Loose Boundary Hydraulics

Loose Boundary Hydraulics

BY

A. J. RAUDKIVI

Associate Professor of Civil Engineering,
University of Auckland, New Zealand.

PERGAMON PRESS

OXFORD · LONDON · EDINBURGH · NEW YORK
TORONTO · SYDNEY · PARIS · BRAUNSCHWEIG

Pergamon Press Ltd., Headington Hill Hall, Oxford
4 & 5 Fitzroy Square, London W.1

Pergamon Press (Scotland) Ltd., 2 & 3 Teviot Place, Edinburgh 1

Pergamon Press Inc., 44–01 21st Street, Long Island City, New York 11101

Pergamon of Canada Ltd., 6 Adelaide Street East, Toronto, Ontario

Pergamon Press (Aust.) Pty. Ltd., 20–22 Margaret Street, Sydney,
New South Wales

Pergamon Press S.A.R.L., 24 rue des Écoles, Paris 5e

Vieweg & Sohn GmbH, Burgplatz 1, Braunschweig

Copyright © 1967 Pergamon Press Ltd.
First edition 1967
Library of Congress Catalog Card No. 66–29601

Printed in Great Britain by Bell and Bain Ltd., Glasgow

Contents

Preface

THE real task in writing this book was the summarizing and correlating of all the publications scattered throughout the technical literature. A staggering number of publications was found to exist. Many of the papers read had been superseded or were too specialized or detailed for this text, which is intended to be introductory in nature, but a great many remained for closer study. I have attempted to give a reference to all the papers which are woven into this text. If some have been omitted this is unintentional and I would like to offer my apologies in advance. The omissions are most likely to be papers which by their universal acceptance have become common knowledge, part of teaching and practice everywhere. The origin and authors of those contributions tend to fade into the background. However, to all the authors of papers on topics associated with loose boundary hydraulics I would like to offer my thanks.

I would also like to thank all authors, societies, institutions, government departments in various countries and publishers, who so kindly gave their permission to use information, figures and diagrams from their publications.

In my own Institution my most sincere thanks go to my colleague R. A. Callander, who sacrificed so much of his time in reading the draft and made so many valuable suggestions. Also, many thanks to David N. Browne for doing the tracing of the illustrations.

Finally, I would like to thank Professor N. A. Mowbray for his help and encouragement, and my family for managing with less than their fair share of my time.

Auckland, New Zealand,   A. J. R.
  January 1965

A*

List of Symbols

a	a reference level $y = a$; amplitude; half-axis of the ellipse of orbital motion; dimensionless quantity
A	area; coefficient; amplitude
b	factor; distance between centres of grains; half-axis of the ellipse of orbital motion; dimensionless quantity
B	Width of channel; coefficient
c	local concentration of sediment; wave celerity
c_r	speed of propagation of ripple
C	Chézy coefficient; concentration
C_D	drag coefficient
C_s	friction coefficient between sediment layers
C_L	lift coefficient
C_o	maximum possible concentration
C^*	equal to g/C^2
C_v	volumetric concentration
d	particle diameter
d_i	incipient particle diameter
d_e	equilibrium particle diameter
D	depth of flow or water; diameter of pipe
E	ratio of tangential stress to grain's normal immersed weight component; coefficient
f	Darcy-Weisbach friction factor; the Lacey silt factor
f_c	factor defining cross-sectional shape of channel
f_g	factor defining plan geometry of channel
f_s	friction coefficient between sediment layers
f_w	Darcy-Weisbach friction factor for fluid alone
F_b	bed factor
F_D	drag force
F_F	form drag

F_G gravity force

F_I inertia force

F_L lift force

F_p pressure force

Fr Froude number

F_{rr} resistance force due to rolling friction

F_s surface drag force; side factor

g gravitational acceleration

G weight of sediment transported per unit time and width; a dimensionless number in section 6.4

G_B weight of bed load transported per unit time and width

H wave height

i_b the fraction of bed sediment of a given size range

i_B fraction of G_B according to particle size

I integral

j the value of ordinate y at which net velocity is a maximum; a dimensionless quantity equal to δ/y_0

k shape factor or volume coefficient; equivalent sand roughness; wave number $2\pi/L$; particle diameter

K coefficient in Strickler formula; erosion coefficient; a coefficient or factor

l Prandtl mixing length

l_1 Lagrangian scale of turbulence

l_s sediment mixing length

L lift; wave length; characteristic path length

m hydraulic mean radius; mass; a coefficient

M mass; moment

n the Manning coefficient; a number or exponent

N a dimensionless number in section 6.4; numerical constant

N_e number of particles eroded

N_d number of particles deposited

p percentage; probability; pressure; factor defining the proportion of bed surface taking fluid shear

P length of wetted perimeter; a function of $(t, u_*/\kappa U)$; a coefficient

P_f power to overcome hydraulic resistance

P_s power to suspend sediment

P_y dispersive pressure

q water discharge per unit width

q_s sediment discharge; volume per unit time per unit width of bed

Q water discharge; a coefficient

Q_s total mass of grains passing a cross-section per unit time and width in suspension

Q_b total mass of grains passing a cross-section per unit time and width as bed load

Q_{sb} total mass of grains passing a cross-section per unit width and time in suspension and as bed load

r ratio y/y_0

R   resistance force; wave reflection coefficient; correlation coefficient

Re   Reynolds number

Re_* particle Reynolds number $u_* d/v$

s clear distance between particles

S slope; specific gravity of sea water

S_e slope of energy gradient

S_s specific gravity of solids

t time

T wave period; total time; overall shear resistance; tangential component of force

T_o overall shear resistance on the bed

T_c critical or threshold value of tractive force

u component of fluid velocity at a point in the x-coordinate direction

u_* shear velocity $\sqrt{(g y_0 S)}$

u_b relative velocity past bed grains

u_e effective velocity (usually assumed at particle crest level)

u_s relative velocity past suspended grains; water surface velocity

u' magnitude of turbulent fluctuation in the u-component of velocity

U mean velocity of fluid

U_e average mass transport velocity

U_b velocity of the bed form in x-direction

v component of fluid velocity at a point in the y-coordinate direction

v_b relative velocity past bed grains

v_g velocity of sand grain

v_s relative velocity past suspended grains

v' magnitude of turbulent fluctuation of the v-component of velocity

V velocity

V_0 stable channel velocity

$\bar{V}_s$ average net sediment velocity

w fall velocity of particles in fluid at rest

$\bar{w}$ waviness

$\mathbf{W}$ weight; work

x coordinate; factor; exponent

X correction parameter; horizontal displacement of water particle in wave motion

y vertical coordinate; exponent

y_0 depth of flow

y' intercept of velocity plot with y-axis on log-natural paper

Y vertical displacement of a water particle in wave motion; a coefficient

z coordinate; exponent equal to $w/\kappa_s B_s u_*$

α an angle or a dimensionless factor or quantity

β an angle; a coefficient; an exponent

γ specific weight of water

γ_s specific weight of sediment

γ_s^* immersed specific weight of sediment

δ the distance by which the local sediment lags behind the velocity at the bed

δ_1 boundary layer thickness

δ' the nominal thickness of the laminar sublayer $11 \cdot 6 \, v/u_*$

ε diffusion coefficient, eddy viscosity; dimensionless quantity; coefficient of rolling friction

ε_s sediment diffusion coefficient

η	time variable parameter; efficiency; sandbed ordinate; viscosity of mixtures
θ	dimensionless applied shear stress, section 6.4; phase angle in radians
θ_*	$= [(\theta - \theta_c)\theta^{1/2}]^{2/3}$
κ	von Karman universal constant
λ	linear concentration d/s; distance jumped by individual grains
μ	absolute or dynamic viscosity; micron
ν	kinematic viscosity
ξ	dimensionless quantity; ordinate of surface waves; a coefficient; displacement of water particle from its mean orbital position
ρ	density of fluid
ρ_s	density of sediment
σ	standard deviation; dimensionless stress, section 6.4.1; surface tension; factor
τ	shear stress
τ^*	component of shear stress arising from grain collisions
τ'	component of shear stress arising from distortion of intergranular fluid
τ_f	shear stress due to skin friction
τ_i	shear stress due to internal distortion of flow
τ_s	spill resistance, energy dissipated at sudden expansions
ϕ	coefficient of friction or angle of repose
ϕ	velocity potential; Einstein bed-load function
ϕ_b	parameter in Bagnold sediment transport theory
ϕ_s	parameter in Bagnold sediment transport theory
ϕ	parameter in Bagnold sediment transport theory
ϕ'	parameter in Bagnold sediment transport theory
χ	a characteristic grain load
ψ	stream function; reciprocal of entrainment function in the Einstein bed-load function
ω	angular velocity $2\pi/T$
$-$	bar above a quantity signifies the mean value of the quantity

o   subscript o signifies the value of a quantity on the bed level, or in deep water

c   subscript c signifies the critical or threshold value of the quantity

–   bar as a subscript signifies the value of the quantity at the depth of one grain layer below the bed level.

b   subscript b signifies the proportion of the quantity occurring as bed load

s   subscript s signifies the proportion of the quantity occurring as suspended load

CHAPTER 1

Introduction

A STUDY of sediment transport seeks to answer the question "What happens when a fluid flows over a bed composed of material whose grains may be set in motion by the flow?" This involves the erosion, transport and deposition of soil or rock particles by air and water.

The civil engineer associates these phenomena with rivers and coast lines. Yet the principles have much wider uses. Many industrial processes use fluids to transport solids or are concerned with separation or mixing of particles, for example pneumatic and hydraulic conveying, coal washing and mineral dressing, chemical reactors based on the fluidized-solid systems, combustion of pulverized or atomized fuels, gas and liquid cleaners, etc.

All these problems are of the same kind, and differences in treatment are only a matter of emphasis. The treatment in the following pages is aimed at the civil engineering student. It deals with the description and mobility of solid particles and their transport by wind and water, the stability of rivers, resistance to flow and with particle movement by surface waves. No attempt is made to include every detail of these problems or to assemble design data.

The emphasis throughout is on discussing the reasoning and trends by which the present-day knowledge and methods have been developed, thus building a framework to which the student can add by his own studies. It is the principles, the mechanism of the various phases of sediment transport that is the theme and not the immense volume of practical know-how.

Sound knowledge of the principles is of great economic

importance. One only needs to think of the expenditure on maintenance and improvements of rivers and estuaries, be it for flood control or navigation, coastal protection, canals and approaches to harbours, or prevention of land erosion by wind or water, to see this. The results and benefits from this expenditure depend largely on the engineer's understanding of the basic principles. The detailed interdependence of the factors involved in practical problems is so complex that these may never be subject to a rigorous analytical treatment. Nevertheless, much can be achieved by careful application of the fundamentals of mechanics and of the results of experiment and experience.

The book closes with introductory remarks on topics which deal with specialized aspects of loose boundary hydraulics and are outside the scope of this book, which is introductory in nature. Therefore only brief reference is made to topics such as geometry of the water-courses, scour at bridge piers and below hydraulic structures, density currents in reservoirs and in tidal estuaries, and transport of solids in pipelines. The brevity of the treatment of these topics should not be taken as an indication or measure of their practical importance but is the result of limitation of space.

CHAPTER 2

Sediment Properties

SEDIMENTS are broadly divided into cohesive and non-cohesive ones. In the case of cohesive sediments the resistance to erosion depends on the strength of the cohesive bond between the particles which may far outweigh the influence of the physical characteristics of individual particles. Once erosion has taken place, however, cohesive material may become non-cohesive in respect to further transport. Characteristics may also change through chemical or physical reactions. On the other hand, the non-cohesive sediments generally consist of larger discrete particles than the cohesive soils and the movement of these particles depends on the physical properties of the individual particles, such as size, shape and density. Non-cohesive soils may be bound together by the roots of the vegetable cover.

The treatment will generally be limited to non-cohesive sediment with a short discussion on critical tractive force of cohesive soils.

The particle's size and its terminal fall velocity are the most important single parameters in current use, relating the sediment properties with the theories of grain motion.

Particle Size and Shape. Grain size affects the transportability of the sediment and ranges from great boulders which are rolled only by violent mountain torrents to fine clays which once stirred up, take days to settle.

3

A frequently used classification is:

			B.S. sieve sizes
Boulders	>200	mm	
Cobbles	200–60	mm	
Coarse gravel	60–20	mm	$2\frac{1}{2}$–$\frac{3}{4}$ in.
Medium gravel	20–6	mm	$\frac{3}{4}$–$\frac{1}{4}$ in.
Fine gravel	6–2	mm	$\frac{1}{4}$–No. 7
Coarse sand	2–0·6	mm	No. 7–No. 25
Medium sand	0·6–0·2	mm	No. 25–No. 72
Fine sand	0·2–0·06	mm	No. 72–No. 200
Coarse silt	0·06–0·02	mm	
Medium silt	0·02–0·006	mm	
Fine silt	0·006–0·002	mm	
Clay	<2 μ		

It should be noted that terms such as bed load, suspended, wash load, do not refer to particle size but to method of transport under particular conditions.

Natural sediments are irregular in shape and therefore the definition of size by a single length dimension is necessarily very incomplete. Such classification is made arbitrarily due to convenience of measurement. Common dimensions used for definition are:

1. Sieve diameter—size of sieve opening through which the given particle will just pass. Sieves do not grade particles entirely by size but partly also by shape. The sieve diameter of a particle is the side length or diameter of the smallest opening through which the given particle will pass.

2. Equivalent or sedimentation diameter—diameter of a sphere of the same density with the same terminal settling velocity in the same fluid at the same temperature as the given particle. The standard sedimentation diameter is measured in water at 24°C. The settling velocity for any particle of a sediment depends on the density of the particle, the grading of the sample, the shape characteristics, the concentration, the fluid and the apparatus in which it is measured. Therefore, the meaning of the sedimentation diameter is ambiguous unless qualified by detailed information.

3. Nominal diameter—diameter of a sphere of equal volume.

4. Triaxial dimensions.

Sands are commonly analysed by sieving so that the sieve diameter is a convenient choice. The nominal diameter is useful in defining the size of large particles for which the volume can be easily measured. In a particular sediment the size of the particles may vary over a very wide range.

The sediment characteristics can be displayed by plotting the results of sieve analysis as a cumulative frequency curve, i.e. the per cent by weight greater than a certain size against the logarithm of that size. From such cumulative frequency plots the median size can be read off and the distribution can be described in statistical terms. The mean diameter or the median diameter and the standard deviation of the particle size distribution will describe the sand more closely than a single dimension. In many natural sands the size distribution is nearly log–normal. However, if the sediment has a wide distribution the larger particles form a protective cover and shelter the finer material and there is as yet no satisfactory definition for description of the most effective size.

For clay, silt and fine sand it is more convenient to determine the sedimentation diameter by settling analysis methods such as pipette, bottom withdrawal tube, hydrometer or visual accumulation tube.

Particle shape affects sediment transport but there is no direct and quantitative way to assess the particle shape and its effects except on fall velocity. The shape of a particle is a measure of the ratio of the surface area of the particle to that of a sphere having the same volume. This definition of shape does not specify whether the particle is rounded or a cube. Terms like sphericity and roundness are used to describe form. Sphericity is defined as the cube root of the ratio of the volume of the particle to the volume of its circumscribing sphere. Roundness is defined as the average radius of curvature of the individual edges to the maximum radius of the circle inscribed within a cross-section of the particle.

Density of the sediment particles is an important property and must be known. Usually the sediment is composed of a variety of minerals and although the mean density may vary little, the variation from particle to particle may be appreciable, from pumice sands to heavy minerals such as magnetite. Such variations in density affect sediment transport by segregation—for example, the armour effect of the heavy minerals on dune crests. In problems involving erosion and deposition bulk density and porosity of the sediment have to be considered. For example, newly formed fluvial deposits in reservoirs may have very high porosity and low weight per unit volume of space occupied.

Fall velocity of a particle in a fluid depends upon the size, shape and density of the particle and the density and viscosity of the fluid. Under steady state conditions the fall velocity is called the terminal velocity and the drag on the particle is equal to its submerged weight.

For a sphere,

$$\pi(d^3/6)g(\rho_s-\rho) = C_D\pi(d^2/4)\rho w^2/2 \tag{2.1}$$

$$w^2 = (4/3)(1/C_D)gd(\rho_s-\rho)/\rho \tag{2.2}$$

where w is fall velocity, ρ_s and ρ are densities of solid and fluid respectively, d is the particle diameter, g is gravitational acceleration, and C_D is drag coefficient and is a function of the Reynolds number. $Re = wd/v$; v being the kinematic viscosity of fluid.

In the laminar range $C_D = 24/Re$ and the expression for fall velocity reduces to Stokes' law. For single spherical particles in fluid the drag coefficient C_D is a unique function of Reynolds number (Fig. 2.1). For ease of application of eqn. (2.2) and Fig. 2.1 a chart can be prepared in the form of particle diameter d versus fall velocity w, with temperature and Reynolds numbers as parameters (Fig. 2.2).

Attempts to define the shapes of non-spherical natural particles, so that for any defined shape C_D will also be a unique function of Reynolds number, have not been successful. Very many definitions

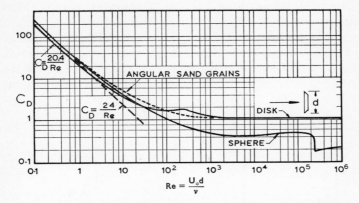

FIG. 2.1. Drag coefficient for spheres and disks as a function of Reynolds number.

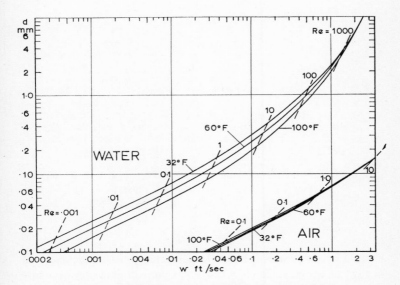

FIG. 2.2. Fall velocity of quartz spheres in water and air.

of shape are in use. For example, Heywood[1] uses a shape factor or volume coefficient k, such that volume = kd^3 and d is the diameter of a circle having an area equal to the projected area of the particle when placed in the most stable position; i.e. the distance of the centre of gravity of the particle above the supporting horizontal plane is a minimum. Heywood also plots

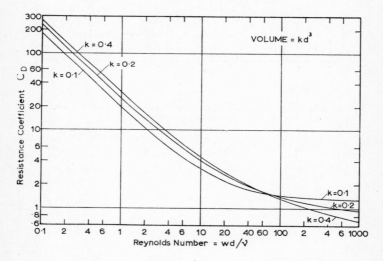

Fig. 2.3. Resistance coefficient $C_D = 8k(\rho_s - \rho)gd/\pi\rho w^2$ plotted against Reynolds number by various shapes of particles. (By permission of the Institution of Mechanical Engineers, London.)

drag coefficient against Reynolds number with k as a parameter (Fig. 2.3). The Sub-Committee on Sedimentation, U.S. Inter-agency Committee on Water Resources, Report No. 12, uses a shape factor

$$\text{S.F.} = c/(ab)^{1/2}, \tag{2.3}$$

where c is the shortest of the three mutually perpendicular axes (a, b, c) of the particle (Fig. 2.4). An indirect measure of shape would be the ratio of the median diameter of the grading to the median equivalent sphere diameter as obtained from fall velocity, i.e. for spherical particles the shape factor would be unity.

In addition to the shape effect it is known from experiment that the drag coefficient with regard to the local fluid velocity past a

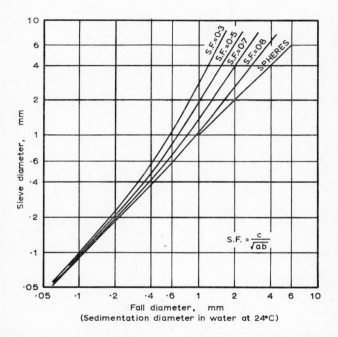

FIG. 2.4. Relation of sieve diameter and fall diameter for naturally worn quartz sand as a function of shape factor (S.F.). (By permission U.S. Dept. of Interior, Geological Survey, Sub-Committee on Sedimentation.)

grain, increases with increase in concentration. Following Richardson and Zaki,[2] Bagnold[3] plotted drag coefficient versus Reynolds number with concentration of C (ratio of grain occupied space to the whole space) as parameter; using Heywood's $k = 0.3$ which is reasonable for most natural grains.

Generally the drag force per unit area is expressed as

$$F = C_D \rho \mathbf{q}^2/2, \tag{2.4}$$

where $\mathbf{q}$ is the velocity vector.

Thus

$$C_D = 2F/(\rho \mathbf{q}^2) \tag{2.5}$$

which is a unique function for an isolated grain.

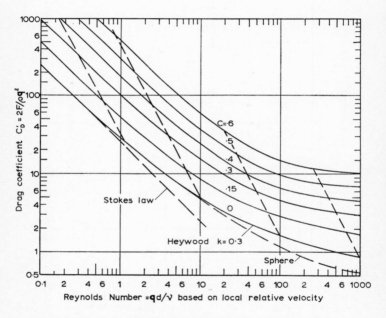

FIG. 2.5. Variation of drag coefficient with grain concentration.
(By permission of the Royal Society, London.)

In Zaki's work, and by Bagnold $\mathbf{q} = V/\varepsilon$, where $V =$ upward fluid velocity—without grains—in the tube in which the experiments were carried out and ε is porosity equal to $(1-C)$. The presence of other grains affects the value of C_D and this new value is called C'_D. The relations indicated on the Fig. 2.5 are assumed to apply to grains in sediment which are subject to fluctuating forces of turbulent or disturbed flow. If in a given fluid–grain system the particle diameter, kinematic viscosity and the fluid force acting on each grain are kept constant, then an increase in the concentration by lowering the local velocity lowers the value of the local Reynolds number. This effect is shown by the inclined dotted lines.

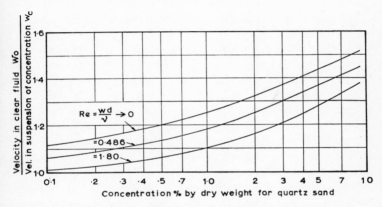

Fig. 2.6. Effect of concentration on fall velocity (McNown and Lin).

Bagnold suggests that a reasonable approximation is

$$C'_D/C_D = (1-C)^{-3} = \varepsilon^{-3}. \qquad (2.6)$$

However, this point needs verification. Due to the interference, the drag coefficient will not be a simple function of the concentration.

McNown and Lin[4] published some experimental data for quartz sand. This is plotted (Fig. 2.6) as the ratio of fall velocity in clear fluid to that in suspension versus concentration.

Maude and Whitmore[5] describe the fall velocity affected by concentration as

$$w = w_0(1 - C)^\beta,$$

where w_0 is the fall velocity of a single grain in a large container, and β is a function of particle shape, size distribution and the Reynolds number. Plotted on a log–log paper as β versus $w_0 d/v$ the value of β is given as 4·65 for Re less than one, and 2·32 for Re greater than 10^3, with a S-curve transition between these values.

2.1. Colloids and Flocculation

The transport of sediment carried by streams may be separated into two kinds:

1. Transport of bed material. This includes all sizes of material found in appreciable quantities in the bed of the stream. It may be transported along the bed or in suspension or both.

2. Transport of fine sediment, known as the wash load. This material is not usually found in quantities in the bed of the stream and is supplied by soil erosion or erosion of the sediment itself. The sediment erosion is important on steep rivers carrying shingle derived from soft rocks, such as greywacke. It may arrive from an external upstream source or by surface runoff over land.

The wash load of many streams consists of very fine particles. With particles of about 10 μ or less not only the gravitational forces are important but also the electro-chemical ones. Suspensions of fine particles are known as colloidal systems and the study of colloids is a branch of science in its own right. No attempt is made here to do any more than to draw the reader's attention to this kind of solid liquid system.

Solid particles of sediment usually have very little attraction for water molecules and the stabilization of such a system may result from an electric charge. The particles are denser than the liquid and tend to fall through it by the action of gravity. The motion of particles is opposed by fluid drag.

In flowing water the suspended load may consist of much larger particles than those of colloidal size, and the size of particles in suspension is governed by the intensity of turbulent mixing. The movement of even the very fine particles in flowing fluid is dominated by turbulent agitation. But when such fine particles come, for example, into a lake the settling may be counteracted by large- and small-scale thermal motion. The large-scale motions are caused by thermal convection. In the small scale the liquid molecules are in a state of continuous agitation caused by their thermal energy. This thermal energy is also transmitted to the solid particles and the resulting motion is known as the Brownian movement. It is important for particle sizes below 1 μ.

A comparison of the effect of Brownian motion with that caused by gravity is interesting. E. F. Burton gives for silver spheres the following results:

Diameter of particles (mμ)	Distance travelled in Brownian movement (mμ)	1 second gravitational fall (mμ)
100	10,000	67·6
1,000	3,162	6,760
10,000	1,000	676,000

The particles may also have electrical charges. If the particles have the same charge, they repel each other and thus counteract sedimentation. However, if an additional agent causes the particles to lose their charges then by mutual attraction of mass they will tend to join together and thus form larger particles or flocs and these settle out more rapidly. For example, kaolin clays consist of hydrous silicates of aluminium having a calcium-magnesium base. The particles have like electric charge in fresh water and repel each other. But if these are carried into the sea, then they come into water containing a high percentage of dissolved salts. The sodium ions of the chlorides are exchanged with the calcium and magnesium ions from the particles. The particles lose their charges, attract one another and form flocs.

References

1. HEYWOOD, H., Measurement of the fineness of powdered materials, *Proc. Inst. Mech. Eng.* **140** (1938).
2. RICHARDSON, J. F. and ZAKI, W. N., Sedimentation and fluidisation, Part 1, *Trans. Inst. Chem. Engrs.* **32** (1954).
3. BAGNOLD, R. A., The flow of cohesionless grains in fluids, *Philosophical Trans. of the Roy. Soc.* (A) **249,** No. 964 (1956).
4. McNOWN, J. and LIN, P. N., Sediment concentration and fall velocity, *Proc. Second Midwestern Conf. on Fluid Mech.*, Ohio State University, 1952.
5. MAUDE, A. D. and WHITMORE, R. L., A generalized theory of sedimentation, *Brit. J. Appl. Phys.* **9,** 477–82 (1958).

CHAPTER 3

Threshold of Particle Transport

WHEN the flow of a fluid, be it gas or liquid, over a flat surface of loose grains is gradually increased, a condition is reached where a few grains here and there begin to move with the fluid owing to the forces exerted by the fluid flow. For more than two centuries workers in this field have attempted to formulate the conditions of incipient motion. One of the earliest expressions is due to Brahms (1753) and gives the critical velocity of water as

$$V_{\text{critical}} = kW^{1/6}, \qquad (3.1)$$

where k is an empirical constant and W is the weight of the grain.

Before dealing with the various theoretical approaches it is useful to consider the physical picture. Familiarity with the hydraulics of flow over smooth and rough boundaries, the boundary layer and the concepts of lift and drag is assumed; topics which are discussed in most of the modern textbooks on fluid mechanics. The moving grains are subject to a weight force which moves them down towards the bed and a tangential force which maintains the forward motion. There are also shear stresses between the grains in motion and those forming the stationary boundary, the fluid between them taking part in this shearing. The tangential force may be transmitted entirely by fluid as in case of transport by fluid over a horizontal bed or at the other extreme it may be due en irely to the component of weight force as when granular material is sliding down a steep slope. In general both can contribute. Confining the attention

15

to an assembly of non-cohesive particles of density ρ_s greater than that of fluid, the picture may be of the kind shown in Fig. 3.1.

In general there will exist near the bed a mean velocity profile $u = f(y)$. Superimposed upon this temporal mean velocity may be turbulent velocity fluctuations. As the fluid passes the particle the stream lines are deflected. The fluid force exerted on the

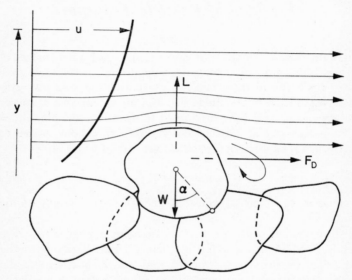

FIG. 3.1. Diagrammatic picture of an exposed grain subject to fluid force.

particle may be resolved into two components, one parallel to the direction of mean flow, called the drag, and the other normal to it, called the lift.

If the flow is laminar near the boundary or if the thickness of laminar sublayer is, say, 5 or more times the height of the surface irregularity then the individual grains will not shed eddies and the drag is due to viscous shear. It will be carried by the whole surface and not by a few more exposed grains. Surface roughness should not influence the drag force. Particle shape would influence the magnitude of the lift and drag components of the fluid force on the particle. These are also functions of the particle surface area as well as of piling position.

As the velocity increases the more exposed particles shed eddies and a wake is formed downstream. The size of the wake depends upon the size and shape of the particle, and the point of separation of the boundary layer formed on the particle. The point of separation in turn is a function of the shape of the particle and of the local Reynolds number.

The drag combines the surface drag or viscous skin friction and the form drag due to pressure difference in front and behind the particle. The point of application of the drag force, relative to the centre of gravity of the particle, is not fixed and depends on the relative magnitudes of the lift and drag components. These in turn are functions of the shape and location of the particle and the local Reynolds number. The lift is analogous to the form drag and is the resultant of the pressure difference above and below the particle. As the flow speeds up over the particle the pressure is reduced whereas underneath the particle, where the interstitial velocity is relatively very small, the pressure is static. It has to be borne in mind that in turbulent flow both lift and drag are fluctuating quantities in magnitude, point of application and in direction.

Opposing these fluid forces is the submerged weight of the particle, plus any constraining forces due to neighbouring particles.

These two sets of forces—fluid and resisting forces—tend to move or roll the particle and one can say that if the moment of the resisting forces about a point of contact is greater than that of the fluid about the same point the particle will be stable. If not, the particle will be rolled downstream until it reaches a position where the combination of forces again renders it stable. The condition of balance—equality of the two opposing moments —signifies incipient motion or the threshold of motion. As soon as some particles are in motion the picture is further complicated by impact forces between moving and stationary grains.

B

In the laboratory the threshold is usually defined by visual observation. The movement of an arbitrarily selected small number of grains is taken to define the threshold.

Jeffreys[1] put forward a theory of fluid dynamic lift as the cause of the initial upward acceleration from the bed. Some experimental work was carried out by Einstein and El-Samni.[2] But as yet there is no generally accepted analytical theory or satisfactory experimental result defining the lift force exerted on the particles.

The analysis of the threshold condition by C. M. White[3] simplifies the picture discussed above to the balance of the moments due to drag and immersed weight.

The immersed weight, assuming a spherical grain, is $W = (\pi/6)d^3(\rho_s - \rho)g$ and acts through the centre of gravity of the particle. The moment about the point of contact is

$$M_w = (\pi/6)d^3(\rho_s - \rho)g(d/2) \sin \alpha, \qquad (3.2)$$

where α is assumed to be given, on the average, by the angle of repose of the submerged material.

The mean drag is expressed as $\tau = \rho u_*^2$, the force on the grain as

$$F_D = \tau A \propto \rho u_*^2 (\pi d^2/4)$$

and the moment as

$$M_D = \beta \rho u_*^2 (\pi d^2/4)(d/2) \cos \alpha, \qquad (3.3)$$

where the coefficient β depends on the ratio of momentary eddy velocity to mean velocity, on the proportion of the drag per unit area which is taken by the individual grain by virtue of its relative position in the piling, on the height at which the drag force acts and on the proportion of the grain's projected area. Equating these two moments yields an expression for the threshold shear velocity.

$$u_{*c}^2 = \frac{2}{3} \frac{\tan \alpha}{\beta} \left(\frac{\rho_s - \rho}{\rho} \right) gd$$

or

$$u_{*c} = B \sqrt{\left[\left(\frac{\rho_s - \rho}{\rho} \right) gd \right]}. \qquad (3.4)$$

From this the critical fluid velocity distribution becomes

$$u_c = 5.75B \sqrt{\left[\left(\frac{\rho_s - \rho}{\rho} \right) gd \right]} \log \left(\frac{y}{y'} \right). \qquad (3.5)$$

If B is constant, then u_{*c} varies as the square root of the grain diameter. But it is not difficult to see (as will be shown later) that B is primarily a function of $\mathrm{Re} = u_* d/v$.

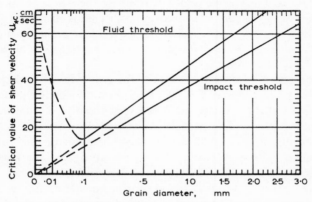

FIG. 3.2. Variation of the threshold velocity in air with grain size, according to Bagnold. Grain size drawn on a square root scale to exhibit the relation $u_* \propto \sqrt{d}$. (By permission of Methuen & Co., Ltd.)

Colebrook and White[4] showed that when $u_* d/v > 3.5$ the grain behaves as an isolated obstacle in the path of the fluid and sheds eddies from its downstream side. A prominent grain lying above the surface can carry the whole of the drag on the area it occupies and a large proportion of that on the area covered by the wake. This shielded area may be 10 or 20 times the projected area of the grain.

If experimental data on threshold conditions in *air* are plotted as u_{*c} versus $(d)^{1/2}$ it is seen that $u_* \propto (d)^{1/2}$ (Fig. 3.2), for d larger than a certain diameter. For fine dune sands $d \doteq 0.25$ mm, and from Fig. 3.2 $u_{*c} \doteq 20$ cm/sec. With $v = 0.14$ cm^2/sec the Reynolds number is $\mathrm{Re} = 20 \times 0.025/0.14 = 3.57$.

It is seen from Fig. 3.2 that this diameter of 0·25 mm is close to the diameter yielding the minimum value of u_{*c}. For the larger grains the coefficient B is found to be nearly constant at 0·1.

When the Reynolds number becomes less than 3·5 (approx.) the surface becomes hydraulically smooth, i.e. the surface becomes covered by a laminar sublayer which is thick relative to particle size and individual grains cease to shed eddies. The drag becomes a viscous one and is carried by the whole surface and not only by the more exposed grains. This is displayed in the relatively greater drag required to set the first grains in motion. The coefficient B changes and the proportionality of u_{*c} to $(d)^{1/2}$ does not hold.

The minimum threshold velocity for grains in air as displayed in Fig. 3.2 is at about $d = 0·08$ mm. For still smaller grains the threshold shear velocity increases very rapidly. In nature this implies that once fine particles have settled on the ground they will be sheltered in the viscous sublayer, are out of reach of the turbulent eddies and cannot be swept up again individually— for example, soft dust on the ground in a strong wind.

The u_* for a smooth Portland cement powder surface is of the same order as that for gravel of 5 mm diameter. An approximate measure of the critical diameter is that the material feels soft instead of gritty for diameters less than 0·07 mm.

The significance of the fluid threshold and impact threshold as observed for air will be discussed in Chapter 4. Only one curve, the fluid threshold, has been observed for grains in water and the value of B is nearer to 0·2.

Approaches to the threshold problem by analytical models of the kind described are gross simplifications and are not sufficient to describe the mechanism of the problem. A different approach was used by Shields[5] who assembled a number of relevant parameters into dimensionless numbers and related these to experimental results. His method can be summarized as follows:

The drag force on a grain is

$$F_D = C_D A \frac{\rho u^2}{2} = f_1\left(\alpha_1, \frac{ud}{\nu}\right)\rho d^2 u^2, \qquad (3.6)$$

where C_D is drag coefficient, α_1 is a grain shape factor, ud/v is a Reynolds number, u is a characteristic velocity at an elevation y above the bed, where $y \propto d$ the grain size, i.e. $y = \alpha_2 d$.

For a smooth boundary

$$\frac{u}{u_*} = 5\cdot75 \log \frac{yu_*}{v} + 5\cdot5 \qquad (3.7)$$

and for a rough boundary

$$\frac{u}{u_*} = 5\cdot75 \log \frac{y}{k} + 8\cdot5. \qquad (3.8)$$

Shields combines these into an expression covering the velocity distribution from smooth, through a transition, to the rough boundary condition as

$$\frac{u}{u_*} = 5\cdot75 \log \frac{y}{k} + f\left(\frac{yu_*}{v}\right). \qquad (3.9)$$

Using $y = \alpha_2 d$ and assuming that $k \propto d$ yields $y \propto k$. The term

$$\frac{yu_*}{v} \propto \frac{ku_*}{v} \propto \frac{k}{\delta'} \quad \text{since } \delta' = \frac{11\cdot6v}{u_*},$$

where δ' is the nominal thickness of the laminar sublayer. Thus

$$\frac{u}{u_*} = 5\cdot75 \log \alpha_2 + f\left(\frac{u_* d}{v}\right) = f_2\left(\alpha_2, \frac{u_* d}{v}\right). \qquad (3.10)$$

Here

$$u_* = \sqrt{\frac{\tau_0}{\rho}} = \sqrt{g y_0 S}$$

since from the balance of forces $\tau_0 = \gamma y_0 S$. Combining the relationship for drag and velocity yields

$$F_D = \tau_0 d^2 f_3\left(\alpha_1, \alpha_2, \frac{d\sqrt{g y_0 S}}{v}\right). \qquad (3.11)$$

Shields further assumed that the resistance of the particle to motion should depend only upon the form of the bed and the immersed weight of particles, i.e.

$$R = \alpha_3(S_s-1)\gamma d^3, \tag{3.12}$$

where α_3 is a factor accounting for the form of the bed. Equating drag and resistance forces and replacing τ_0 by τ_c, the critical shear stress, the relationship for threshold condition is

$$\alpha_3(S_s-1)\gamma d^3 = \tau_c d^2 f_4(\alpha_1, \alpha_2, d(gy_0S)^{1/2}/v). \tag{3.13}$$

For the specific case of level bed and uniform particle size, this yields a relationship, usually referred to as the Shields entrainment function

$$\left.\begin{array}{c}\dfrac{\tau_c}{\gamma(S_s-1)d} = f\left(\dfrac{d\sqrt{gy_0S}}{v}\right) = f\left(\dfrac{du_*}{v}\right)\\[4mm]\text{or}\\[2mm]\dfrac{\tau_c}{\left(\dfrac{\rho_s-\rho}{\rho}\right)\rho gd} = \dfrac{u_{*c}^2}{\left(\dfrac{\rho_s-\rho}{\rho}\right)gd} = f(\text{Re}_*) = f_1\left(\dfrac{d}{\delta'}\right)\end{array}\right\} \tag{3.14}$$

(using $\delta' = 11\cdot6v/u_*$, i.e. $du_*/v = 11\cdot6d/\delta'$).

Equation

$$u_{*c} = B\sqrt{\left[\left(\dfrac{\rho_s-\rho}{\rho}\right)gd\right]}$$

can be written as

$$\dfrac{u_{*c}^2}{\left(\dfrac{\rho_s-\rho}{\rho}\right)gd} = B^2.$$

Comparing this with eqn. (3.14) shows that $B = f(u_*d/v) = f(\text{Re}_*)$ as was stated previously. When B becomes constant it is also seen that since u_* is proportioned to u and d is proportional to

$W^{1/3}$ the entrainment velocity $u_{\text{crit}} \propto W^{1/6}$, which is the Brahms formula.

Shields plotted experimental results in terms of entrainment function $\tau_c/[\gamma(S_s-1)d]$ versus the particle Reynolds number $\text{Re}_* = du_*/\nu$ and obtained a reasonably defined curve, Fig. 3.3. Since then many more results have been added by various

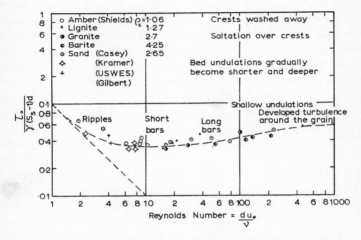

FIG. 3.3. Sediment entrainment as a function of Reynolds number, according to Shields.

experimenters. The effect of hydrodynamic lift on the particle entrainment has not been specifically considered in any of these approaches, thus implying that the lift is zero or uniquely related to the drag.

There is a great similarity between the general shape of this function and functions such as the Darcy-Weisbach coefficient f versus Re, the drag coefficient C_D versus Re for a sphere, cylinder, etc., in particular, the first of these for artificially roughened pipes of uniform roughness. There is the laminar flow region with characteristic variation with Re, the transition region and the turbulent region where the entrainment function settles down to a constant value. It may be reasonable to expect that with a strongly non-uniform particle size distribution the larger ones will disturb the laminar sublayer earlier and that the curve will deviate from the straight line earlier, cf. the f versus Re curve for non-uniform roughness. Shields also indicated that the type of bed formation which gradually develops after the motion has begun is characterized by the position on the "entrainment function–particle Reynolds number" plane. Short ripples were observed at low values of particle Reynolds number Re_* and long bars at higher values. This observation is used in hydraulic model studies where relatively coarse material of low specific gravity is frequently used for movable bed studies. The larger particle size increases model Re_* without making the particle too heavy. However, evidence presented by Shields on the post-entrainment conditions is very limited.

Although the Shields results have been confirmed by experimenters, some unanswered questions still remain and papers can be found containing conclusions in variance with those of Shields. Rubey[6] suggested that for particles of 5 mm diameter and less the size is unimportant and velocity only dominates. Hjulstrom[7] stated that particle size and not the velocity is the controlling factor for incipient motion. Harp[8] concludes that the $\tau_0/\gamma(S_s-1)d$ versus Reynolds number relation plots as discontinuous lines, that is parallel straight lines slightly sloping downwards to the right on Shields' coordinate plane, and that no evidence of a transitional function between the laminar and turbulent regimes was found. However, the latter experiments were carried out in a channel with converging sides (27·8° included angle) and results will be strongly influenced by suppression of turbulence and boundary layer development. In the laminar flow and boundary layer region Tison[9] concluded that the points lie perpendicular to the 45° downward sloping line of Shields.

In studying the motion of sediment particles in water, Ippen and Verma[10] concluded, "Nothing is known in detail as yet concerning the turbulent pressure fluctuations near the bed". By including the lift L_c, Chepil[11] wrote for the threshold drag acting on a spherical grain

$$F_c = \left(\frac{\pi}{6} \gamma_s^* d^3 - L_c\right) \tan \alpha, \qquad (3.15)$$

where γ_s^* is the immersed weight of the grain. From experiments he found that L_c is equal to about $0.85 F_c$ for any size of spherical elements, such as soil grain on the surface, and for any wind velocity within the range required to move different sizes of soil grains. Thus

$$F_c = 0.52 \gamma_s^* d^3 \tan \alpha / (1 + 0.85 \tan \alpha) \qquad (3.16)$$

or taken per unit cross-sectional horizontal area occupied by the grain $-\pi d^2/4$,

$$\tau_c = 0.66 \gamma_s^* d \tan \alpha / (1 + 0.85 \tan \alpha). \qquad (3.17)$$

Drag and lift per unit horizontal area occupied by the topmost grains are much higher than drag and lift per unit area on the whole bed, because the topmost grains take up most of the drag and lift and shelter other grains. If N is the ratio of drag and lift on the topmost grain moved by the fluid, then the threshold value of drag per unit area of the whole bed is

$$\tau_c = 0.66 \gamma_s^* d N \tan \alpha / (1 + 0.85 \tan \alpha). \qquad (3.18)$$

White[3] estimated N to be about 0.3. The angle α, assumed to be equal to the angle of repose ϕ, Chepil[11] found by experiments to equal 24 degrees. By actual measurements of pressure on topmost spherical bodies—soil grains—and from drag on the whole surface computed from the threshold drag velocity of the wind, Chepil[11] found that $N = 0.2$.

Chepil and Siddoway[12] also devised a strain gauge anemometer for measuring turbulence near the bed. Oscillograms obtained with this instrument indicated that both lift and drag pressures at a level of the topmost grains are distributed statistic-ally according to a "somewhat skewed normal error law". Hence, from a statistical standpoint, the maximum lift or drag has no definite limit. To take into account the fluctuation of lift and drag in turbulent flow eqn. (3.18) was written as

$$\tau_c = 0.66\gamma_s^* dN \tan \alpha/(1+0.85 \tan \alpha)T. \tag{3.19}$$

The turbulence factor T was defined as $(\bar{p}+3\sigma)/\bar{p}$, and was found to be approximately 2.5. Here $\bar{p}$ is the mean pressure of drag and lift and σ is the standard deviation of the fluctuations.

For water Kalinske[13] concluded that in general the instan-taneous shear stress acting on the bed is up to 3 times the temporal mean shear.

Raudkivi[14] suggested that the entrainment of particles and transport of bed load can take place at values of temporal mean shear stress τ_0 which is well below the value of Shields' critical shear stress. Measurements along a ripple face showed that the temporal mean shear varied from zero at the reattachment point (downstream of the ground roller at the lee of the ripple) to maximum at the crest. The Shields critical value was reached well up the ripple slope but sediment transport took place all along the ripple face. This proves that the sediment entrainment is a function of both the temporal mean drag on the bed and of the turbulence of flow over it. It follows that the mobility of grains is a function of the turbulent agitation and temporal mean shear; the turbulence makes the particles mobile and the shear stress transports them. Here it should be realized that turbulence can effect entrainment of particles in two ways: the particles may be moved by the drag exerted by a passing eddy or if the eddy lowers the local pressure then the particles may be ejected from the bed by the hydrostatic pressure. By this latter mechanism sheltered particles can be entrained as well as particles in the wake of larger ones. This is manifested in the form of scour observed around these obstacles to flow. The subject of impulse forces on grains and their relationship to pressure–velocity correlations has not yet been studied in detail. Theoretical considerations indicate that the impulsive forces should be more important than mean boundary shear for entrainment of grains, whenever the boundary layer is turbulent.

References

1. JEFFREYS, H., *Proc. Camb. Phil. Soc.* **25**, 272 (1929).
2. EINSTEIN, H. A. and EL-SAMNI, El-S. A., Hydrodynamic forces on a rough wall, *Reviews of Modern Physics*, **21**, No. 3, 520–4 (July 1949).
3. WHITE, C. M., The equilibrium of grains on the bed of a stream, *Proc. Roy. Soc.* (A) **174**, No. 958 (1940).
4. COLEBROOK, C. F. and WHITE, C. M., Experiments with fluid friction in roughened pipes, *Proc. Roy. Soc.* (A) **161**, 367–81 (1937).
5. SHIELDS, A., Anwendung der Ähnlichkeits-Mechanik und der Turbulenzforschung auf die Geschiebebewegung, *Preussische Versuchsanstalt für Wasserbau und Schiffbau*, Berlin, 1936.
6. RUBEY, W. W., *The Force Required to Move Particles on the Bed of a Stream*, U. S. Geological Survey Paper 189E, 1938.
7. HJULSTROM, P., Transportation of detritus by moving water, *Recent Marine Sediments*, Am. Assoc. of Petroleum Geologists, 1939.
8. HARP, J. F., Critical tractive force of uniform sands, A Dissertation submitted to the Faculty of Department of Civil Engineering for the degree of Doctor of Philosophy. The University of Arizona, 1963. University Microfilms, Inc., Ann Arbor, Michigan.
9. TISON, L. J., Recherches sur la tension limité d'entraînement des materiaux constitutifs du lit, *Ann. Soc. Tech., Brux*, ser. 1, **61**, 163–83 (June 2, 1947).
10. IPPEN, A. T. and VERMA, R. P., The motion of discrete particles along the bed of a turbulent stream, *Proc. Minnesota International Hydraulics Convention*, 1953.
11. CHEPIL, W. S., Equilibrium of soil grains at the threshold of movement by wind, *Proc. Soil Science, Soc. of America*, **23**, 422–8 (1959).
12. CHEPIL, W. S. and SIDDOWAY, F. H., Straingage anemometer for analyzing various characteristics of wind turbulence, *Journal of Meteorology*, **16**, 411–8 (1959).
13. KALINSKE, A. A., Movement of sediment as bed in rivers, *Trans. Am. Geophys. Union*, **28**, 615–20 (1947).
14. RAUDKIVI, A. J., Study of sediment ripple formation, *Proc. A.S.C.E.*, No. Hy 6 (Nov. 1963).

CHAPTER 4

Sand Transport by Air

ONCE particles have been set in motion it is necessary to distinguish between dust storms and sand storms. The small particles of dust are kept in suspension by upward currents of the air movement. It is a suspension phenomenon and the dust cloud may rise to a height of several thousand feet. In an erosion desert, where there is very little dust, the initial dust cloud is blown away, and soon after the wind exceeds the threshold strength, one can observe a thick low lying sand cloud driving across the country. It has a clearly marked upper surface about 3–4 ft above the ground.

The problem is to explain how large grains get up to heights of 3–4 ft and what keeps them there. Measurements show that the upward eddy currents near the surface are not sufficiently strong to keep these grains in suspension or to lift them up. Particularly since the vertical component of turbulence is much reduced by the presence of the solid boundary, the ground.

R. A. Bagnold *et al.* have shown that the grains move like ping-pong balls. Once the grain is in the air, it receives a supply of energy from the forward drag of the wind. The wind drives them onwards until on falling to the ground they bounce up again and so on. Immediate observational support is furnished when the sand cloud moves over a stretch of hard ground or one covered with pebbles; then the sand cloud thickness increases appreciably. When the sand cloud moves over a surface composed of loose grains similar to those in movement the falling grains splash into the loose mass and frequently become buried but in the process they eject a number of other particles into the air.

28

These particles do not rise as high as the particle did which ejected them because some energy has been lost in disturbing the surface.

Theoretical considerations[1,2] as well as experiment, show that the downward velocity of the grain is very near to the terminal velocity when it hits the ground. By this time the forward velocity of the grain is nearly that of the wind. Hence the angle at which the grain hits the ground is given by

$$\tan \beta = \frac{\text{terminal velocity of grain}}{\text{wind velocity}} .$$

Observations show that the angle of impact remains remarkably constant over a wide range of conditions at $10° < \beta < 16°$. For example, if the grain does not rise high enough to reach full wind velocity, it will also not reach the full terminal velocity of fall and the angle β will not be affected much.

This bouncing movement of sand grains has been called "saltation".

4.1. The Surface Creep

The grain in saltation strikes the surface at a flat angle. A portion of its energy is passed on to the grains which are ejected upwards as it hits the loose surface. The rest of the energy is transmitted to the loose surface in disturbing many grains. This continued bombardment results in a slow forward creep of the grains composing the surface, i.e. the grains in the surface creep are not affected directly by wind, and receive their momentum by impact from saltating grains. The surface creep amounts to about one-quarter to one-fifth of total transport, but it plays a very important part in sand movement by wind. It is the means of transport of grains whose weight is far too great to be shifted by the wind drag alone. A high speed grain in saltation can by impact move a surface grain of about 200 times its own weight or 6 times its diameter.

Owing to the great difference in speed between the grains in saltation and in surface creep, the surface creep is responsible for the changes in the size grading of sand deposits.

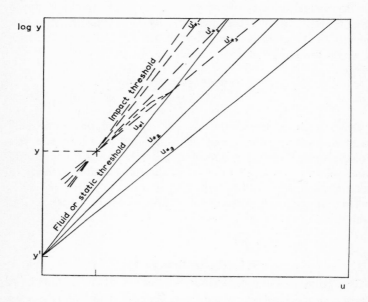

FIG. 4.1. Diagrammatic plots of wind velocity distributions, according to Bagnold. (By permission of Methuen & Co., Ltd.)

4.2. Effects of Sand Movement on Wind

When velocity measurements, taken over a wind-blown sand surface fixed by moistening, are plotted on log–normal paper (Fig. 4.1) they all converge at a point y', which is somewhat greater than $k/30.2$ if k is taken to mean the grain diameter. The equivalent roughness height k corresponds better to the depth of the little bombardment craters. If the measurements are repeated over the same sand surface but now dried out, the wind can be increased in strength up to a threshold velocity without any movement taking place and without change in velocity distribution.

But once movement has started at some point the velocity of the wind close to the surface downstream drops to a lower value—the impact threshold—due to the extra drag of the saltating grains.

The impact threshold is the limiting value at which particle motion can be maintained once it has been started. It is recalled here that the two threshold values, that is fluid (or static) and impact threshold have been observed in transport by air only.

Within about an inch of the surface the velocity distribution for a stronger wind does not plot as a straight line, but approaches a straight line higher up. Extending the straight parts of such lines they converge to a point. Irrespective of the wind strength, velocity at the elevation of this point remains constant, and closer to the ground the wind velocity actually falls as the wind above increases.

Thus (according to Bagnold) at a shear velocity of $u'_* = 3$ ft/sec the state over a moving fine sand ($d = 0.25$ mm) is the same as over a fixed surface of gravel of $d = 1\frac{1}{2}$ in. This must be due to the saltating sand grains.

Theory as well as observation show that the kink in the velocity distribution curve corresponds to the height of the statistical mean path of the saltating grains. This in turn corresponds with the mean height of the sand grains above the surface as obtained from concentration measurement.[3,4]

4.3. Instability of a Flat Sand Surface

If it is assumed that the distribution of descending grains is uniform over the whole area, then they can be represented diagrammatically by parallel equidistant lines, Fig. 4.2.

If it is further assumed that the mass flow in surface creep q_s at any point is proportional to the number of forward impulses which each unit area at that point receives per second, it follows that q_s at that point is proportional to the closeness to one another of the points of impact in the diagram. If now by one cause or another a tiny hollow is formed, then on the lee side AB these points are further apart and on the windward side they are closer together. Hence many more grains are driven up the slope BC than down the reverse slope AB. This means that the original hollow will get bigger. Grains excavated from the hollow will accumulate at C because they are not removed down wind as quickly as they are arriving, thus forming a second lee slope beyond C.

Each grain in saltation describes a certain path through the air from the place of its ejection from the surface to the point where

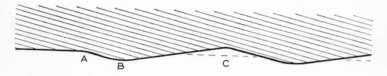

Fig. 4.2. Diagrammatic distribution of falling sand grains.

it strikes the surface and ejects another grain. From grain to grain the paths may be very different, but for any given strength of wind there exists in a statistical sense a mean grain path. In other words, of all the grains which are ejected from any given small area of the surface a greater number will fall on a second small area a distance of one characteristic path length L down-wind, than on any other area.

If grains were ejected in equal numbers from all over the surface, the distribution of their impacts would still be uniform; but if owing to a local tilting of the surface, a greater number of ejections occur at one point, then the effect is most markedly felt at another point distance L downstream. This is the principle of the mechanism of ripple formation. The initial irregularity is exaggerated by the surface creep up the downwind slope of the hollow and the mean path length of saltating grains leads to the systematic repetition. (Fig. 4.3.)

Ripple length and the mean path length are in close agreement. However, for a uniform sand, ripples disappear when u_* exceeds about three times the corresponding threshold value. The problem gets more complicated when the sands are non-uniform. A knowledge of the relationships between ripple length and wind gradient for natural non-uniform sands would be extremely useful. The mean wind velocity at any place could be determined with a tape measure.

The explanation as it stands would make the ripple crests continuously higher and the hollows deeper, but as the height of the crests increases, so does the wind velocity. Over the crests

FIG. 4.3. Schematic ripple pattern and characteristic path of saltating grains.

the wind velocity increases with the height at a greater rate than over the hollows, due to convergence of streamlines. Therefore, as the crests rise, more and more grains are pushed over and deposited in the hollows. This soon stabilizes the shape.

With uniform sands the ripple height to length ratio is usually about 1 : 20 to 1 : 30. With non-uniform sands this ratio may be 1 : 15 to 1 : 10 because coarser grains collect and pave the crests. Ripples of the latter type become decidedly asymmetrical and the cross-section is controlled by the proportion of coarse grains in the sand.

4.4. Ridges and Dunes

If there is over a surface of non-uniform sand a wind of lower strength than the ultimate threshold needed to set the largest grains in motion, the sand movement lasts for a limited time only, until the surface becomes paved by coarse grains. And it produces ripples whose crests are paved by coarse grains. If, however, there is a continuous supply of saltating grains coming into the area, the picture changes. By impact the saltating grains can dislocate grains more than 6 times their own diameter, so that coarse grains are still kept in motion. The falling grains can penetrate into the hollows, which were sheltered, and expose more bed material. The finer grains of this bed material go into

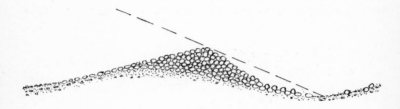

FIG. 4.4. Ridge formation.

saltation and are carried off, so that more and more coarse grains are excavated and driven up the windward slope.

The grains moving over the crest come into the complete shelter of the lee slope. (Fig. 4.4.)

Since new grains continue to arrive and no corresponding grains leave the crest (they arrive by creep) the characteristic path length ceases to be relevant. The ripples will go on growing and become ridges, some of which are about 2 ft high and a chain in wavelength.

The essential difference between ripples and ridges lies in the relative magnitudes of the wind strength and the dimensions of the crest grains. The wind conditions favourable for ridge formation are between the fluid or static threshold and the impact threshold. For the ripple, the wind is strong enough to carry away the topmost crest grains when the crest rises above a limiting height, whereas in the case of a ridge the wind is not strong enough to do this.

This leads to the basic features of dune formation. Imagine a stretch of sand which has reached a non-erosion stage in a given wind, i.e. covered by pebbles larger than those movable by this wind. These pebbles shelter the finer particles. Let this area be followed by a patch of fine sand.

If now the wind increases, more sand goes into motion from between the pebbles over the pebble covered area. But for any given wind the rate of sand flow over a surface containing pebbles, that is a harder surface, is greater than the rate possible over the surface of plain soft sand, where much of the energy in saltation goes to friction and surface creep. Hence the new supply of sand, with the increased wind, passes downwind over the pebble area at a greater rate than it can pass over the sand patch. Consequently, a strong wind causes accretion of sand on the soft sand patch. The slowing down of sand transport over the sand patch causes the air to become overloaded with sand and this has the effect that accretion starts upwind of the upwind border of the soft sand patch and the sand patch extends upwind as well as increases in thickness. This action lasts only as long as there is a plentiful supply of sand stored on a pebbly upwind surface, and stops where equilibrium is reached, i.e. when the pebbles shelter the sand so that no more erosion at given wind strength occurs. After that the movement on the sand patch still continues and the patch becomes longer downwind and thinner.

If the wind slackens, then any sand coming in from a sand source will be stored in the area dotted with pebbles. The pebbles shelter the sand until a new equilibrium condition is reached.

Hence, the pebble area acts as an accumulator of sand during slight winds, which may be from any direction, and this "stored" sand is used by the strong dune-building wind. For coastal dunes the sand supply is also independent of dune-building wind. The sand arrives on a beach by the action of the sea and becomes available for dune-building by wind when it dries out.

Excellent descriptions and explanations on the formation of various forms of dunes, on grading of sand deposits, etc., are given by R. A. Bagnold.[4]

Wind erosion is a very complex problem in relation to soil conservation and agriculture. The factors influencing wind erosion are numerous but the most important ones may be grouped as follows:

I. *Air*	II. *Ground*	III. *Soil*
Velocity	Roughness	Soil structure
Turbulence	Obstructions	Texture
Humidity	Topographic features	Content of organic matter
Viscosity	Cover	Lime
Pressure	Temperature	Specific gravity
		Moisture content

Wind erosion depends on the mutual relationship of these factors and the effect of any one may be to aggravate or to reduce the erosion. A simple example is that of wind turbulence which increases erosion. But although surface roughness increases the turbulence, the erosion decreases because the wind velocity near the surface is reduced. For aspects of wind erosion the reader is referred to literature.[5,6]

References

1. BAGNOLD, R. A., *Proc. Roy. Soc.* (A) **157**, 594 (1936).
2. BAGNOLD, R. A., *J. Geogr.* **89**, 409 (1937).
3. BELLY, P. Y., *Sand Movement by Wind*, U. S. Army Coastal Engineering Research Center TM No. 1, Jan. 1964.
4. BAGNOLD, R. A., *The Physics of Blown Sand and Desert Dunes*, Methuen, 1941.
5. CHEPIL, W. S. and WOODRUFF, N. P., The physics of wind erosion and its control, *Advances in Agronomy*, Vol. 15, pp. 211–302, 1963.
6. ——— ——— ———, Wind erosion and transportation, Progress Report Task Committee on Preparation of Sediment Manual, *Proc. Am. Soc. Civil Engineering, Journ. of Hydr*. Div., HY 2, March 1965.

CHAPTER 5

Sand Movement in Water

ALTHOUGH the physics of sand movement by air is fairly well understood, there is no such clarity when the transporting fluid is water, in spite of intensive research all over the world.

In the first place the difficulties of both observation and measurement are far greater in the case of water than in air. But more significant is the fact that the density ratio between the fluid and transported material is so little different from unity in the case of sand in water that it is extremely difficult to separate the effect of the motion of the surrounding water from that of the motion of the grains in it. Taking buoyancy into account, the density ratio for air and quartz sand is 1/2000 and 1/1·65 for water and quartz sand.

Thus, in order that a stationary grain gains a velocity equal to that of the fluid, the fluid must lose momentum equivalent to 2000 grain volumes in air and 1·65 grain volumes in water. Hence the reduction in the velocity of a stream of water by a given saltation of sand along the bottom is less than 1/1000 of the reduction in velocity in an identical case in air.

In air the reduction in velocity close to the surface is so great that the residual drag due to the stationary surface underneath can be neglected. It makes very little difference whether this surface is plane or rippled. The velocity of the air is entirely controlled by the intensity of saltation.

In water, however, the direct effect of saltation appears to be negligible and the velocity of water is controlled largely by the unevenness of the surface, such as ripples, dunes, etc. But the form and magnitude of this unevenness depends on the movement of the grains of which the surface is composed. These surface features not only translate but also change with changes of parameters defining the flow.

The bed features which may develop as the flow is increased can be classed as follows:

1. Ripples, regular wavy bed features with a flat upstream face and a steep downstream face but irregular in plan. These occur when the flow conditions are a little in excess of the threshold of sediment movement.

2. Dunes, much larger bed forms, usually with long straight crests. They may have ripples superimposed and occur at flow greater than that forming ripples.

3. Flat or slightly wavy bed occurs when the flow has been increased sufficiently to wipe out the dunes.

4. Anti-dunes form at still higher flow, generally in super-critical flow. The form is that of the dune but with the steep face upstream.

Exactly what controls the mechanism of sediment entrainment, formation of bed forms and sediment suspension is as yet not known. But fluid turbulence cannot be regarded as the only essential requirement for suspension. It has been observed in laboratory experiments[1] that a mean grain concentration of 35 per cent, at which the flow became laminar and the mean separation distance was still 0·3 of a grain diameter, the grains were maintained at this dispersion against the action of gravity.

In the conventional approach the problem of particle movement by water is divided into two parts, the bed load and the suspended load. This division lacks physical meaning, but so long as there is no general theory explaining all phases of sediment transport by one function it is justified.

References

1. BAGNOLD, R. A., Some flume experiments on large grains but little denser than the transporting fluid, and their implications, *Proc. Inst. Civil Eng.*, **4**, Part III, 174 (1955).

CHAPTER 6

The Sediment Load

IN THE following, several of the bed-load functions are discussed. It is not intended to give a complete record of all the formulae proposed but rather to discuss the types of formulae in the sequence of development.

6.1. The Du Boys Formula and Formulae of Similar Form

The Du Boys bed-load function (1879) is one of the oldest still in use.[1] Although based on a very simple model, it has considerably influenced many subsequent formulae.

The bed is arbitrarily considered to move as a series of superimposed layers of thickness d', presumably the same magnitude as the particles. The velocity of the layers is assumed to vary linearly by equal increments from zero to maximum.

Hence, if the nth layer from the top remains at rest, the surface layer must have a velocity

$$(n-1)\Delta v.$$

The discharge q_s of sediment in motion–volume per unit time per unit width of bed—may be found by multiplying the mean velocity of the layers

$$(n-1)\Delta v/2$$

by the total thickness nd'.

$$\therefore \ q_s = nd'(n-1)\Delta v/2.$$

The longitudinal component of fluid weight, $\gamma y_0 S$, is assumed to be balanced by the friction of the sediment water mixture at the bed. The friction coefficient between successive layers is assumed constant f_s so that the force balance is

$$\gamma y_0 S = f_s(\gamma_s - \gamma)nd' = \tau = \text{tractive force}$$

per unit area.

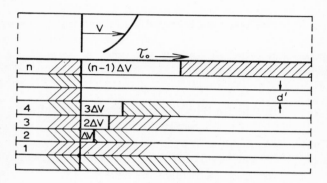

FIG. 6.1. Du Boys model of bed-load transport.

The threshold conditions are given when the top layer just resists motion. This yields a critical value of τ, marking the limit of motion, i.e. $n = 1$.

$$\therefore \ \tau_c = f_s(\gamma_s - \gamma)d'$$

hence

$$\tau = n\tau_c \quad \text{or} \quad n = \tau/\tau_c.$$

Introducing this value of n into the rate of transport equation yields

$$q_s = (d'\tau/\tau_c)(\tau/\tau_c - 1)\Delta v/2$$

$$= (\Delta v d'/2\tau_c^2)\tau(\tau - \tau_c).$$

$$\therefore \ q_s = C_s\tau(\tau - \tau_c), \tag{6.1}$$

where $C_s = vd'/2\tau_c^2$ is considered to depend entirely upon sediment characteristics.

The tractive force τ can be replaced by the use of Manning's formula

$$q = (1 \cdot 49/n)y^{5/3}S^{1/2}$$

$$yS = S^{7/10}(qn/1 \cdot 49)^{3/5} = \tau/\gamma$$

Substituting for τ in eqn. (6.1) yields

$$q_s = C_s \frac{S^{1 \cdot 4}\gamma^2}{(1 \cdot 49/n)^{1 \cdot 2}} q^{3/5}(q^{3/5} - q_c^{3/5}) \tag{6.2}$$

where q is the actual water discharge per foot, and q_c is the discharge per unit width of channel of slope S_c at which sediment transport begins.

Straub[2] gave some average values.

d (mm)	1/8	1/4	1/2	1	2	4
C_s (ft^6/ lbf^2 sec)	0·81	0·48	0·29	0·17	0·10	0·06
τ_c (lbf/ft^2)	0·016	0·017	0·022	0·032	0·051	0·09

Meyer-Peter and Müller,[3] for example, proposed a formula deduced from experiments with particles of uniform size, with mixtures, with natural gravel, with lignite and with baryta. Results cover a wide range of conditions and satisfy the formula

$$(K_s/K_r)^{3/2}\gamma DS = 0 \cdot 047(\gamma_s - \gamma)d_m + 0 \cdot 25(\gamma/g)^{1/3}[(\gamma_s - \gamma)/\gamma]^{2/3}G^{2/3} \tag{6.3}$$

where G is the weight of sediment transport per unit time and width, K_s/K_r is the ratio of the coefficient of roughness of the bed to that due to grain roughness of the surface, and K is the coefficient in the Strickler formula

$$V = Km^{2/3}S^{1/2}. \tag{6.4}$$

For wide channels the hydraulic mean radius m is replaced by the depth D. The ratio (K_s/K_r) introduces an allowance for the observed fact that with the formation of bed features, ripples, etc., the resistance to the flow changes. The resistance to the flow is taken to be the sum of the surface resistance due to grain roughness and the resistance due to ripples, dunes and irregularities. The value of K_s can also be adjusted for side effects.

With fully developed turbulence and hydraulically rough boundaries the resistance measurements by Nikuradse can be described by the simple formula of Strickler

$$K_r = \frac{\text{constant}}{d^{1/6}}.$$

Furthermore, the Chézy coefficient is related to the Darcy–Weisbach coefficient f as follows:

$$(1/f)^{1/2} = C/(8g)^{1/2}$$

and the Chézy coefficient $C = K_r m^{1/6}$. Thus for surface roughness in a wide channel

$$K_r = (8g/f)^{1/2} D^{-1/6}. \qquad (6.5)$$

Combining eqns. (6.4) and (6.5) yields

$$K_s/K_r = (f/8)^{1/2} V/(gDS)^{1/2}.$$

The Reynolds number is expressed as

$$\text{Re} = 4DV/\nu$$

and the relative roughness

$$k/D = d_{90}/4D,$$

d_{90} being the size of sediment in bed for which 90 per cent of the material by weight is finer. There is a tendency for the bed to become armoured by the larger particles of the bed material since these move less readily than the finer fractions. This has led to empirical selections of characteristic or effective particle sizes, such as the d_{90} here. The above form of Re expresses the linear dimension—diameter in case of pipelines—by the hydraulic mean radius m which for a circular cross-section is $D/4$. Hence,

$4m$ or 4 times the depth (hydraulic mean radius for two-dimensional flow) becomes equivalent to the diameter of a pipeline. Thus it is possible to use the available pipe flow charts of f versus Reynolds number with k/D as a parameter for evaluation of the ratio of K_s/K_r.

The effective particle size d_m in eqn. (6.3) is expressed as

$$d_m = 1/100 \, \Sigma \, d_i \Delta p_i, \qquad (6.6)$$

where Δp_i is the percentage of particle size d_i, the latter being the mean size of the fraction.

It is seen that the left-hand side of this transport formula [eqn. (6.3)] expresses the bed shear stress τ_0. The first term on the right-hand side is the critical or threshold shear stress τ_c which is proportional to $(\gamma_s - \gamma)d$.

Hence

$$G = N(\tau_0 - \tau_c)^{3/2},$$

where

$$N = 8(g/\gamma)^{1/2}\gamma/(\gamma_s - \gamma)$$

and it is seen that this formula is basically of the same form as the Du Boys formula.

A large number of formulae of basically the same form, either in terms of G or q_s, have been published of which only a few are listed:

Shields proposed from his experimental results a dimensionally homogeneous transport function of the form

$$(G/\gamma q)[(\gamma_s - \gamma)/\gamma S] = 10(\tau - \tau_c)/(\gamma_s - \gamma)d, \qquad (6.7)$$

where $G/\gamma q$ is the weight ratio of sediment and water discharges.

Meyer-Peter[3]

$$G^{2/3} = 39{\cdot}25q^{2/3}S - 9{\cdot}95d_m, \qquad (6.8)$$

where d_m is given by eqn. (6.6). This expression was derived from experiments with uniform sand and gravel and the values of the coefficient are for the ft-lbf-sec system of units.

Schoklitsch[4]

$$G = (A/d^{1/2})S^{3/2}(q-q_c) \qquad (6.9)$$

derived for uniform sand. The critical discharge at which the grain movement commences is given as

$$q_c = Bd/S^{4/3}. \qquad (6.10)$$

MacDougall[5]

$$G = AS^B(Sq-C). \qquad (6.11)$$

A and B are constants dependent only upon the specific gravity and mechanical composition of the sand,

$$C = Sq_c = S\tau_0 = \frac{100}{6} - d_g(\gamma_s - \gamma)/M.$$

Here d_g is the mean grain size, and M is a sand modulus found by dividing the area under the arithmetical sand grading curve along the 50 per cent abscissa. The ratio of area below the dividing line to the area above is the value M. The constant C may be found by extending the plot of bed load against tractive power (Sq) to the zero bed-load point. A has been found to range from 100 to 1000 and B from 0·25 to 1·0.

There are many more formulae of the same kind. When applying any of them it is essential to ascertain that the conditions and sediment are similar to those from which the particular formula was derived.

6.2. Einstein Bed-load Formula

Einstein[6,7] departed from the mean tractive force concept used by Du Boys and other authors of similar formulae. By the time of Einstein's original paper[6] the concepts of fluid turbulence and boundary layer had been well established and numerous attempts had been made, or were in progress, to apply these theories to the problem of sediment transport.

In turbulent flow the fluid forces acting on the particle vary with respect to both time and space, and it is assumed that the movement of any particle depends upon the probability that at a particular time and place the dynamic forces exceed the resisting forces. The probability of movement of any one particle is expressed in terms of the weight rate of sediment transport, the size and immersed weight of the particle, and a characteristic time which is taken to be a function of the quotient of the particle size divided by its fall velocity. It is postulated that a given particle size moves in a series of steps and that a given particle does not stay in motion continuously, but is deposited on the bed after a few steps.

The rate at which the bed load G_B moves through unit width of cross-section is subdivided into fractions i_B according to particle size. The rate at which the given size moves through unit width per unit time is then $(G_B i_B)$. Particles with diameter d are assumed to be performing individual steps of length $(A_L d)$ on the average. They are assumed to be deposited anywhere between the measuring section and $(A_L d)$ downstream, since on passing the measuring section they have already travelled an unknown part of the total step $A_L d$. Thus the area of deposition is $(A_L d)$ times unit width. The volume of the particle is $(A_2 d^3)$. The number of such particles deposited per unit time on a unit area of bed is expressed as

$$N_d = G_B i_B / (A_L d A_2 d^3 \rho_s g) = G_B i_B / (A_L A_2 \rho_s g d^4). \quad (6.12)$$

The fraction of the bed sediment of a given size range is i_b, and it is assumed that this also represents the fraction of the surface covered by particles of this size, that is the number of particles per unit area is $i_b / (A_1 d^2)$. If p_s is the probability of such a particle being eroded during a unit time, then the number of particles eroded per unit time and area is

$$N_e = i_b p_s / A_1 d^2. \quad (6.13)$$

For equilibrium the number of particles eroded must equal the number deposited. Transposing all quantities pertaining to the grain to the left

$$\frac{G_B i_B}{\rho_s g d^2} \frac{A_1}{A_2} = A_L i_b p_s. \quad (6.14)$$

Note that for uniform grain size the i = fractions become unity.

The probability p_s has the dimensions of sec^{-1}. If the time t_1 necessary to replace a bed grain by another similar one were known, p_s could be replaced by the absolute probability $p = p_s t_1$, and the eqn. (6.14) would become dimensionless. It is seen that p_s is the number of exchanges per second, t_1 is the time taken per exchange and p implies the total exchange time per second or the fraction of the total time taken by these exchanges.

The time t_1 is assumed to be proportional to the time the grain takes to settle in the fluid through the distance of its own diameter

$$t_1 = A_3'd/w = A_3[\rho d/g(\rho_s-\rho)]^{1/2}.$$

The latter form with $A_3 = 1/F$ follows from the expression for settling velocities by W. W. Rubey.[8]

F is a parameter for settling velocity w and $F = 0·816$ for particles of quartz greater than 1 mm settling in water at normal temperature. For smaller grains Rubey expressed the fall velocity as

$$w = [\tfrac{2}{3}g(\rho_s-\rho)/gd+36\mu^2/\rho^2d^2]^{1/2} - 6\mu/\rho d$$

$$= F[(dg(\rho_s-\rho)/\rho)]^{1/2}$$

and $$F = (\tfrac{2}{3}+36v^2/gd^3(\rho_s-\rho))^{1/2} - (36v^2/gd^3(\rho_s-\rho))^{1/2}.$$

Substituting for t_1 and p_s

$$N_e = (i_b p/A_1 d^2 A_3)[g(\rho_s-\rho)/\rho d]^{1/2}. \qquad (6.15)$$

Equating with N_d and rearranging

$$\frac{G_B}{\rho_s g}\sqrt{\left[\frac{\rho}{\rho_s-\rho}\frac{1}{gd^3}\right]} = \frac{i_b}{i_B}\frac{A_2 A_L}{A_1 A_3}p \qquad (6.16)$$

The left-hand term is called ϕ and is a transport rate function.

If p is small, deposition of a particle is possible everywhere, and for a given particle size A_L is assumed to be a general constant with a value of about 100. On that part of the bed where the lift force exceeds the particle weight, the values of p are large and deposition cannot occur.

By averaging the distances travelled by individual particles, $A_L d$ is expressed as

$$A_L d = \sum_{n=0}^{\infty} (1-p)p^n(n+1)\lambda d = \lambda d/(1-p),$$

where $(1-p)$ particles have been deposited after travelling λd; p particles are not deposited after travelling λd. Of these $p(1-p)$ particles have been deposited after travelling $2\lambda d$; $p^2(1-p)$ particles have been deposited after $3\lambda d$; etc. Substituting for A_L in eqn. (6.16)

$$\frac{p}{1-p} = \frac{A_1 A_3}{A_2 \lambda} \frac{i_B}{i_b} \frac{G_B}{\rho_s g} \sqrt{\left[\frac{1}{gd^3} \frac{\rho}{\rho_s - \rho} \right]}$$

$$\frac{p}{1-p} = A_* \frac{i_B}{i_b} \phi = A_* \phi_*. \tag{6.17}$$

The term ϕ is a dimensionless measure of bed-load transport and is independent of the size of the stream. Thus, for example, it is invariant between model and prototype.

From the preceding reasoning the probability p may also be interpreted as the fraction of the bed on which at any time the lift on a given particle is sufficient to cause motion. Thus p is assumed to be also the probability of the dynamic lift L on the particle being larger than its submerged weight

$$W' = g(\rho_s - \rho)A_2 d^3.$$

The lift is expressed as

$$L = C_L A_1 d^2 \frac{\rho u^2}{2}.$$

The flow parameters are based on the logarithmic velocity distribution formulae. Following Keulegan[9] the vertical velocity distribution is written as

$$\bar{u}_y/u_* = 5 \cdot 50 + 5 \cdot 75 \log_{10} (yu_*/v) = 5 \cdot 75 \log_{10} (9 \cdot 05 yu_*/v)$$

for smooth boundaries and

$$\bar{u}_y/u_* = 8\cdot50 + 5\cdot75 \log_{10}(y/k_s) = 5\cdot75 \log_{10}(30\cdot2y/k_s)$$

for hydraulically rough boundaries.

The transition between the two, including the rough and smooth conditions, is combined in the form

$$\bar{u}_y/u_* = 5\cdot75 \log_{10}(30\cdot2yx/k_s) = 5\cdot75 \log_{10}(30\cdot2y/\Delta).$$

Here $\bar{u}_y$ is the average velocity at a point distance y from the bed; $u_* = (\tau_0/\rho)^{1/2} = (gmS)^{1/2}$ = average shear velocity; k_s is the roughness of the bed; y is measured from a reference $0\cdot2k_s$ down from the plane containing the prominent roughness heights; x is the correction parameter; and $\Delta = k_s/x$ = apparent roughness of the surface.

For plane beds the roughness k_s is taken equal to the grain size of uniform sediment and d_{65} size (65 per cent of mixture by weight finer) for non-uniform sediment. The additional form drag of beds covered by bed features is accounted for by dividing the cross-section A into a fraction A' related to grain roughness and A'' related to form drag. Both have assigned to them the same length of wetted perimeter, so that two hydraulic mean radii m' and m'' are defined. Then

$$m' + m'' = m.$$

Thus the velocity distribution near the grain on the bed surface is expressed in terms of u_*, m' and $\delta' = 11\cdot6v/u_*$. It is also stated that in the lift calculation the velocity acting on all particles of a mixture must be measured at a distance $0\cdot35X$ from the theoretical bed, in which

$$X = 0\cdot77\Delta \quad \text{if } \Delta/\delta' > 1\cdot80,$$
$$X = 1\cdot39\delta' \quad \text{if } \Delta/\delta' < 1\cdot80.$$

The correction is introduced because particles smaller than X are sheltered between larger ones and in the laminar sublayer.

The lift is divided by a parameter ξ which is a function of d/X. When dealing with sediment mixtures a further correction factor

Y is introduced to describe the change of the lift coefficient in mixtures with various roughness conditions.

Thus

$$u = 5 \cdot 75 u_* \log_{10}[30 \cdot 2(0 \cdot 35 X/\Delta)],$$

$$u^2 = 5 \cdot 75^2 g m_B' S \log^2(10 \cdot 6 X/\Delta),$$

where m_B' is the m' value referred to bed only. The mean magnitude of lift coefficient C_L is taken to be $0 \cdot 178$, based on experiments[10] with 3 in. hemispheres, and at any given instant

$$L = 0 \cdot 178 A_1 d^2 \frac{\rho}{2} g m_B' S 5 \cdot 75^2 \log^2(10 \cdot 6 X/\Delta)(1+\eta),$$

where η is a parameter varying with time.

Next p is expressed as the probability that W'/L will be smaller than unity

$$1 > W'/L = \left(\frac{1}{1+\eta}\right)\left(\frac{\rho_s - \rho}{\rho}\frac{d}{m_B' S}\right)\left(\frac{2A_2}{0 \cdot 178 A_1 5 \cdot 75^2}\right)\frac{1}{\log^2(10 \cdot 6 X/\Delta)}$$

$$= \left(\frac{1}{1+\eta}\right)\psi B/\beta_x^2, \tag{6.18}$$

where the meaning of the latter symbols is in the sequence of bracketed terms above. Here η may be positive or negative but the lift is always positive so that

$$|(1+\eta)| > (B/\beta_x^2)\psi.$$

If the factors ξ and Y are introduced, this becomes

$$|(1+\eta)| > \xi Y B' \frac{\beta^2}{\beta_x^2}, \tag{6.19}$$

where $B' = B/\beta^2$, $\beta = \log_{10} 10 \cdot 6$, and $\xi, Y, \beta^2/\beta_x^2$ are all unity for uniform grain size and $x = 1$. Next η is expressed as $\eta = \eta_0 \eta_*$, where η_0 is the standard deviation of η.

C

Equation (6.19) is squared and divided by η_0 yielding

$$\left[\frac{1}{\eta_0}+\eta_*\right]^2 > \xi^2 Y^2 B_*^2 \psi^2 (\beta^2/\beta_x^2)^2 = B_*^2 \psi_*^2, \qquad (6.20)$$

where

$$B_* = B'/\eta_0 \quad \text{and} \quad \psi_* = \xi Y(\beta^2/\beta_x^2)\psi.$$

The limiting case of motion is given by

$$\left[\frac{1}{\eta_0}+\eta_*\right]^2 = [B_*\psi_*]^2$$

or

$$\eta_*\big|_{\text{limit}} = \pm B_*\psi_* - \frac{1}{\eta_0}. \qquad (6.21)$$

The η_* values are assumed to be normally distributed, so that with the use of the error function the probability for motion becomes

$$p = 1 - \frac{1}{\sqrt{\pi}} \int_{-B_*\psi_* - 1/\eta_0}^{B_*\psi_* - 1/\eta_0} e^{-t^2} dt.$$

Thus, by eqn. (6.17)

$$p = 1 - \frac{1}{\sqrt{\pi}} \int_{-B_*\psi_* - 1/\eta_0}^{B_*\psi_* - 1/\eta_0} e^{-t^2} dt = \frac{A_*\phi(i_B/i_b)}{1 + A_*\phi(i_B/i_b)}$$

$$= \frac{A_*\phi_*}{1 + A_*\phi_*}. \qquad (6.22)$$

There η_0, A_* and B_* are, by the development, universal constants, and the equation may be represented by a single function between the intensity of bed-load transport ϕ_* and the shear intensity ψ_*.

It should be noted that, in application the value of m_B' is assumed and values of u_*', δ, k_s/δ, x, Δ and ψ are calculated. For these calculations

$$\psi' = \frac{\rho_s - \rho}{\rho} \frac{d_{35}}{m_B' S}.$$

The empirical selection of d_{35} as the effective diameter for description of the resistance effects of bed features was proposed by Einstein. Then with the aid of an empirical function[7] of ψ' versus U/u''_* the calculated ψ' yields U/u''_* and u''_*. From u''_* the value of m'' is obtained and the sum of m' and m'' must yield m. In subsequent calculation the diameter of the size fraction considered is used in ψ.

Although Einstein gave the result as

$$\phi = f(\psi) \tag{6.23}$$

it is frequently given as

$$\phi = f\left(\frac{1}{\psi}\right), \tag{6.24}$$

because

$$\frac{1}{\psi} = \frac{\rho}{\rho_s - \rho} \frac{mS}{d}$$

is the same expression as the Shields entrainment function. Thus eqn. (6.24) represents the rate of sediment transport versus the entrainment function in the form of $G = f(\tau_0)$. It will be realized that this relationship was developed on a semi-rational basis of the same kind as used by C. M. White for threshold conditions. The relationship also dispenses with the critical shear stress implying transport at all velocities different from zero.

The constants and the function relating ϕ and ψ have to be obtained experimentally. The analytical model does not explain mechanism of the transport problem although various concepts of fluid mechanics are used to justify the steps. Fundamentally the result is not superior to the empirical formulae, although in its later form[7] it is more flexible for practical use. The derivation has been reproduced here because of the very wide use of this formula in the U.S.A.

From the plot of experimental data, from Zürich and the data by Gilbert, as ϕ versus ψ, Einstein obtained for uniform material

$$0 \cdot 465\phi = e^{-0 \cdot 391\psi}$$

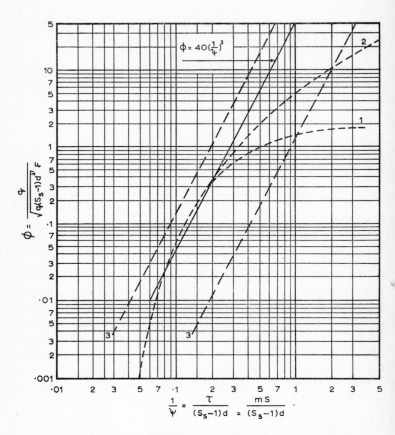

FIG. 6.2. Plot of the Einstein bed-load function. (By permission of John Wiley & Sons, Inc.) 1. The Einstein linear semilogarithmic relation for uniform material ($0 \cdot 465 \, \phi = e^{-0 \cdot 391 \psi}$), eqn. (6.23). 2. Deviation in Einstein presentation (ref. 6) of the plotted data for uniform material from the relationship (1). 3. These lines indicate the approximate limits to which the available data plot. The uniform material data in the above coordinates plot closely to the line $\phi = 40(1/\psi)^3$ for ϕ values less than 0·01 and follow line (1) for ϕ values less than 0·1. The uniform materials ranged from 0·315 mm sand to 28·6 mm gravel and included barite and coal.

with distinct deviation at the higher and more important values of ϕ. Sediment suspension may be at least partly responsible for this.

C. B. Brown[11] presented the same data as ϕ versus $1/\psi$ (Fig. 6.2) and all the data appears to reduce to one function only, which is approximated by

$$\frac{q_s}{\sqrt{[(S_s-1)gd^3]}F} = 40\left[\frac{\tau}{\gamma(S_s-1)d}\right]^3 \tag{6.25}$$

$$F = \sqrt{\left[\frac{2}{3}+\frac{36v^2}{gd^3(S_s-1)}\right]} - \sqrt{\left[\frac{36v^2}{gd^3(S_s-1)}\right]} \tag{6.26}$$

or

$$\phi = 40\left(\frac{1}{\psi}\right)^3. \tag{6.27}$$

At lower values the data tend to approach the same threshold limit as given by Shields (Fig. 6.2).

6.3. Kalinske Formula

Kalinske[12] proposed a sediment transport formula based on reasoning similar to that used by C. M. White for the threshold of bed movement.

The resultant of the fluid forces acting on the particle at the threshold of movement is taken to be equal to

$$F = \frac{\pi}{6}(\rho_s-\rho)gd^3 \tan\phi,$$

where ϕ is the coefficient of friction, taken to be the angle of repose. The number of grains per unit area effective in taking the shear is assumed to be $p/(\frac{1}{4}\pi d^2)$, where p is a factor defining the proportion of the bed surface taking the fluid shear.

Thus the product of fluid forces on the particle and the number of particles per unit area taking this force yields

$$\tau_c = \alpha p(\rho_s-\rho)gd \tan\phi. \tag{6.28}$$

For spherical particles the factor α from the above values is 2/3, but it will vary with particle shape for non-spherical particles.

The product of the weight of the particle and the number of these uniform grains moving at mean velocity $\bar{u}_s$ yields the transport rate per unit width.

$$G = \left[\frac{\pi}{6}(\rho_s - \rho)gd^3 p \Big/ \left(\frac{\pi}{4}d^2\right)\right]\bar{u}_s = \alpha_1 \gamma_s^* d^3 \bar{u}_s p / (\alpha_2 d^2)$$

$$= \alpha_3 p \gamma_s^* d \bar{u}_s \qquad (6.29)$$

or

$$G/(\bar{u}_s \gamma_s^* d) = \alpha_3 p. \qquad (6.30)$$

Any single particle at any instant is assumed to have a speed equal to

$$u_s = b(u - u_c), \qquad (6.31)$$

where u is the instantaneous fluid velocity at the particle level, and u_c is the critical fluid velocity that is required to initiate movement of the particle. In order to evaluate $\bar{u}_s$ it is assumed that deviations from the mean velocity at the particle level, $\bar{u}$, are distributed according to the normal law of error

$$f(u) = \left[e^{-(u-\bar{u})^2/2\sigma^2}\right]/(\sqrt{2\pi})\sigma, \qquad (6.32)$$

where $\sigma = \sqrt{[(u-\bar{u})^2]}$ is the standard deviation and $f(u)$ is the frequency distribution function.

Thus

$$\bar{u}_s = b \int_{u_c}^{\infty} (u - u_c)f(u)du.$$

The integral

$$\int_{-\infty}^{\infty} f(u)du$$

is unity.

Writing $(u - \bar{u})/\sigma = t$ and $(u_c - \bar{u})/\sigma = t_c$ and dividing $\bar{u}_s$ by $\bar{u}$

$$\frac{\bar{u}_s}{\bar{u}} = b\left[\frac{\sigma e^{-t_c^2/2}}{\bar{u}(\sqrt{2\pi})}\right] - b\left[\frac{u_c}{\bar{u}} - 1\right]\left[\frac{1}{2} - \int_0^{t_c} \phi(t)dt\right] = f_1\left(\frac{u_c}{\bar{u}}\right),$$

(6.33)

where

$$\phi_{(t)} = \frac{1}{\sqrt{2\pi}} e^{-t^2/2}.$$

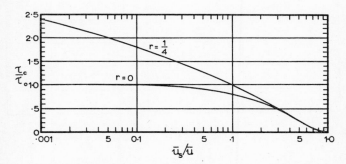

FIG. 6.3. Computed values of $\bar{u}_s/\bar{u}$ in terms of τ_c/τ_0 in the Kalinske bed-load formula.

If $\sigma/\bar{u} = r$, then $t_c = (u_c/\bar{u} - 1)/r$ and the ratio of $\bar{u}_s/\bar{u}$ is a function of the relative intensity of turbulence as given by r, and the ratio of u_c to $\bar{u}$. The equation yields a finite magnitude for u_s, the value depending on r. If $r = 0$, the flow is laminar and the equation reduces to $u_s = b(\bar{u} - u_c)$.

The ratio $u_c/\bar{u}$ is expressed in terms of $(\tau_c/\tau_0)^{1/2}$, where τ_0 is the applied fluid shear stress at the bed.

An interesting feature of the plot of $(\bar{u}_s/\bar{u})$ versus (τ_c/τ_0) is that the $\bar{u}_s/\bar{u}$ values are not influenced by turbulence for τ_c/τ_0 less than $\frac{1}{2}$. (Fig. 6.3.)

The bed-load equation is now written as

$$G/(\bar{u}\gamma_s^* d) = \alpha_3 p \bar{u}_s/\bar{u}.$$

(6.34)

Here $\bar{u}$ is the mean fluid velocity at grain level and from boundary layer theory it is taken that $\bar{u}$ can be expressed as $c\sqrt{(\tau_0/\rho)}$. The value of c is taken to be 11 and p is taken to be equal to 0·35. A value of $\sigma/\bar{u} = \frac{1}{4}$ was taken by Kalinske as typical of the turbulence intensity of natural streams and was used for evaluation of $\bar{u}_s/\bar{u}$, viz., τ_c/τ_0. The value of α_3 is of the order of 2/3 for near spherical particles.

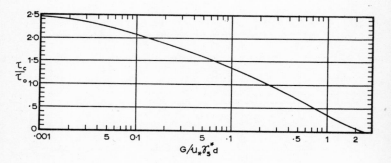

Fig. 6.4. Kalinske transport function $G/u_*\gamma_s^*d$.

Thus

$$G/(u_*d\gamma_s^*) = 2\cdot5(\bar{u}_s/\bar{u})$$

or

$$G/(u_*d\gamma_s^*p) = 7\cdot3f(\tau_c/\tau_0) \qquad (6.35)$$

or

$$G/(u_*d\gamma_s^*) = 2\cdot5f(\tau_c/\tau_0).$$

Kalinske proposes the median size of the grains for d in this formula which is displayed on Fig. 6.4.

Analogous to the Einstein–Brown formula, the Kalinske formula can be plotted as

$$\frac{q_s}{u_*d} = f\left[\frac{\tau_0}{\gamma(S_s-1)d}\right]. \qquad (6.36)$$

It is apparent that the form of the function is similar to that of ϕ versus $1/\psi$ (Fig. 6.2).

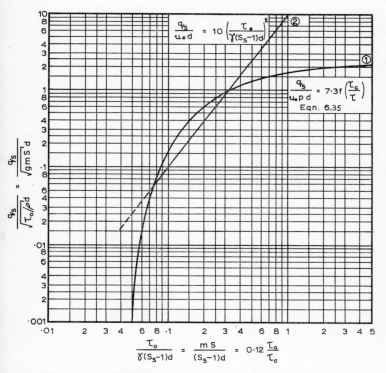

FIG. 6.5. Plot of Kalinske bed-load function. (By permission of John Wiley & Sons, Inc.) Experimental points follow line 1 closely for ordinate values less than 1·0. From ordinate value of 0·05 up the line 2 is a good fit to experimental points.

The straight part is satisfied by

$$\frac{q_s}{u_* d} = 10 \left[\frac{u_*^2}{(S_s-1)gd} \right]^2 \qquad (6.37)$$

C*

and the function curves round to the asymptotic value of $\tau_0/[\gamma/S_s - 1)d] = 0\cdot056$.

6.4. Bagnold's Sediment Transport Theory

Bagnold[13] started from the observation that a static grain mass cannot be sheared without some degree of dispersion, and this dispersion must be upwards, against the weight force. Consequently, the shear stress causing movement of grain layers must be accompanied by a normal stress between the moving grains and between the moving grains and the stationary bed grains.

Einstein in 1906 studied the effect on apparent viscosity of spherical grains dispersed in a fluid and solved analytically the problem of the grain effect on the fluid, when the concentration is very low, so that the grains may be assumed not to interfere with one another.

As the concentration increases the effects of the grain collisions cannot be ignored. The collisions should lead to increased dispersion of grains in a direction normal to the planes of shear and the normal dispersive stress should increase with grain concentration. The grain interference and displacement should give rise to an additional shear resistance due to the momentum transferred by the grains. This shear resistance would be additional to that due to intergranular fluid.

Bagnold carried out both theoretical and experimental studies of grain dispersion under the action of a shear stress.

A mass of rigid spheres of uniform diameter d and density ρ_s is assumed to be assembled in contact in a close-packed array. This mass is now dispersed uniformly so that the distance d between the centres is increased to (bd). If the resulting clear distance between grains is s, then

$$b = \frac{s}{d} + 1 = \frac{1}{\lambda} + 1,$$

where $\lambda = d/s$ represents the linear concentration, analogous to the volume-concentration concept of dense gases. The ratio of grain-occupied space to the whole space, the volume concentration, is given by

$$C = \frac{C_0}{b^3} = \frac{C_0}{(1/\lambda+1)^3}$$

or

$$\lambda = \frac{1}{(C_0/C)^{1/3} - 1},$$

where C_0 is the maximum possible concentration when $\lambda = \infty$ ($s = 0$) and is equal to $\pi/3\sqrt{2} = 0.74$.

The close-packed array is such that parallel planes can include the centres of adjacent spheres either as a square or a triangular pattern. If such a bed is uniformly expanded, the distance between centres of adjacent triangular pattern grain layers is $(\sqrt{\frac{2}{3}})bd$. In order that one of these layers may just slide over another, the value of λ cannot exceed 22.5. For the square pattern these values are $[\frac{1}{2}(\sqrt{2})bd]$ and $\lambda = 8.3$ respectively.

If the packing is not perfect or the spheres not of the same size, or shearing takes place along parallel curved surfaces, then the general shearing may become possible at some value of λ between 22.5 and 8.3.

At lower values of λ the grains will pass with increasing ease and the changes of shear stress transmitted by continuous and simultaneous contact between many grains should decrease rapidly with decreasing λ.

A value of $C_0 = 0.65$ is assumed for natural reasonably rounded uniform grains, which yields the relationship between linear concentration λ and volume concentration C shown in Fig. 6.6.

The overall shear resistance T is assumed to be

$$T = \tau^* + \tau',$$

where τ^* is the component due to the grain collisions, and τ' is due to the distortion of the intergranular fluid.

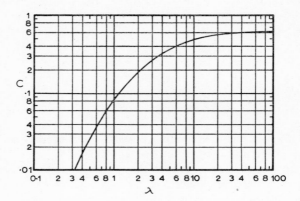

FIG. 6.6. Relation between linear concentration λ, and volume concentration C, for $C_0 = 0.65$, where C_0 is the maximum concentration of natural grains at rest and $\lambda = 1/[(C_0/C)^{1/3} - 1]$. (With the permission of the Royal Society, London.)

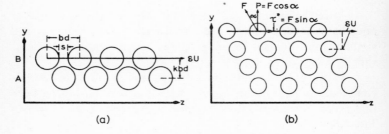

FIG. 6.7. (a) Cross-section of equidistant grain arrangement (three dimensional) with grains of alternate layers displaced in z-direction. (b) Two-dimensional sketch of a possible statistically preferred grain arrangement (non-equidistant) which might be associated with dispersive pressure proportional to shear stress in a viscous fluid.

The fluid shear may be of negligible inertia (laminar) or inertial (turbulent). Similarly, the grain motion independent of the fluid, may be inertial or of negligible inertia.

Bagnold sets up two simple analytical models for the cases when grain inertia effects dominate and when the effect of fluid viscosity dominates.

In the grain inertia case he derives for the dispersive pressure

$$P_y \propto f(\lambda)\rho_s d^2 \left(\frac{dU}{dy}\right)^2 \cos \alpha_i,$$

where α_i is the angle between the resultant force and its normal component.

The grain layer is considered to be sheared over another layer at a mean relative velocity δU. Collisions lead to an exchange of momentum which yields the force or pressure components P_y and τ^*.

The latter is expressed as (Fig. 6.7)

$$\tau^*_{xy} = P_y \tan \alpha_i.$$

This shear stress is assumed to be due to grain stresses only and is regarded as additive to fluid shear stress, τ', due to fluid turbulence in the intergranular space. It should vanish when $\lambda \to 0$.

For the viscous case, the grains are considered to move relative to each other giving rise to a temporary reduction of the mean value of δU during the approach of one grain to another and an increase as they move apart. It is also reasoned that this should lead to a preferred arrangement of grains. Assuming harmonic velocity fluctuations an expression for the combined grain and fluid mean shear stress is obtained as

$$\overline{T} = \mu(1+\lambda)\left(1+\frac{f_1(\lambda)}{2}\right)\frac{dU}{dy}.$$

To test these theories Bagnold carried out experiments in an annulus of which the outer boundary rotated, using grains of the same density as the fluid (in order to prevent the grains from settling out). The results were plotted as shear stress and grain pressure against corresponding values of $\rho_s d^2 (dU/dy)^2$.

When plotted as τ^*/λ or P/λ versus $\rho_s \lambda d^2 (dU/dy)^2$ both τ^* and P, for all values of λ within the experimental range, became

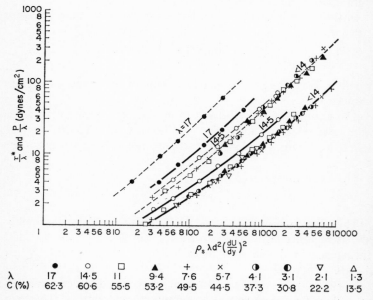

λ	• 17	○ 14·5	□ 11	▲ 9·4	+ 7·6	× 5·7	◗ 4·1	◑ 3·1	▽ 2·1	△ 1·3
C (%)	62·3	60·6	55·5	53·2	49·5	44·5	37·3	30·8	22·2	13·5

FIG. 6.8. (From ref. 13 by permission of the Royal Society, London.)

proportional to $(dU/dy)^2$ at sufficiently high speeds. In this inertia region τ^* and P also become proportional to λ^2 for all values of λ less than about 14 and plot on the same line (Fig. 6.8).

It was also found that $\tau^*/P = \tan \alpha_i$ for $\lambda < 14$ approaches a constant value of 0·32 approx.; for $\lambda > 14$, $\tan \alpha_i$ is approximately 0·4.

In the low speed region further tests were carried out with the viscosity increased sevenfold. The results for $\lambda < 14$ lie on one line and the plot shows that the pressure P persists. Here at the lowest speeds laminar flow conditions were approached.

The persistence of the dispersive grain stress P in the absence of grain inertia effects is interesting. It implies that fluid turbulence is not the only means of support for the suspended grains.

Bagnold introduces two dimensionless numbers G and N. The number G is a dimensionless number formed from μ, τ^* or P, ρ_s and d and combined with λ as

$$G^2 = \frac{\tau^* \rho_s d^2}{\lambda \mu^2} \quad \text{and} \quad \frac{P \rho_s d^2}{\lambda \mu^2}.$$

It is a form of Reynolds number, i.e.

$$\frac{d \sqrt{(\tau^*/\rho_s \lambda)}}{\mu / \rho_s}$$

and is analogous to $u_* d / \nu$. The number N is the ratio of

$$\frac{\text{shear stress resulting from grain inertia}}{\text{viscous shear stress}}.$$

Inertia stress at the high speed, P or τ^*, was proportional to $\lambda^2 \rho_s d^2 (dU/dy)^2$.

From the experiment it was observed that the shear stress was proportional to $\lambda^{3/2}$.

Thus

$$N = \frac{\lambda^2 \rho_s d^2 (dU/dy)^2}{\lambda^{3/2} \mu (dU/dy)} = \frac{\lambda^{1/2} \rho_s d^2 (dU/dy)}{\mu}.$$

Plotted in terms of these dimensionless numbers the curves for the two different viscosities join into a continuous line.

The ratio $\tau^*/P = \tan \alpha_i$ increases from $0 \cdot 32$ steadily to another constant value of about $0 \cdot 75$. The transition region range is approximately $450 > N > 40$ or $3000 > G^2 > 100$ or in terms of Reynolds number

$$\left[\frac{d\sqrt{(\tau^*/\rho_s\lambda)}}{\mu/\rho_s}\right], \ 55 > Re > 10.$$

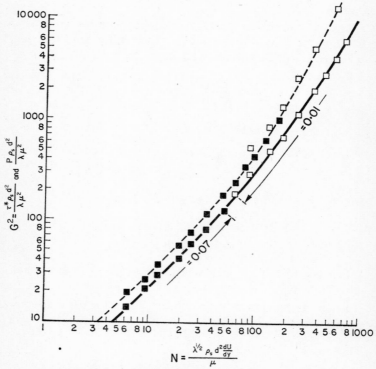

FIG. 6.9. Conformity of experimental results at different viscosities. Complete line shows shear stress; broken line pressure. $\lambda = 11$. $\square$, $\mu = 0.01$ (water); $\blacksquare$, $\mu = 0.07$. (From ref. 13 by permission of the Royal Society, London.)

6.4.1. Stress equilibrium in steady two-dimensional flow

In his paper[14] Bagnold proposes a theory for sediment transport based on the concepts developed above.

In an ideal case, where the top layer of grains slides simultaneously, the applied shear stress plus the component of weight of grains equals the resisting stress and can be expressed as

$$T_0 = (\rho_s - \rho)gd \cos \beta(C_- \tan \alpha_-) - (\rho_s - \rho)gdC_- \sin \beta$$

$$= (\rho_s - \rho)gd \cos \beta C_-[\tan \alpha_- - \tan \beta],$$

where β is the slope of the bed, C_- is the grain concentration within the bed, and $\tan \alpha_-$ is the ratio of τ^*/P.

For natural cohesionless grains C_- is constant at approximately 0·63. Tan α_- may be assumed to be equal to the tangent of the angle of repose, and for rounded grains is also of the order of 0·63. The product $(C_- \tan \alpha_-)$ is stated to have a value of 0·4 with very little deviation, i.e. if the grains are more angular and stand at a steeper slope their static concentration for random packing is usually less.

The product $(\rho_s - \rho)gd \cos \beta$ is used as a unit for stress measurement

$$\sigma = (\rho_s - \rho)gd \cos \beta \qquad (6.38)$$

and is the same expression as used by Shields. The resisting stress thus becomes

$$T_0 = \sigma C_-[\tan \alpha_- - \tan \beta].$$

The total applied shear stress (the impelling force) at any plane y in the flow can also be expressed as

$$T_y = T_y' + (\rho_s - \rho)g \sin \beta \int_y^{y_0} C dy,$$

where T_y' is the weight component of water and the other term on the right-hand side is the weight component of the grains, both parallel to the bed.

The integration is from level y ($y = 0$ at the surface of stationary bed) to the free surface. Dividing by the unit stress and converting

y into units of grain diameter $y = ad$, then a dimensionless measure of the applied tangential stress is obtained.

$$\theta_a = \frac{T_a}{\sigma} = \theta'_a + \tan \beta \int_a^{a_0} C\,da$$

or at the bed surface

$$\theta_0 = \theta'_0 + \tan \beta \int_0^{a_0} C\,da.$$

But

$$\theta_0 = \frac{\tau'_0}{\sigma} + \frac{\tau^*_0}{\sigma},$$

where τ'_0 is the intergranular fluid shear stress and τ^*_0 is the shear stress arising from grain dispersion.

Hence,

$$\theta_0 = \theta'_0 + \tan \beta \int_0^{a_0} C\,da = \frac{\tau'_0}{\sigma} + \frac{\tau^*_0}{\sigma}. \tag{6.39a}$$

In two-dimensional parallel flow

$$T'_y = (y_0 - y)\rho g \sin \beta$$

dividing by σ and substituting ad for y, then

$$\frac{T'}{\sigma} = \frac{(a_0 - a)d\rho g \sin \beta}{(\rho_s - \rho)g d \cos \beta} = \left(\frac{\rho}{\rho_s - \rho}\right)(a_0 - a) \tan \beta$$

$$\theta_0 = \left[\frac{\rho}{\rho_s - \rho}(a_0 - a) + \int_0^{a_0} C\,da\right] \tan \beta. \tag{6.39b}$$

The force component, normal to the bed of dispersed grains over any plane $a = y/d$ is the normal component of the immersed weight of all the grains above that plane. Thus per unit of bed area

$$\text{load of grains} = (\rho_s - \rho)g \cos \beta \int_a^{a_0} C\,dy = \sigma \int_a^{a_0} C\,da$$

and a characteristic load χ can be introduced as

$$\chi = \frac{\text{load}}{\sigma} = \int_a^{a_0} C\,da,$$

i.e., the mass per unit area of the load χ is $\chi \rho_s d$.

The total load is assumed to consist of (1) *the bed load* which is that part of the load whose normal immersed weight component is in equilibrium with the grain stress P. This load is transmitted downwards via the dispersed grains and rests on the stationary bed; (2) *the suspended load* which is the part of the total load whose weight component is carried by the fluid turbulence. It is assumed that this load is not transmitted to the bed grains but appears as an excess static fluid pressure. Bagnold[15] measured such an excess pressure over the pressure due to an equal column of grainless fluid.

How the load divides into these parts is not yet known. It can only be written in general terms that the grain content C of every unit volume consists of components C_b and C_s and

$$\left.\begin{array}{ll}
\text{bed load} & \chi_b = \displaystyle\int C_b\,da = \frac{P}{\sigma} \\[2ex]
\text{suspended load} \;\; \chi_s = \displaystyle\int C_s\,da \\[2ex]
\therefore \;\; \text{total load} & \chi = \chi_b + \chi_s
\end{array}\right\} \qquad (6.40)$$

If the suspended load is not carried by the stationary bed, then the normal stress between the bed-grain layers at any depth $-a$ is

$$\chi_{b\,(\text{static})} = \int_0^{a_0} C_b\,da + C_- a_-. \qquad (6.41)$$

Consequently, for normal stresses the moving bed-load grains may be considered as an upper part of the bed, which happens to be dispersed.

With

$$\theta = \theta' + \tan \beta \int Cda = \frac{\tau'}{\sigma} + \frac{\tau^*}{\sigma},$$

$$\tau^* = P \tan \alpha = \sigma \chi_b \tan \alpha, \tag{6.42}$$

$$\theta = \theta' + \tan \beta (\chi_b + \chi_s) = \frac{\tau'}{\sigma} + \chi_b \tan \alpha. \tag{6.43}$$

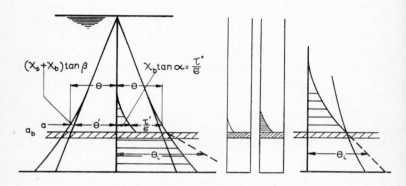

FIG. 6.10. Diagrammatic presentation of the stress equilibrium.
(By permission of the Royal Society, London.)

According to this concept the applied tangential stress can be subdivided in the following ways:

(a) Into the tangential components of the weight of fluid and the weight of dispersed grains.

(b) The shear stress in the intergranular fluid and that arising from the grain dispersion.

With increasing concentration the fluid resistance term becomes progressively less.

When the seepage flow through the bed is neglected then τ' is zero below the surface and $\tan \alpha$ is constant at $\tan \alpha_-$. The value of the static friction is unknown, but from the diagram (Fig. 6.10) it is seen that the limiting yield stress θ_L of the bed below the top layer will exceed θ_-.

From eqn. (6.43)

$$\theta_L = \chi_{b\,(\text{static})} \tan \alpha_-,$$

since $\tau'/\sigma = 0$ below surface and $\tan \alpha = \tan \alpha_-$.

By eqn. (6.41)

$$\chi_{b\,(\text{static})} = \int_0^{a_0} C_b\,da + C_- a_- = \chi_{b0} + C_- a_-,$$

but since the load on the bed $\chi_{b0} \neq f(a)$

$$\left| \frac{\partial \theta_L}{\partial_a} \right| = C_- \tan \alpha_- = 0.4 \quad \text{by experiment.} \tag{6.44}$$

From eqn. (6.39a) for the top layer of grains between 0 and $-a$

$$\left| \frac{\partial \theta}{\partial a} \right|_{a=0} = \frac{\partial \theta'}{\partial a} \bigg|_{a=0} + \tan \beta C_-,$$

where $\partial \theta'/\partial a$ is zero below the sand surface, since θ_0' is assumed to vanish below the sand surface.

For the bed to shear only at its surface

$$\left| \frac{\partial \theta}{\partial a} \right|_0 < \left| \frac{\partial \theta_L}{\partial a} \right|$$

or

$$C_- \tan \alpha_- = 0.4 > \left| \frac{\partial \theta'}{\partial a} \right|_0 + \tan \beta C_-, \tag{6.45}$$

c.f.

$$\frac{T_0}{\sigma} = C_-[\tan \alpha_- - \tan \beta].$$

For 2-D parallel flow from eqn. (6.39b)

$$0.4 > \left[\left(\frac{\rho}{\rho_s - \rho} \right) + C_- \right] \tan \beta. \tag{6.46}$$

The above implies that in a plane bed of uniform spheres perfectly piled, no grains should move as long as the applied shear stress does not exceed the above limit of 0·4. On reaching this limit all grains would be stripped from the top layer. Bagnold reasons that when the tangential fluid stress θ_0 on the bed boundary is raised to the value $C_-\tan\alpha_-$, the whole top layer should then be "peeled" off simultaneously and become dispersed. If this dispersion were to be removed or carried in suspension, the successive top layers would be peeled off continuously.

Observation does not substantiate this. In the first instance from experiment the threshold values θ_c range between 0·03 and 0·06 for turbulent flow, and reach about 0·2 in laminar flow. And secondly, Bagnold[15] found that the grain bed could persist at an applied tangential stress more than 12 times the value of $C_-\tan\alpha_- = 0·4$. Consequently, the dispersed grains must give rise to an additional bed load (χ_{bo}) which increases the resisting stress at the bed surface. Bagnold now expanded his theory to reconcile it with the observations. The argument goes that the surface grains of a natural surface are not uniformly exposed, and the applied tangential stress under turbulent fluid flow conditions is not steady. Therefore individual grains start to move at a lower value of θ_0.

If θ_c is the threshold value of $\theta_0 = T_0/\sigma$, which for the special case of level bed is

$$\tau_c \Big/ \left[\left(\frac{\rho_s - \rho}{\rho} \right) g\rho d \right] = u_{*c}^2 \Big/ \left[\left(\frac{\rho_s - \rho}{\rho} \right) gd \right],$$

then it is known that

$$\theta_c = f(\mathrm{Re}),$$

where

$$\mathrm{Re} = \frac{u_* d}{\nu}.$$

In a randomly piled plane bed of natural grains there are assumed to be grains which may be moved by the fluid at the threshold stress θ_c, but not at any lesser. There are also no grains

which by virtue of their own weight and surroundings only will
withstand an evenly distributed tangential stress exceeding
$\theta_0 = C_- \tan \alpha_- = 0\cdot4$.

When θ_0 is increased beyond θ_c grains continue to be eroded
until the extra resisting stress $\tau_0^*/\sigma = \chi_{b0} \tan \alpha_0$ at the bed surface
offsets the applied stress difference $\theta_0 - \theta_c$ due to the load of
dispersed grains. Equation (6.43)

$$\theta - \frac{\tau'}{\sigma} = \chi_b \tan \alpha$$

then becomes at the bed surface

$$\chi_{b0} \tan \alpha_0 = \theta_0 - \frac{\tau_0'}{\sigma}, \qquad (6.47)$$

where $\tan \alpha_0$ is to be determined by the G value just over the bed
surface. It is also assumed that during this happening the concentration λ_0 just over the bed is not large enough to affect
seriously the internal shear stress of the intergranular fluid, i.e.
$\tau_0' = \tau_c$ and as θ_0 is increased the stress element τ_0'/σ will remain
at the value of θ_c so long as $\tau_0' = \tau_c$.

Thus

$$\chi_{b0} \tan \alpha_0 = \theta_0 - \theta_c. \qquad (6.48)$$

It is then suggested that as $\theta_0 \to 0\cdot4$ the shear due to the intergranular fluid approaches zero, so that when $\theta_0 > 0\cdot4$ the equation becomes

$$\chi_{b0} \tan \alpha_0 = \theta_0. \qquad (6.49)$$

In the case of wind-blown grains this condition is obtained
at the threshold of grain movement, because the agitation of the
whole bed surface by the "ballistic" type of saltation destroys all
the inherent shear strength of the bed grains as soon as the chain
reaction is set off by the first grains moved.

Thus the bed-load flow of grains under a turbulent water
stream should become quantitatively similar to that of wind-
blown sand when θ_0 in water exceeds about $0\cdot4$.

Curves corresponding to eqns. (6.48) and (6.49) are plotted on double logarithmic scales for three representative cases (Fig. 6.11).

Curve (a) is for wind-blown grains; θ_c becomes zero at first movement. Curve (b) is for turbulent liquid flow over a plane bed

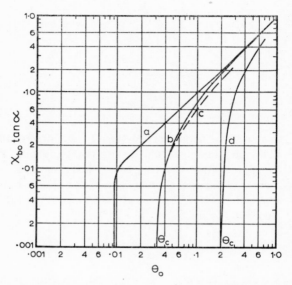

FIG. 6.11. Curves of $\chi_{bo} \tan a = \theta_0 - \tau_0'/\sigma$, wind-blown grains (a), (b) and (c) turbulent flow, (d) a hypothetical viscous flow. (By permission of the Royal Society, London.)

surface τ_0'/σ constant at θ_c until concentration C_0 begins to suppress turbulence at the bed surface; τ_0'/σ has been given Shields minimum value of θ_c (0·033 or, if required, 0·056) up to $\theta_0 = 0·2$ and has thereafter been diminished progressively to zero at $\theta_0 = 0·4$. (At $\theta_0 = 0·4$ the resulting increase in χ amounts to 8 per cent.)

It is now suggested that the difference between the applied shear and the threshold shear stress which is not already opposed by the bed-load resistance, is carried by grains scattered over the exposed surface and that these can be assumed to form a thin layer (in a statistical sense) over the surface. This layer of thickness less than grain diameter causes a static grain load $\delta\chi$ and it is assumed that this gives rise to an increment in θ defined as (Fig. 6.12)

$$\theta_0'' = \delta\chi \tan \alpha_-. \qquad (6.50)$$

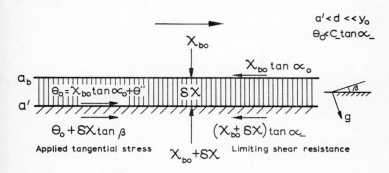

Fig. 6.12. Diagrammatic distribution of the difference in applied and threshold shear, according to Bagnold. (By permission of the Royal Society, London.)

Thus eqn. (6.47) becomes

$$\theta_{-a'} = \chi_{b0} \tan \alpha_0 + \theta_0'' + \delta\chi \tan \beta$$

yielding for the stability of these grains

$$(\chi_{b0} + \delta\chi) \tan \alpha_- > \theta_{-a'}.$$

Substituting for $\delta\chi$ from eqn. (6.50)

$$\chi_{b0} \tan \alpha_- > \chi_{b0} \tan \alpha_0 + \theta_0'' \frac{\tan \beta}{\tan \alpha_-} \qquad (6.51)$$

and as before $\theta_0'' = \theta_c$ for the lower range of θ_0.

When eqn. (6.51) is not satisfied there is a resistance deficit of a plane grain bed which is

$$\theta_0''' = \chi_{b0}(\tan \alpha_0 - \tan \alpha_-) + \theta_0'' \frac{\tan \beta}{\tan \alpha_-} \qquad (6.52$$

and bed grains will be eroded continuously.

But since these cannot be supported as a bed load, without an increase in the applied stress (χ_{b0} is the total bed load) they must be redeposited on the bed. Hence, the plane bed surface becomes wavy. The form drag of these bed forms will equal the drag deficit θ_0''' in the bed resistance.

The resistance deficit θ_0''' should disappear when $\theta_0 \to 0.4$ and the bed features due to it should also disappear. It was also suggested that at this stage θ_0'' vanishes so that the shear resistance arising from dispersed grains alone is sufficient to balance the applied shear.

This reasoning implies that bed features should develop on any bed surface with downward ($+$) slope regardless of grain size when θ_0 is slightly larger than θ_n^c.

For small grains $\tan \alpha_-$ may be less than $\tan \alpha_0$. Then the features should get more prominent with increasing θ_0. For large grains ($G^2 > 440$), $\tan \alpha_- > \tan \alpha_0$ and the features which develop when $\theta_0 \doteq \theta_c$ should disappear as θ_0 and, in consequence, χ_{b0} increase. The persistence of the bed features should then depend on the downward slope ($+ \tan \beta$).

Further, making the approximation that the form drag is concentrated at the downstream faces of the ripples means that on the upstream faces of these primary bed features the resistance deficit can be accounted for by the slope. Writing for the local upstream slope β', then $\tan \beta'$ should be limited to [by eqn. (6.52)]

$$\tan \beta' = -\chi_{b0}(\tan \alpha_0 - \tan \alpha_-) \frac{\tan \alpha_-}{\theta_0''},$$

where θ_0'' could be replaced by θ_c. This also suggests that the upstream faces become plane surfaces.

The steady state could be expressed as

$$\chi_{b0} \tan \alpha_0 = \theta_0 - \theta_0'' - 0_0'''. \qquad (6.53)$$

Substituting for θ_0''' by eqn. (6.52) yields

$$\chi_{b0} \tan \alpha_0 = K\left[\theta_0 - \theta_0''\left(1 + \frac{\tan \beta}{\tan \alpha_-}\right) \right] \doteq K(\theta_0 - \theta_c),$$

where

$$K = \frac{\tan \alpha_0}{2 \tan \alpha_0 - \tan \alpha_-}.$$

This with $\tan \alpha_0 = 0.32$ and 0.75 at the limits and $\tan \alpha_- = 0.63$ yields for $K = 32$ and 0.86 respectively.

The effect of the initial form drag on the bed load χ_{b0} is small, and the growth of this effect with θ_0 was indicated by curve (c) in Fig. 6.11.

Bagnold further suggests that with the increase of the primary ripple form a stage is reached where this perturbation leads to formation of vortices in the hollows, strong enough to scour. The scoured material is deposited on the upstream slope of the next ripple downstream making these steeper and so aggravating the situation, leading to a sudden instability of the primary ripple system. Thus when the vorticity gets strong enough to cause scour in the hollows there should be a discontinuity in the relationship between χ_{b0} and θ_0.

No theory is offered as to the size or shape of these secondary bed features, but it is reasoned that the form drag created by the new system should exceed the value needed for the steady state, because of the extra erosion and deposition. A discontinuity in the relationship between $\chi_{b0} \tan \alpha_0$ and θ_0 would therefore be expected and this is shown to happen in the plot of experimental results on Fig. 6.13.

Equation (6.52), by neglecting $\theta'(\tan \beta / \tan \alpha_-)$ becomes

$$\chi_{b0} = \frac{\theta_0'''}{\tan \alpha_0 - \tan \alpha_-}$$

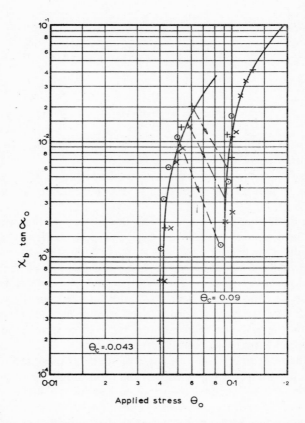

FIG. 6.13. Bed loads, reduced from relevant experimental transport rates of Fig. 6.14d, curve III, showing discontinuity on passing from the "primary ripple" system to secondary bed features, according to Bagnold. Symbols O, ×, + refer to different constant bed-slope settings and to relative flow depth decreasing in this order. (By permission of the Royal Society, London.)

suggesting that the critical value χ_{b0} at which the discontinuity and change from primary ripple system occurs should increase with grain size, since $\tan \alpha_0 \rightarrow \tan \alpha_-$, till the breakdown fails to occur.

6.4.2. *Bagnold's transport formula*

Following the ideas expounded in 6.4.1, Bagnold[14] developed a sediment transport formula based on concepts of work done. The mass of grains Q_{sb} passing the cross-section per unit width and time is expressed as

$$Q_{sb} = \rho_s \int_y^{y_0} Cu \, dy = \rho_s d \int_a^{a_0} Cu \, da,$$

where u is the local fluid velocity and the other symbols are as defined in section 6.4.1.

Next, this relationship is expressed in terms of work done. With the aid of simplifying assumptions the relative velocity past bed-load grains is expressed as

$$u_b = \left(\frac{\frac{4}{3}\sigma \tan \alpha}{\rho C'_{Db}}\right)^{1/2} ; \quad v_b = 0$$

and past the suspended grains as

$$u_s = \tan \beta \left(\frac{\frac{4}{3}\sigma \cos \beta}{\rho C'_{Ds}}\right)^{1/2} ; \quad v_s = (\tfrac{4}{3}\sigma \cos \beta/\rho C'_{Ds})^{1/2},$$

where C'_D is the drag coefficient of the particles at the given concentration of sediment. These expressions indicate that at a given location u_b/v_s is proportional to $(\tan \alpha)^{1/2}$.

The mean relative velocity is expressed as

$$\bar{u}_b = (2/3\sigma \tan \alpha/\rho C_D)^{1/2},$$

where C_D is the drag coefficient for an isolated grain at Reynolds number $\text{Re} = \bar{u}_b d/\nu$ and $\tan \alpha$ is the mean stress ratio within the bed-load dispersion.

The actual rate of work done in grain transport along the bed is expressed as the tangential stress opposing the motion times the grain speed relative to the bed, that is

$$W = T_R U.$$

The tangential stress is taken to be proportional to the grain's normal immersed weight component and their ratio is

$$E = \frac{T_R}{\sigma \chi_b}.$$

Thus

$$T_R = E\sigma\chi_b = E\sigma \int_a^{a_0} C\,da$$

and

$$W = E\sigma \int_a C u\,da = E\sigma Q_{sb}/(\rho_s d).$$

For the bed load $E = \tan \alpha_0$, since all the bed-load grains are supported by the bed-surface grains, and

$$W_b = \frac{\sigma Q_b}{\rho_s d} \tan \alpha_0.$$

Allowing for the slope of the bed surface the rate of work done by the fluid in transporting sediment becomes

$$W_{bF} = \frac{\sigma Q_b}{\rho_s d} (\tan \alpha_0 - \tan \beta).$$

The tangential stress applied to the bed surface by the weight of the fluid is T_0' and the total applied shear stress $T_0 = T_0' + \sigma\chi_b \tan \beta$. The non-effective applied shear stress is $T_c = \sigma\theta_c$ and the effective fluid stress is $T_0' - T_c$.

The available energy is now expressed as force times velocity

$$(T_0' - T_c)A(T_0'/\rho)^{1/2},$$

where $(T'_0/\rho)^{1/2}$ is the fluid's shear velocity at the effective plane of application taken to describe the fluid velocity and A is a coefficient. Thus

$$W_{bF} = (T'_0 - T_c)A(T'_0/\rho)^{1/2}\eta,$$

where η is the efficiency factor of the transport.

The rate of energy loss of the fluid per unit of bed load is taken to be $\bar{u}_b\sigma \tan \alpha$ and η is defined by

$$\eta = \frac{u_b\sigma \tan \alpha}{\sigma(\sigma/\rho)^{1/2}} = \tan \alpha \left(\frac{2 \tan \alpha}{3C_D}\right)^{1/2}.$$

Here $u_b\sigma \tan \alpha$ is a "standard rate of energy loss of fluid per unit of bed load", and the product of the unit of stress σ and $(\sigma/\rho)^{1/2}$—interpreted as velocity—is taken to define the energy available per unit of bed load. Thus the ratio of the rate of work done by the fluid to the rate of energy loss of the fluid can be expressed as

$$\frac{W_{bF}}{\bar{u}_b\sigma \tan \alpha} = \frac{(T'_0 - T_c)A(T'_0/\rho)^{1/2}}{\sigma(\sigma/\rho)^{1/2}} = (\theta' - \theta_c)A(\theta')^{1/2}$$

which is a dimensionless relationship between the bed-load transport rate function and the stress applied by the fluid at the bed surface. The function on the left is denoted by

$$\phi_b = \frac{Q_b}{\rho_s d(\sigma/\rho)^{1/2}} \frac{\tan \alpha_0 - \tan \beta}{\tan \alpha} \frac{1}{(2 \tan \alpha/3C_D)^{1/2}}$$

and

$$\phi_b = \phi'_b \frac{1}{B_b}.$$

The group $\phi'_b = Q_b/\rho_s d(\sigma/\rho)^{1/2}$ is essentially the same group of parameters as deduced by H. A. Einstein from an entirely different approach. Bagnold suggests that the value of $\tan \alpha$ be obtained from the appropriate value of G^2. In liquids $\tan \alpha_0$ at the base should not be very different from $\tan \alpha$ within the dispersion.

For wind transport it is reasoned that within the dispersion G^2 is so large that tan α is constant at 0·32 and that the surface creep, resulting from the saltating movement of grains, leads to conditions similar to mechanical shearing. Therefore tan α_0 is approximately the static value (angle of repose) which for average grains was taken to be 0·63 or approximately twice tan α. Thus for liquids

$$B_b = \frac{\sqrt{(2 \tan \alpha / 3C_D)}}{1 - \tan \beta / \tan \alpha} \xrightarrow[\beta \to 0]{} \sqrt{\frac{2 \tan \alpha}{3C_D}}$$

and for wind

$$B_b = \frac{\sqrt{(\frac{2}{3} \tan \alpha / C_D)}}{2 - (\tan \beta / \tan \alpha)} \xrightarrow[\beta \to 0]{} \frac{1}{2} \sqrt{\left(\frac{2 \tan \alpha}{3C_D}\right)}.$$

The bed-load equation is then expressed as

$$\phi_b = A(\theta' - \theta_c)(\theta')^{1/2}$$

or

$$\phi_b' = AB_b(\theta' - \theta_c)(\theta')^{1/2}$$

or

$$Q_b = AB_b\rho_s d\left[\left(\frac{\rho_s - \rho}{\rho}\right)gd \cos \beta\right]^{1/2}(\theta' - \theta_c)(\theta')^{1/2}.$$

In the case of transport by wind $\theta_c = 0$, and a value of 8·5 is suggested for A.

An analogous expression is developed for the suspended load transport. The suspended grains are assumed, in a statistical sense, to be falling through the fluid with a relative velocity whose normal component is $\bar{v}_s$. In order to maintain a steady suspended load, work has to be done at a rate $\sigma \chi_s \bar{v}_s$, which is visualized as being expanded in pushing an equal frictionless grain load up an imaginary slope of $(\bar{v}_s / \bar{U}_s)$. This ratio is the equivalent of E or tan α_0 in the case of the bed load. Here $\bar{U}_s$ is the mean sediment velocity.

Thus

$$\phi_s = \frac{Q_s}{\rho_s d} \frac{(\bar{v}_s/\overline{U}_s - \tan \beta)}{(\bar{v}_s/\overline{U}_s)\bar{v}_s}$$

$$= \frac{Q_s}{\rho_s d(\sigma/\rho)^{1/2}} \frac{1}{B_s},$$

where

$$B_s = \frac{(\frac{4}{3} \cos \beta / n C_{Ds})^{1/2}}{1 - (\overline{U}_s/\bar{v}) \tan \beta}$$

which becomes $(4/3C_{Ds})^{1/2}$ when $\overline{U}_s \tan \beta \ll \bar{v}_s$. Here C_{Ds} is the drag coefficient on individual grains and n is a correction factor which allows for the presence of other grains. Suspended load concentration is considered to be small (less than 1 per cent) so that grains can be regarded as isolated, i.e. $n = 1$. B_s will begin to increase very rapidly as $\overline{U}_s \tan \beta \to \bar{v}_s$.

Little is known of the mechanism which renders a given turbulent fluid flow capable of maintaining a suspension of grains of a given size and density. However, the rate at which the necessary internal turbulent energy is supplied to the fluid must be associated with the fluid shear at the boundaries and with the nature of these boundaries. At the threshold of grain movement the bed is essentially a fixed boundary of grain roughness. As the flow is increased the nature of the boundary changes progressively until, for liquids, $\theta_0 \doteq 0.4$. By then the boundary to the fluid flow has become a zone of moving bed-load grains. From θ_c to $\theta_0 \doteq 0.4$ the nature of the turbulence generation must also be transitional. At a still higher value of bed shear stress the liquid flow should be virtually independent of the underlying stationary boundary. The resistance should be entirely granular and independent of θ_c which can be discarded. The turbulence generation should by now have reached another stable state and if grain suspension occurs at all it should be fully developed. ϕ_s should become proportional to $\theta^{3/2}$, the new measure of the available rate of energy supply for the transport of both bed and suspended bed load.

D

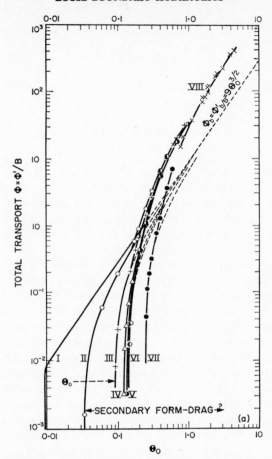

FIG. 6.14a. Transport rates plotted in terms of the general function
$$\phi = \phi'/B.$$

I. Experimental data for wind-blown sand; values of B from ref. 14.
II–VII. Experimental data for quartz grains in water; mean curves
of Figs. 6.14c, d, e replotted with ordinates ϕ' divided by the
appropriate values of B from ref. 14. VIII. Wax–lead stearate
grains ($d = 1\cdot36$ mm) in water and Perspex grains ($d = 1\cdot58$ mm)
in brine; density difference $\rho_s - \rho = 0\cdot004$; from data given in ref. 15.

(*cont.* p. 83)

Instead of adding

$$\phi_b' + \phi_s' = \frac{Q_b + Q_s}{\rho_s d(\sigma/\rho)^{1/2}} = \phi_b\left(1 + \frac{\phi_s}{\phi_b}\frac{B_s}{B_b}\right) = \phi',$$

Bagnold introduces an equal work concept as

$$\phi_{s(b)} = \phi_b\left(\frac{B_s}{B_b}\right)$$

and writes the total transport rate as

$$\phi = \phi_b\left(1 + \frac{B_s}{B_b}\right) = A\theta'^{3/2}\left(1 + \frac{B_s}{B_b}\right).$$

If suspended load is zero

$$\phi' = \phi_b' = A'(\theta' - \theta_c)\theta'^{1/2},$$

where $A' = AB_b \doteq 9B_b$.

If suspension occurs, it should be fully developed when $\theta > 0\cdot4$ and θ_c can be discarded. So the total value of ϕ' should be

$$\phi' = A'\theta'^{3/2}\left(1 + \frac{B_s}{B_b}\right).$$

Bagnold has calculated a table of values for the bracket term.

When experimental results are plotted as ϕ versus $\theta_* = [(\theta_0 - \theta_c)\theta_0^{1/2}]^{2/3}$ they define approximately a single function (Fig. 6.14)

$$\phi = 9\theta_*^{3/2}\left(1 + \frac{B_s}{B_b}\right),$$

Calculated extrapolations of transport rates of bed load alone are shown by the dashed curves; all these are now asymptotic to $\phi = 9\theta_0^{3/2}$. Departure of the experimental plots from the bed-load curves are assumed to be due to the development of a suspended load in addition to the bed load. The plotting symbols connect with those of Fig. 6.14b. (From ref. 14 by permission of the Royal Society, London.)

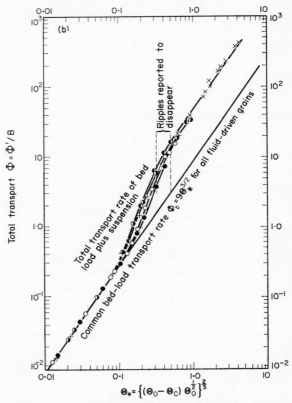

FIG. 6.14b. Replot of Fig. 6.14a in terms of $\theta_* = \{(\theta_0 - \theta_c)\theta_0^{1/2}\}^{2/3}$ showing the common range over which the suspended load appears to develop, the narrow range of θ_* over which the bed features disappear, and the apparent ultimate proportionality of the transport rates of bed load and suspended load. Plotting symbols connect with Fig. 6.14a: ○, II; + III; ◑, V; ◔, VI; ●, VII; ×, VIII. (From ref. 14 by permission of the Royal Society, London.)

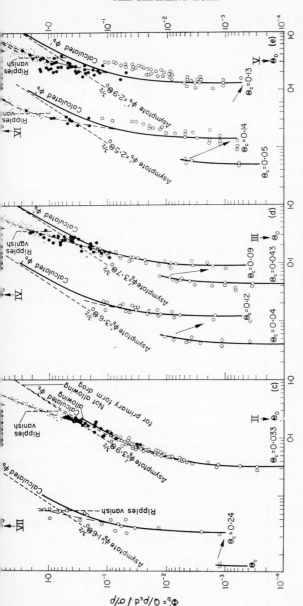

Fig. 6.14c, d and e. Sediment transport rates.

Fig. c. Plot II: ○, U.S.W., 0·586 mm; ●, Gilbert, 0·787 mm, subcritical flow;·; Gilbert, supercritical flow. Plot VII: U.S.W., 0·205 mm. Showing close agreement at low values of θ_0 between experimental rates of θ_0 with calculated rates of total load with calculated rates for bed load rate alone as given by $\phi_b{}' = 9aB(\theta_0 - \theta_c)\theta_0^{\frac{1}{2}}$, where the constant 9 comes from wind-blown sand data; $a = 1$ except for plot II (primary form-drag only, $a = 0.9$); B is given by ref. 14, calculated from a mean drag coefficient $C_D = 2C_D$ and θ_c is the experimental parameter given by the value of θ_0 at the foot of the plot.

Fig. d. Plot III: ●, Gilbert 0·507 mm; ○, U.S.W., 0·524 mm. Plot IV: ○, U.S.W., 0·483 mm.

Fig. e. Plot V: ○, U.S.W., 0·347 mm; ●, Gilbert, 0·376 mm, subcritical flow;; Gilbert, supercritical flow. Plot VI: ○, U.S.W., 0·31 mm; ●, Gilbert, 0·305 mm, subcritical flow;·; Gilbert, supercritical flow. The U.S.W. data seem anomalous in these two cases, possibly owing to an error in the difficult estimation of the mean water depth over a deeply rippled bed. (From ref.14, by permission of the Royal Society, London.)

where B_s is taken to be zero from threshold up to about $\theta = 4\theta_c$ for liquid-driven grains and up to the experimental limit of $\theta = 0\cdot2$ for wind-blown grains. For liquid-driven grains from $\theta = 0\cdot4$ upwards, an analytical expression was developed.

A comparison of observed results with the Bagnold sediment transport formula is made in the U.S. Geological Survey Water-Supply Paper 1498-F. *A Study of Fluvial Characteristics and Hydraulic Variables Middle Rio Grande, New Mexico*, by J. K. Culbertson and D. R. Dawdy, 1964.

6.5. Comparison of the Bed-load Formulae

At the present stage of knowledge it is difficult to compare meaningfully the various sediment transport formulae. The sediment discharge formulae are generally based on laboratory data and very little is known about the way the transport relationships will depend on the size of the water course. Transport rates obtained in the laboratory usually apply to straight flumes. But natural watercourses are irregular in cross-section and alignment. Published comparisons of measured rates of sediment transport with those calculated by various formulae are rather inconclusive and the amount of satisfactory data available from natural rivers for comparison purposes is also very limited.

Any of the transport formulae can be transcribed in terms of another. Thus Chien,[16] for example, showed that the Meyer-Peter and Müller bed-load equation can be transcribed as

$$\phi = (4/\psi - 0\cdot188)^{3/2},$$

where ϕ and ψ are as defined for Einstein bed-load formula. This equation and the Einstein formula both fitted the data analysed quite well for values of ϕ up to 10. For larger values the Einstein bed-load equation yields smaller transport rates. Comparison of the plot of ϕ versus $1/\psi$ with the Kalinske bed-load equation $q_s/u_* d$ versus $u_*^2/(S_s - 1)gd$ shows an obvious similarity.

The logarithmic plots of most of the sediment transport functions usually approximate to straight lines of the form

$$G = Aq^n$$

or in terms of mean concentration

$$\frac{G}{q} = Aq^{n-1}.$$

Experience shows that n is larger than unity, implying that concentration as well as sediment transport will increase with increasing discharge q.

In this connection interesting comparisons can be made with the aid of the Shields entrainment function $\tau_c / \gamma(S_s - 1)d \doteq 0.056$. With $S_s = 2.6$ and $\tau_c / \gamma = y_0 S$ this yields

$$d \doteq 11 y_0 S.$$

The ratio of τ_0 / τ_c upon substitution of $d/11$ for $y_0 S$ becomes $11 y_0 S / d$. Hence,

$$\frac{\tau_0 - \tau_c}{\gamma(S_s - 1)d} = \frac{\tau_0}{\gamma(S_s - 1)d} - \frac{\tau_c}{\gamma(S_s - 1)d}$$

$$= \frac{y_0 S}{(S_s - 1)d} - 0.056$$

$$= \frac{0.056}{d}(11 y_0 S - d).$$

With this value the various bed-load functions can be described as follows:

(1) Shields:

$$\frac{G(S_s - 1)}{\gamma q S} = 10 \frac{\tau_0 - \tau_c}{\gamma(S_s - 1)d}$$

yields

$$\frac{G}{\gamma q} = 0.35 \frac{S}{d}(11 y_0 S - d).$$

If $d \ll 11 y_0 S$, then

$$\frac{G}{\gamma q} \doteq 3.85 \frac{y_0 S^2}{d}.$$

The water discharge q in terms of the Chézy formula is proportional to $y_0^{3/2}S^{1/2}$ so that for a constant S

$$q_s \propto q^{5/3}.$$

Or expressed in terms of the Manning formula $q \propto y_0^{5/3}S^{1/2}$ and for a constant S

$$q_s \propto q^{8/5}.$$

(2) Du Boys:

$q_s \propto q^{4/3}$ in terms of the Chézy formula.

$q_s \propto q^{6/5}$ in terms of the Manning formula.

(3) Einstein–Brown:

$$q_s/[g(S_s-1)F^2d^3]^{1/2} = 40[\tau/\gamma(S_s-1)d]^3$$

becomes with $q \propto Vy$

$$q_s \doteqdot 27Fd^{3/2}(y_0S/d)^3$$
$$q_s/q = 27Fy_0^{3/2}S^{5/2}/d^{3/2},$$

so that

$q_s \propto q^2$ in terms of the Chézy formula

$q_s \propto q^{9/5}$ in terms of the Manning formula.

(4) Kalinske:

$$q_s/u_*d = 10[u_*^2/(S_s-1)gd]^2,$$

substituting $u_*^2 = gy_0S$

$$q_s/[(gy_0S)^{1/2}d] = 3{\cdot}9(y_0S/d)^2$$
$$q_s/(y_0S)^{1/2} \doteqdot 22(y_0S)^2/d$$
$$q_s/q \propto y_0S^2/d,$$

so that

$q_s \propto q^{5/3}$ in terms of the Chézy formula

$q_s \propto q^{8/5}$ in terms of the Manning formula

which is the same as by Shields' formula.

If one plots these relationships between q_s and q on logarithmic scales, then variations are apparent both in the slope and in the

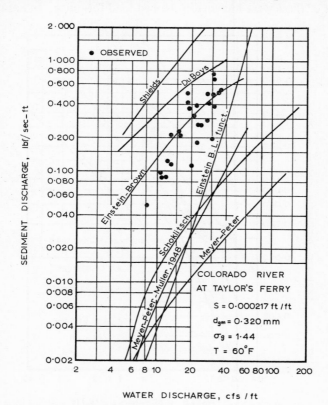

FIG. 6.15. Sediment rating curves for Colorado River at Taylor's Ferry, according to several formulae, compared with measurements. By permission of the California Institute of Technology.)

location on this plane. Data obtained from observations on natural watercourses, however, are equally widely spread from river to river.

D*

With most formulae the slope becomes too flat with high discharge and sediment load. This only underlines the fact that most of these were intended to be bed-load formulae. In natural

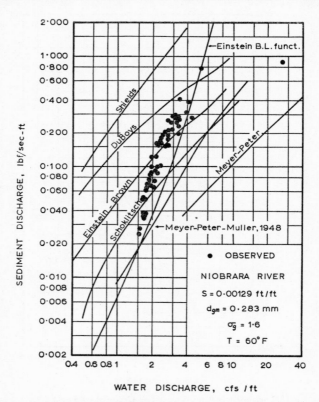

FIG. 6.16. Sediment rating curves for Niobrary River near Cody, Nebraska, according to several formulae, compared with measurements. (By permission of the California Institute of Technology.)

rivers much of the sediment is transported in suspension. But even between formulae accounting for both bed and suspended sediment load, see, for example, refs. 7 and 17, the variations are appreciable. Experience shows that in applying formulae of this kind to particular cases, errors of 100 per cent are to be

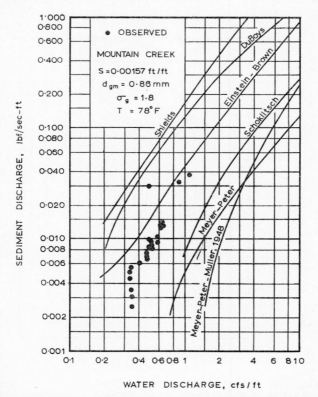

FIG. 6.17. Sediment rating curves for Mountain Creek near Greenville, South Carolina, according to several formulae, compared with measurements. (By permission of the California Institute of Technology.)

expected. In other words the formulae provide estimates only. Therefore it is most desirable that more than one formula be used. The sediment and flow conditions should be compared to those from which the constants of the particular bed-load formula were obtained.

Figures 6.15, 6.16, 6.17 and 6.18 from ref. 18 illustrate the point.

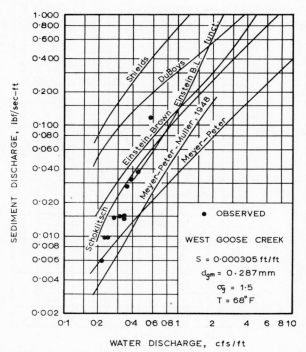

Fig. 6.18. Sediment rating curves for West Goose Creek near Oxford, Mississippi, according to several formulae, compared with measurements. (By permission of the California Institute of Technology.)

One of the primary causes for discrepancies in the sediment transport rates calculated from the various formulae is the definition of shear stress τ_0 or shear velocity u_* to be used in the formulae. Figure 6.19 shows a plot of the total drag (equal to surface drag plus form drag) versus the mean velocity, and the friction factor f against the mean velocity and the shear velocity. It is seen that the shear velocity actually decreases a little as the mean velocity increases from 1·8 to 3·5 ft/sec. What happens is that on passing the threshold shear for movement of given granular bed material the initially flat bed changes into a rippled

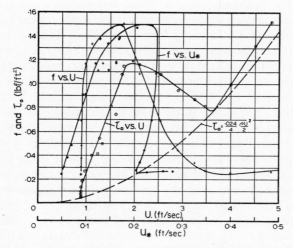

FIG. 6.19. Plot of total shear stress against mean velocity and of friction factor against mean and shear velocity.

bed and the friction factor increases rapidly, while the mean velocity changes relatively little. The friction factor attains its maximum value when the steepness (height to wavelength ratio) of the bed forms reaches a maximum. Thereafter, although the bed forms may grow, their steepness decreases with increasing velocity and the friction factor also decreases. By the time the transition flat bed has been reached the friction factor is approximately the same as at the threshold of particle movement. A further increase in velocity leads to the formation of antidunes and the friction factor increases again. This concept is discussed in greater detail in Chapters 12 and 13.

The total shear also reaches a maximum when the bed forms have their maximum steepness and a large part of this total is form drag. As the bed forms flatten the form drag diminishes also. The surface drag corresponding to a flat surface of sand grain roughness is shown by the dashed line on Fig. 6.19.

On the upstream faces of these bed features the temporal local surface drag varies from zero at the reattachment region of the surface of discontinuity formed at a crest, to a maximum at the next crest downstream (see also Chapter 12). Underneath the interface (in the ground roller) the surface drag is in the upstream direction but small in magnitude. The maximum at the crest is approximately equal to the surface drag indicated by the flat grain bed. The deficit in the local surface drag over the rest of the upstream face of the bed forms is compensated for by a part of the form drag which, by means of the turbulence generated, stirs up the particles and makes these mobile at lower values of the local temporal surface drag. The general turbulence level also increases and thus the rate of sediment transport could also be expected to increase. Just how much of the form drag contributes to the sediment transport is not known. Einstein[7] uses an empirical subdivision but most authors do not refer to a subdivision of the drag at all (see also Chapter 13).

References

1. DU BOYS, P., Études du régime du Rhône et l'action exerceé par les eaux sur un lit à fond de graviers indefiniment affouillable, *Annales des Ponts et Chaussées*, Ser. 5, **18**, 141–95 (1879).

2. House Document 238, 73rd Congress, 2nd Session, U.S. Govt. Printing Office Washington, D.C., 1935, p. 1135. Also in *Engineering Hydraulics* edited by Hunter Rouse, Wiley and Sons.

3. MEYER-PETER, E. and MÜLLER, R., Formulae for bed-load transport, *Proc. 2nd Meeting IAHR*, Stockholm, 1948, pp. 39–64.

4. SCHOKLITSCH, A., *Der Geschiebetrieb und Geschiebefracht*, Wasserkraft und Wasserwirtschaft, 1934, p. 37.

5. MACDOUGALL, C. H., Bed-sediment transportation in open channels, *Trans. Am. Geophysical Union*, pp. 491–5 (1934).

6. EINSTEIN, H. A., Formulae for the transportation of bed-load, *Trans. A.S.C.E.* **107**, 561–77 (1942).

7. EINSTEIN, H. A., *The bed-load function for sediment transportation in open channel flows*, Techn. Bulletin No. 1026, Sept. 1950, U.S. Dept. of Agriculture, Soil Conservation Service, Washington, D.C.

8. RUBEY, W. W., Settling velocities of gravel, sand and silt, *Am. J. Sci.* **25**, No. 148 (April 1933).

9. KEULEGAN, G. H., Laws of turbulent flow in open channels, *Nat. Bureau of Standards*, *J. Res.* **21**, 701–41 (1938).

10. EINSTEIN, H. A. and EL-SAMNI, El-S. A., Hydrodynamic forces on a rough wall, *Rev. Mod. Phys.* **21**, 520–4 (1949).

11. BROWN, C. B., *Engineering Hydraulics*, edited by Hunter Rouse, p. 796.

12. KALINSKE, A. A., Movement of sediment as bed in rivers, *Trans. Am. Geophys. Union*, **28**, 615–20 (1947).

13. BAGNOLD, R. A., Experiments on a gravity free dispersion of large solid spheres in a newtonian fluid under shear, *Proc. Roy. Soc. London* (A) **225**, 49 (1954).

14. BAGNOLD, R. A., The flow of cohesionless grains in fluids, *Phil. Trans. Roy. Soc.* Series A, No. 964, **249** (1956).

15. BAGNOLD, R. A., Some flume experiments on large grains but little denser than the transporting fluid, and their implications, *Proc. Inst. Civil Eng.* **4**, part 3, 174 (1955).

16. CHIEN, NING, The present status of research on sediment transport, *Trans. A.S.C.E.* **121** (1956); or *Proc. A.S.C.E.* **80**, Sept. No. 565 (Dec. 1954).

17. LAURSEN, E. M., The total sediment load of streams, *Proc. A.S.C.E.* **84**, No. HY 1 (February, 1958).

18. VANONI, VITO A., BROOKS, N. H. and KENNEDY, J. F., Lecture notes on sediment transportation and channel stability, W. M. Keck Laboratory of Hydraulics and Water Resources California Institute of Technology, Report No. KH–R–1, January, 1961.

CHAPTER 7

Discussion of Sediment Transport by Dimensional Analysis

DIMENSIONAL analysis is extensively used in discussions of the sediment transport problem. The process of dimensional analysis arranges the variables thought to be involved in a systematic way. It yields convenient dimensionless coordinates for the experimental study of the problem and these are less in number than the variables.

The assembly of the variables is necessarily speculative because the mechanism of the problem is not known explicitly. In principle the problem could be expressed as a function of:

(Parameters defining geometry; flow; fluid and sediment).

An assembly of the parameters could be as follows:

D = depth of flow = y_0

B = width of channel

f_c = factor defining cross-sectional shape of channel

f_g = factor defining plan geometry of channel

Q = discharge

S = slope of energy gradient

G = weight of sediment transported per unit time and unit width

ρ = density of fluid

γ = submerged weight of fluid, e.g. $\gamma_{water} - \gamma_{air}$, or $\gamma_{salt-water} - \gamma_{fresh-water}$; in the first of these γ_{air} is negligible, but with problems involving sediment-laden steam flows into a reservoir, fresh and sea water, hot and cold water, and the like—that is problems involving density currents—the difference becomes an important factor

μ = viscosity of fluid

d = characteristic particle size

σ = standard deviation of particle size distribution

α = particle shape factor

γ_s^* = submerged weight of sediment

ρ_s = density of sediment. The submerged weight of particles or liquid represents the net effect of gravity, i.e. the impelling force for downward motion. The density of particles or liquid represents the inertia effect which resists any change in motion and should be important in turbulent motion.

If appreciable wash load is present, the concentration of fine suspended material has to be introduced as it affects both density and viscosity of the fluid.

Many of these parameters can be expressed in terms of other variables. τ_0 may be replaced by γDS, α by the fall velocity w and following Shields' work[1] the velocity distribution has usually been replaced by the shear velocity u_*.

Thus one can write

$$f(D, B, f_c, f_g, Q, S. G, \rho, \mu, \gamma, d, \sigma, w, \gamma_s^*, \rho_s) = 0.$$

Three physical dimensions (mass, length, time) are involved and hence one can obtain $(n-3)$ independent dimensionless groups or π-numbers. Generally, the total number N of possible forms of dimensionless numbers is

$$N = \frac{n!}{(k+1)!(n-k-1)!},$$

where k is the number of physical dimensions.

Thus, for example, $n = 15$ yields $N = 1365$, but only $n-3 = 12$ are independent. For example, with ρ, Q and D as the repeating variables

$$f\left(\frac{B}{D}, f_c, f_g, S, \sigma, \frac{GD^6}{\rho Q^3}, \frac{\mu D}{\rho Q}, \frac{\gamma D^5}{\rho Q^2}, \frac{d}{D}, \frac{wD^2}{Q}, \frac{\gamma_s^* D^5}{\rho Q^2}, \frac{\rho_s}{\rho}\right) = 0.$$

$$(7.1)$$

Terms involving Q may be multiplied by $(B/D)^n$, that is, dividing Q by the area BD, so that U can be substituted for Q.

For example,

$$\frac{GD^6}{\rho Q^3}\left(\frac{B}{D}\right)^3 = \frac{G}{\rho(Q/DB)^3} = \frac{G}{\rho U^3}\ .$$

Or direct substitution $Q = UBD$ yields for the example

$$\frac{G}{\rho U^3}\left(\frac{D}{B}\right)^3\ .$$

Thus

$$f\left(\frac{B}{D}, f_c, f_g, S, \sigma, \frac{G}{\rho U^3}, \frac{\mu}{\rho UD}, \frac{\gamma D}{\rho U^2}, \frac{d}{D}, \frac{w}{U}, \frac{\gamma_s^* D}{\rho U^2}, \frac{\rho_s}{\rho}\right) = 0.$$

$$(7.2)$$

The term $\mu/\rho UD$ is the inverse of the Reynolds number, and $\gamma D/\rho U^2 = gD/U^2$ is the inverse of the Froude number squared. Although the term involving γ_s^* is frequently called the particle Froude number, the physical meaning is that of a drag coefficient. Generally $C_D = \Delta p/\rho V^2$ and since $\gamma_s^* d$ is equivalent to Δp it follows that when V is replaced by w

$$C_D = \frac{\gamma_s^* d}{\rho w^2} = \frac{\gamma_s^* D}{\rho U^2}\frac{d}{D}\left(\frac{U}{w}\right)^2$$

and therefore $\gamma_s^* D/\rho U^2$ can be replaced by C_D.

Hence

$$f\left(\frac{B}{D}, f_c, f_g, S, \sigma, \frac{G}{\rho U^3}, \text{Re}, \text{Fr}, \frac{d}{D}, \frac{w}{U}, C_D, \frac{\rho_s}{\rho}\right) = 0\ . \quad (7.3)$$

Further rearrangement is possible as follows:

1. If the Reynolds number term is multiplied by w/U and d/D, the term known as particle Reynolds number is obtained $\text{Re}_r = wd/\nu$.

2. Following Shields' example and defining the velocity distribution by $u_* = (\tau_0/\rho)^{1/2}$ and k, then U may be omitted.

3. The slope is defined by $\tau_0 = \gamma DS$ and with τ_0, γ and D known, S may be omitted.

Thus one would obtain

$$f\left(\frac{B}{d}, f_c, f_g, \sigma, \frac{G}{\rho u_*^3}, \frac{\mu}{\rho u_* d}, \frac{gd}{u_*^2}, \frac{D}{d}, \frac{w}{u_*}, \frac{\rho_s^*}{\rho}\right) = 0. \tag{7.4}$$

Any of these groups could be combined with others and ρ_s^*/ρ or γ_s^*/γ and gd/u_*^2 often are so combined to yield

$$\frac{1}{(\rho/\rho_s)\text{Fr}_*^2} \quad \text{or} \quad \frac{1}{(\gamma/\gamma_s^*)\text{Fr}_*^2} \quad \text{where } \text{Fr}_*^2 = \frac{u_*^2}{gd}.$$

This is equivalent to considering a π-term of the form

$$\pi = \rho^a d^b u^c \gamma_s^*, \text{ which yields } (\gamma_s^*/\gamma)\, gd/u_*^2.$$

Thus

$$f\left(\frac{d}{B}, f_c, f_g, \sigma, \frac{G}{\rho u_*^3}, \text{Re}_*, \frac{\gamma}{\gamma_s^*}\text{Fr}_*^2, \frac{d}{D}, \frac{u_*}{w}\right) = 0. \tag{7.5}$$

It should be realized that eqns. (7.1)–(7.5) are versions of the same equation, and that one could obtain many more. Which combination of the dimensionless variables is the best must be established from experimental results.

Shields[1] studied

$$f\left(\text{Re}_*, \frac{\gamma}{\gamma_s^*}\text{Fr}_*^2\right) = 0 \quad \text{and} \quad f\left(\frac{\gamma}{\gamma_s^*}\text{Fr}_*^2, \frac{G}{\rho u_*^3}\right) = 0$$

and Liu[2] studied

$$f\left(\text{Re}_*, \frac{u_*}{w}\right) = 0.$$

In effect these two are interchangeable since u_*/w can be computed if $\mathrm{Re} = u_* d/v$ and $(\gamma/y_s^*)\mathrm{Fr}^*$ are given. In terms of the fall velocity the drag on particle is

$$F_D = C_D(\mathrm{Re}_w)\rho d^2 w^2,$$

where $C_D(\mathrm{Re}_w)$ is the drag coefficient as a function of $\mathrm{Re}_w = wd/v$. The effective weight is

$$F_W = \alpha d^3 \gamma_s^*,$$

where α is a form coefficient and $\gamma_s^* = \gamma(S_s - 1)$.

Thus for dynamic equilibrium $F_D = F_W$ yielding

$$C_D(\mathrm{Re}_w)\rho d^2 w^2 = \alpha d^3 \gamma_s^*$$

$$\frac{C_D(\mathrm{Re}_w)}{\alpha} \frac{\gamma}{\gamma_s^*} \frac{w^2}{gd} = 1$$

$$C_D\left(\mathrm{Re}_* \frac{w}{u_*}\right)\left(\frac{w}{u_*}\right)^2 \frac{\gamma}{\gamma_s^*} \mathrm{Fr}_* = \alpha = \mathrm{const.},$$

i.e.
$$\frac{u_*}{w} = f\left(\mathrm{Re}_*, \frac{\gamma}{\gamma_s^*} \mathrm{Fr}_*^2\right).$$

It must be clearly understood that the dimensional analysis only arranges the parameters in convenient dimensionless form and reduces the number (usually by 3), but gives no information on the functional relationships among these parameters or on the additional constant terms, which these parameters may have. From experimental evidence through laboratory and field study one has to determine which parameters are important and what relationship binds them. The evaluation of field information may become very difficult, because the cross-section as well as the plan of the channel may have complicated geometry, and have very different roughness characteristics from point to point. Also the presence of secondary currents will have a bearing upon the general problem.

Shields' study was mainly concerned with finding a criterion for the threshold conditions of sediment movement (Fig. 7.1). The type of bed formation likely is described by the position of the point on Shields' graph of $\tau_0/\gamma(S_s-1)d$ versus du_*/ν, but the information on this aspect is very sketchy.

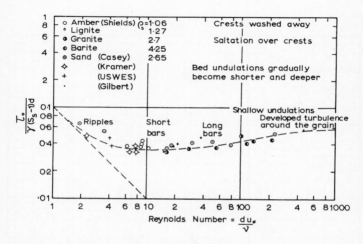

FIG. 7.1. Sediment entrainment as a function of Reynolds number, according to Shields.

Shields' work in the laminar flow region shows that

$$u_*^2/[(S_s-1)gd] \propto (u_*d/\nu)^{-1}$$

or

$$u_*^3 \propto g\nu(S_s-1)$$

which is independent of particle size. This is in keeping with the observation that the surface finish does not affect the resistance of laminar flow over it. Thus so long as the particle size is small compared to the thickness of the laminar sublayer the drag is carried by the surface as a whole and not by a smaller number of prominent grains. Tison[3] found that the experimental results covered the region of Shields' curve, but for any given grain size they tended to lie across Shields' curve instead of along it. If these results are considered in the light of Fig. 7.1, they suggest varying degrees of surface waviness giving rise to additional drag (form drag) during the experiment with a given grain size.

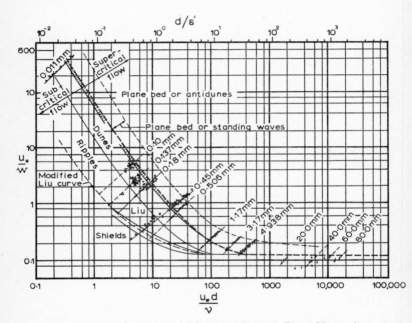

FIG. 7.2. Plot of experimental data as u_*/w versus Reynolds number, according to Liu. (From ref. 29, section 12, by permission of the U.S. Geological Survey.)

Liu found that experimental data plotted with less scatter with u_*/w as ordinate than with $\tau_0/\gamma(S_s-1)d$ (Fig. 7.2).

Figure 7.2 seems to indicate in a systematic way which type of bed formation is likely under given conditions.

The use of shear velocity is satisfactory for flow over a fixed boundary and for the study of threshold conditions, since there the mean roughness is constant and the shear velocity uniquely defines the flow. However, when sediment transport takes place the mean equivalent roughness height is not known because of the bed features and u_* defines only the slope of the velocity plot on the semilog paper, but not its location. For $u = 5.75u_*$ $\log(y/y')$ and u_* is proportional to the slope of the velocity plot with respect to the log y axis.

7.1. Bed-load Transport Formulae

It can be readily shown that most of the sediment transport formulae have the form

$$G = \rho u_*^3 f\left(\mathrm{Re}_*, \frac{\gamma}{\gamma_s^*}\frac{u_*^2}{gd}\right).$$

Such as the Meyer-Peter formula

$$G = 8\sqrt{(g/\gamma)} \cdot (\gamma DS - 0.047\gamma_s^* d_m)^{3/2}$$

$$= \rho u_*^3 8\left[1 - \frac{0.047}{(\gamma/\gamma_s^*)(u_*^2/gd)}\right]^{3/2},$$

since $\gamma DS = \tau_0 = \rho u_*^2$ and $\gamma/g = \rho$.

This shows that the effect of Reynolds number is not included. Hence the formula is not applicable for cases where the effect of viscosity has to be considered, as in the case of silt transport. The values of the constants 8 and 0.047 apply only for the type of sediment investigated, in this case river shingle with a convex sieve curve. The threshold conditions correspond to $G = 0$, showing that the value of the entrainment function is 0.047 instead of the more commonly given value of 0.056.

With a little more manipulation the Einsten's bed-load formula can be expressed as

$$G = \rho_s u_*^3 f\left(\mathrm{Re}_*, \frac{\gamma}{\gamma_s^*}\frac{u_*^2}{gd}\right).$$

The Einstein formula is

$$\phi_* = f(\psi_*),$$

where

$$\phi_* = (G/\gamma_s)(\gamma/\gamma_s^*)^{1/2}[1/(gd^3)]^{1/2}$$
$$\psi_* = (\gamma_s^*/\gamma)[d/(DS)]a.$$

Here a is a function of the ratio of the roughness height to the particle size d, and the ratio of the thickness of the laminar sublayer δ' to the particle size d. By multiplying and dividing ϕ_* by u_*^3

$$\phi_* = (G/\gamma_s)(\gamma/\gamma_s^*)^{1/2}[1/(gd^3)]^{1/2}(u_*/u_*)^3$$
$$= [G/(\rho_s u_*^3)](\gamma/\gamma_s^*)^{1/2}\mathrm{Fr}_*^3$$
$$= G/(S_s\rho u_*^3)f[\gamma/\gamma_s^*\mathrm{Fr}_*].$$

With $DS = \tau_0/\gamma = u_*^2/g$ the ψ term can be written as

$$\psi_* = a/[(\gamma/\gamma_s^*)\mathrm{Fr}_*^2].$$

The thickness of the sublayer δ' depends on the Reynolds number Re_* and on the surface roughness, so that δ'/d is a function of Re_*, a is a function of Re_* and $(\gamma/\gamma_s^*)\mathrm{Fr}_*$, and it follows that

$$G/(S_s\rho u_*^3)f[(\gamma/\gamma_s^*)\mathrm{Fr}_*] = F\{f[\mathrm{Re}_*, (\gamma/\gamma_s^*)\mathrm{Fr}_*]/[(\gamma/\gamma_s^*)\mathrm{Fr}_*^2]\}$$

or

$$G = \rho_s u_*^3 f[\mathrm{Re}_*, (\gamma/\gamma_s^*)\mathrm{Fr}_*].$$

References

1. SHIELDS, A., *Anwendung der Aenlichkeits Mechanik und der Turbulenzforschung auf die Geschiebe Bewegung*, Preussische Versuchsanstalt für Wasserbau und Schiffbau, Berlin, 1936.
2. LIU, H. K., Mechanics of sediment ripple formation, *J. Hydr. Div. A.S.C.E.* **83**, No. HY 2 (April, 1957).
3. TISON, L. J., Recherches sur la tension limité d'entraînment des materiaux constitutifs du lit, *Proc. Minnesota International Hydraulics Convention*, p. 21 (September, 1953).

CHAPTER 8

Sediment Suspension

THE turbulent suspension of sediment may be visualized as an advanced stage of saltation and bed-load movement, but the available analytical methods are not yet capable of describing the transport of bed load and suspended load by one relationship only. There are formulae of empirical or semi-empirical nature[1] which attempt such an overall solution, but as yet a completely successful analysis is still outstanding.

The various analytical treatments of the suspended sediment problem consider only those regions that lie at some distance from the bed, so that the boundary effects due to the bed-load transport need not be accounted for directly. The elementary treatment follows the principles of turbulent mixing and diffusion. It is assumed that the motion is steady and the mean values of sediment and velocity distribution remain the same along the water course. The vertical turbulent velocity components carry fluid upwards and downwards, but the net rate of flow through a unit area is zero. The fluid elements transport sediment particles. Superimposed upon the movement of the sediment particles by turbulent velocity fluctuations is the settling or fall velocity of the particles w.

$$y \quad \begin{array}{ll} \overline{\uparrow} & \cdots \quad \left(c + \dfrac{dc}{dy}\dfrac{\delta y}{2} \right) \\[2mm] \dfrac{\delta y}{2} & \cdots \quad c \\[2mm] \downarrow & \cdots \quad \left(c - \dfrac{dc}{dy}\dfrac{\delta y}{2} \right) \end{array}$$

Let the concentration of particles of a given size at elevation y be c, then as a first approximation the concentration at elevation $(y+\delta y/2)$ is $(c+dc/dy\ \delta y/2)$ and at elevation $(y-\delta y/2)$ it is $(c-dc/dy\ \delta y/2)$. Here $\delta y/2$ is a short distance over which the small fluid-sediment parcel is assumed to retain its identity. For steady state the transport rate upwards must equal that downwards so that

$$(c-dc/dy\ \delta y/2)(v'-w) = (c+dc/dy\ \delta y/2)(v'+w)$$

$$cw = -v'\ \delta y/2\ dc/dy.$$

By analogy with the mixing length concept of turbulent flow and the momentum transfer or exchange coefficient ε (the kinematic eddy viscosity) the term $\delta y/2$ can be interpreted as a mixing length and $v'\ \delta y/2$ as the exchange coefficient. Writing l_s and ε_s for the corresponding sediment diffusion quantities, then the equation becomes

$$cw+\varepsilon_s\ dc/dy = 0. \tag{8.1}$$

This is known as the diffusion equation and is frequently taken as the starting equation. This equation implies a state of equilibrium between the rate of fall of sediment and the rate of movement upwards due to turbulence, that is down the concentration gradient.

In the simplest analysis the sediment diffusion coefficient ε_s is taken to be equal to the momentum transfer coefficient ε.

Integration then yields

$$\ln(c/c_a) = -w \int_a^y dy/\varepsilon, \tag{8.2}$$

where $y = a$ is a reference level where the concentration c_a is known. Combination of a linear shear stress distribution relationship with $\tau = \rho\varepsilon\ du/dy$ yields

$$\tau = \tau_0 - \tau_0 y/y_0 = \rho\varepsilon du/dy \tag{8.3}$$

$$\frac{dy}{\varepsilon} = \frac{\rho du/dy}{\tau_0(1-y/y_0)}\ dy.$$

Furthermore

$$du/dy = (\tau_0/\rho)^{1/2}/l = \frac{u_*}{\kappa y} = 2 \cdot 5 \frac{u_*}{y}$$

assuming the Karman universal constant to be 0·40. Note also that $\varepsilon = u_* \kappa y [1 - (y/y_0)]$ is a parabolic distribution of ε with respect to y, the maximum value of ε being $0 \cdot 25 u_* \kappa y_0$ at $y = 0 \cdot 5 y_0$. The apparent inconsistency between the linearly decreasing shear stress and the logarithmic velocity distribution is not serious. The logarithmic velocity distribution was extended to turbulent flow in general from boundary layer considerations and was based on the assumption of constant shear stress. However, this distribution has been verified experimentally so that its combination with the linearly decreasing shear stress is not inconsistent. Thus the integral can be evaluated, yielding

$$\frac{c}{c_a} = \left(\frac{y_0 - y}{y_0 - a} \frac{a}{y} \right)^{2 \cdot 5 w/u_*}. \tag{8.4}$$

This relationship [eqn. (8.4)] is plotted on Fig. 8.1. It should be noted that the equation is not valid at the bed.

Hunt[2] proposed a refinement to the elementary sediment diffusion theory. Taking into account the space occupied by the sediment particles, assuming uniform flow so that the local mean velocity is a function of the vertical coordinate only, and assuming that sediment concentration does not vary with time, the general equations for turbulent diffusion of uniform material reduce to

$$\varepsilon_s \frac{\partial c}{\partial y} + c \frac{\partial c}{\partial y} (\varepsilon - \varepsilon_s) + (1 - c) c w = 0. \tag{8.5}$$

By neglecting the volume of water displaced this becomes

$$\varepsilon_s \frac{\partial c}{\partial y} + c \frac{\partial c}{\partial y} (\varepsilon - \varepsilon_s) + c w = 0 \tag{8.6}$$

and with $\varepsilon = \varepsilon_s$ is identical with the result from the simple approach discussed before. When ε is taken to be equal to ε_s

and the correction for displacement is retained then eqn. (8.5) becomes

$$\varepsilon_s \frac{\partial c}{\partial y} + (1-c)cw = 0. \qquad (8.7)$$

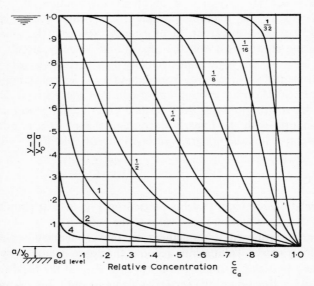

FIG. 8.1. Distribution of suspended load in a flow according to eqn. (8.4), with $z = w/(\kappa\sqrt{\tau_0/\rho})$ as parameter and $a/y_0 = 0.05$.

It is assumed that the turbulent mixing processes for the sediment and the water are similar, but not necessarily identical. By using von Karman's definition of the mixing length

$$l = \kappa \frac{du}{dy} \bigg/ \frac{d^2u}{dy^2}$$

and

$$\tau = \rho l^2 \left(\frac{du}{dy}\right) \frac{du}{dy}$$

the mixing length is eliminated giving

$$gS(y_0 - y) = \kappa^2 \left(\frac{du}{dy}\right)^4 \bigg/ \left(\frac{d^2u}{dy^2}\right)^2$$

from which by integration

$$\frac{du}{dy} = \frac{(gy_0 S)^{1/2}}{2\kappa y_0 [B - (1 - y/y_0)^{1/2}]}, \tag{8.8}$$

where B is a constant of integration (equal to one in clear water).

Thus the distribution of the local temporal mean velocity u is given by

$$\frac{u_{max} - u}{(gy_0 S)^{1/2}} = -\frac{1}{\kappa} \left\{ \left(1 - \frac{y}{y_0}\right)^{1/2} + B \ln \left[\frac{B - (1 - y/y_0)^{1/2}}{B}\right] \right\}. \tag{8.9}$$

The same expressions are assumed for the sediment mixing length and for suspended sediment velocities, terms relating to sediment being distinguished by subscript s. It means that the sediment particle is assumed to move in the same manner as the fluid particles. The sediment concentration is assumed to tend to zero at the free surface so that the maximum water and sediment velocities, occurring at the free surface, are equal.

By analogy with the Boussinesq formula

$$\varepsilon = \frac{\tau}{\rho(du/dy)}$$

$$\varepsilon_s = \frac{\tau_0(1 - y/y_0)}{\rho du_s/dy} = 2\kappa_s y_0 (gy_0 S)^{1/2} \left(1 - \frac{y}{y_0}\right)\left[B_s - \left(1 - \frac{y}{y_0}\right)^{1/2}\right] \tag{8.10}$$

by substitution from eqn. (8.8).

Using this expression in eqn. (8.7)

$$\ln \left(\frac{c}{1 - c}\right) = -w \int \frac{dy}{\varepsilon_s} + \text{const.}$$

and integrating yields

$$\left(\frac{c}{1-c}\right)\left(\frac{1-c_a}{c_a}\right) = \left\{\left(\frac{1-y/y_0}{1-a/y_0}\right)^{1/2}\left[\frac{B_s-(1-a/y_0)^{1/2}}{B_s-(1-y/y_0)^{1/2}}\right]\right\}^z = G^z, \tag{8.11}$$

where

$$z = \frac{w}{\kappa_s B_s(gy_0 S)^{1/2}} = \frac{w}{\kappa_s B_s u_*}. \tag{8.12}$$

For small concentration eqn. (8.11) approximates to

$$\frac{c}{c_a} = \left\{\left(\frac{1-y/y_0}{1-a/y_0}\right)^{1/2}\left[\frac{B_s-(1-a/y_0)^{1/2}}{B_s-(1-y/y_0)^{1/2}}\right]\right\}^z. \tag{8.13}$$

From eqn. (8.9) the relationship between the mean velocity and the surface velocity is determined by integration yielding

$$\frac{\kappa}{(gy_0 S)^{1/2}}(u_{max} - U) = B(B+\tfrac{1}{2}) + B(B^2-1)\ln\frac{B-1}{B} - \frac{2}{3} = f(B)$$

for $B \geqq 1$. The function $f(B)$ may also be written as

$$f(B) = 2\left\{\frac{1}{2\cdot4}\left(\frac{1}{B}\right) + \frac{1}{3\cdot5}\left(\frac{1}{B}\right)^2 + \frac{1}{4\cdot6}\left(\frac{1}{B}\right)^3 + \cdots\right\}$$

which is convergent for $B \geqq 1$.

For $B < 1$

$$\frac{\kappa}{(gy_0 S)^{1/2}}(u_{max} - U) = \frac{5}{6}B + B^2(B+1)\ln B.$$

The depth below the surface $y_* = y_0 - y$ at which $u = U$ is given by

$$(y_*/y_0)^{1/2} + B\ln\left[\frac{B-(y_*/y_0)^{1/2}}{B}\right] + f(B) = 0.$$

Using Vanoni's[3] data which were obtained with flows carrying suspended load at concentrations from zero to $3\cdot36 g/l$, the values of κ and B were chosen to give the best fit to the observed points by assigning the values of u at $y/y_0 = 0.02$ and 0.2.

Vanoni's data on distribution of sediment, c/c_a, were plotted against the distribution function given by eqn. (8.11). The value of B_s was chosen for each curve so that points lie about a line which must pass through the point $c/c_a = 1$, $y = a$, and κ_s was found from the slope of this line $z = w/\kappa_s B_s (gy_0 S)^{1/2}$.

This comparison with Vanoni's data yielded values of B which were greater than unity, ranging from 1.016 to 1.031, and B_s generally less than unity from 0.991 up, with two values 1.005. The values of κ were from 0.256 to 0.311 and values of κ_s from 0.296 to 0.444.

The results obtained from these one-dimensional approaches agree fairly well with observations for small values of z or $2.5w/u_*$ but for larger values the observed exponent appears to be smaller than the calculated one. This seems to indicate that the distribution of suspended load is more uniform than predicted by the theory.

This observation has been attributed to the inaccuracy of the assumption that ε is equal to ε_s[3, 4, 5] and ε_s has been expressed as

$$\varepsilon_s = \beta \varepsilon \qquad (8.14)$$

with β being a function of particle size. Then the exponent of the suspended sediment distribution function becomes $z_1 = w/\kappa_s \beta u_*$ which is of the same form as the z by Hunt.

Ismail[5] obtained from his experiments that

$$\varepsilon_s = 1.5\varepsilon \text{ for } 0.10 \text{ mm sand}$$

$$\varepsilon_s = 1.3\varepsilon \text{ for } 0.16 \text{ mm sand.}$$

H. A. Einstein and Ning Chien[6] proposed a second order approximation of the sediment suspension theory. They took into account the following aspects:

(a) The difference in sediment concentration $l_s(dc/dy)$ between two points on a vertical and a distance l_s apart, where l_s is taken to be the mixing length of the turbulent flow, may be true for fine sediment. For coarse sediment a strongly skew distribution of concentration with elevation may be expected so that higher order derivatives of c need to be included. Alternatively, l_s could be very much smaller than l for water mixing and also vary in a different manner.

(b) The process of turbulent mixing is assumed to be much more active near the origin of the eddy than at points farther away. Whence the mixing length is assumed to vary according to a certain probability distribution instead of having a particular value.

(c) The turbulence is generated at the bed and is dissipated towards the water surface; therefore the characteristics of turbulence are not necessarily symmetrical. The mixing length and instantaneous velocity distribution of the upward flow may be different from those of the downward flow.

Assuming the fluctuating velocity to follow the normal error law and the mixing length of the turbulent flow to follow the prescribed probability distribution function, and including the higher derivative terms of the concentration gradient, Einstein and Chien showed that

$$z_1 = \frac{z}{e^{-L^2 z^2/\pi} + zL \frac{2}{\sqrt{(2\pi)}} \int_0^{\sqrt{(2/\pi)}zL} e^{-x^2/2} dx}, \qquad (8.15)$$

where $L = \log_e (1 + B\kappa)$, and B is a constant.

Figure 8.2 shows that for practical purposes the difference is small and that it only affects the coarse particles of which there are few in suspensions.

The observation that ε_s is larger than ε for fine sediment and is smaller than ε for coarse sediment, is interesting. If one recalls here the familiar plot of drag coefficient C_D versus Reynolds number (e.g. Fig. 2.1), then it is apparent that the drag on a sphere, that is on a sediment particle, varies strongly with its size in addition to the velocity and turbulence characteristics of the water flow. It may be that this variation helps to explain the larger ε_s values for fine sediment.

It is also important to realize that temperature significantly affects the suspended sediment load. Lane, Carlson and Manson[7] found that for sediment smaller than 0·3 mm the load increased with decreasing temperature, but for coarser than 0·3 mm material temperature effects, if any, were very small. This observation appears to be a direct result of the variation of drag with Reynolds

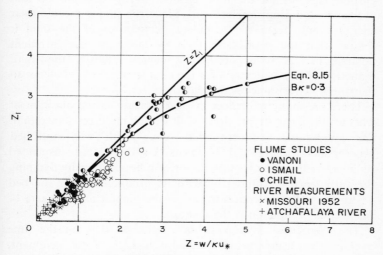

FIG. 8.2. Relationship between z and z_1. (Fig. 3 of ref. 9, by permission of the American Society of Engineers.)

number. With small particles the drag decreases with increasing temperature, i.e. Reynolds number, and hence the sediment carrying capacity must drop.

A further very important feature calls for attention. Various experimenters have found that the sediment suspension does not distribute evenly over the cross-section, even in laboratory flumes. Vanoni, for example, found that the sediment was distributed in longitudinal bands. This agrees with the observation that the flow in straight open channels consists of two or more spiral currents, depending on the width–depth ratio. These

E

secondary currents strongly modify the flow pattern and have an effect on suspended sediment distribution.

The difficulties in the treatment of the suspended sediment problem generally stem from the unknown form of the diffusion coefficient. A relative velocity or "slip" between the fluid and sediment is necessary for force transmission to take place. The particle lags behind the fluid element during acceleration and overtakes it during deceleration. Since the grains receive their energy supply from the turbulent fluctuations of the fluid it follows that the grains also tend to damp out the turbulent fluctuations. A reduction of turbulence intensity implies a reduction of energy demand for the maintenance of turbulence so that the flow resistance is decreased.

There are many references in the literature to the question of whether the clear stream flows with less or more resistance than the comparable sediment-laden one. With well-controlled experiments Vanoni and Nomicos[8] showed that suspended sediment reduces the friction factor of a flow, either by damping the turbulence or interfering with its production near the bed where the sediment concentration is the highest and the rate of turbulence production is the greatest.

The theoretical treatments have assumed that on the time average the instantaneous vertical velocities of the sediment, relative to the fluid, equal the fall velocity w in still fluid. But during periods of acceleration, for example, the relative velocity will be greater than w and the sediment should be carried a shorter distance than assumed. From this it could be inferred that ε_s is less than ε. Also during acceleration the virtual mass of the particle should be considered.

An argument advanced for the increased value of ε_s is that the momentum diffusion coefficient ε requires a correlation between vertical and horizontal fluctuations, whereas this is not necessary for the sediment diffusion and random fluctuations also transport sediment and hence make ε_s larger. However, in a shear flow, where there is a velocity gradient, any velocity fluctuation v' will effect a momentum transfer. Most of these elementary treatments do not differentiate between diffusivity, momentum and mass transfer, or take into account that there is no complete analogy between momentum and mass transfer.

This question of the relative magnitudes of ε and ε_s is put into a better perspective by considering conditions at a point. The rate of sediment transport through a unit horizontal area is $v'c$, or $\overline{v'c}$ as the time average. The sediment concentration is

$$c = \bar{c} + c'. \tag{8.16}$$

But the term $\overline{v'\bar{c}}$ is zero because $\overline{v'}$ is zero. Thus only $\overline{v'c'}$ remains. This is a time average of the product of instantaneous fluctuations of quantities, in form analogous to $\overline{u'v'}$ in momentum exchange in turbulent flow. Here a correlation coefficient may be defined as

$$R_s = \frac{\overline{v'c'}}{\sqrt{\overline{v'^2}}\sqrt{\overline{c'^2}}}. \tag{8.17}$$

An analogy to the Prandtl mixing length concept where

$$\sqrt{\overline{u'^2}} = l \left| \frac{d\bar{u}}{dy} \right| \tag{8.18a}$$

may be used to give

$$\sqrt{\overline{c'^2}} + l_s \left| \frac{d\bar{c}}{dy} \right|. \tag{8.18b}$$

This yields

$$R_s \sqrt{\overline{v'^2}} l_s \left| \frac{d\bar{c}}{dy} \right| = \overline{v'c'} = \varepsilon_s \left| \frac{d\bar{c}}{dy} \right|.$$

That is

$$\varepsilon_s = R_s \sqrt{(\overline{v'^2})} l_s. \tag{8.19}$$

The momentum coefficient—the kinematic eddy viscosity—is

$$\varepsilon = R \sqrt{(\overline{v'^2})} l, \tag{8.20}$$

where

$$R = \frac{\overline{u'v'}}{\sqrt{\overline{u'^2}}\sqrt{\overline{v'^2}}}$$

and these are related by

$$\tau = \rho R \sqrt{(\overline{v'^2})} l \left| \frac{d\bar{u}}{dy} \right| .$$

This shows that

$$\frac{\varepsilon_s}{\varepsilon} = \frac{R_s l_s}{R l} \tag{8.21}$$

and that this ratio depends on the magnitudes of the correlation coefficients as well as the mixing lengths. Thus if the correlation R_s is stronger than R the value of ε_s could be larger than the value of ε and l_s could still be smaller than l. It is clear that a non-zero value of R_s is necessary for sediment diffusion to take place, but how any of these terms varies with the elevation and concentration is still not clear. From eqn. (8.3)

$$\varepsilon = \kappa u_* \left(\frac{y_0 - y}{y_0} \right) y \tag{8.22a}$$

and by eqn. (8.14)

$$\varepsilon_s = \beta \kappa u_* \left(\frac{y_0 - y}{y_0} \right) y. \tag{8.22b}$$

Substituting from $z = w/\beta \kappa u_*$ for $\beta \kappa u_*$ yields

$$\varepsilon_s = \frac{w}{z} \left(\frac{y_0 - y}{y_0} \right) y. \tag{8.23}$$

Here w is a function of particle size, which usually varies with elevation, and z is a function of particle size and concentration, the latter affecting κ.

It should also be kept in mind that these treatments are based on the two-dimensional fluctuations of turbulent velocity and the simplifications introduced through the mixing length assumptions. Hunt[2] showed with Vanoni's data a variation in von Karman's κ. Vanoni[4] carried out further experiments in a flume with a fixed artificially roughened bed and varying suspended sediment

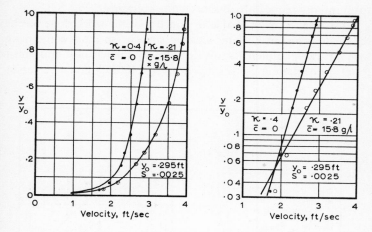

FIG. 8.3. Linear and semi-logarithmic graphs of velocity profiles in a flow 0·295 ft deep and 33·5 in. wide with clear water and with heavy suspended load of 0·1 mm sand. (By permission of the American Society of Civil Engineers, ref. 8.)

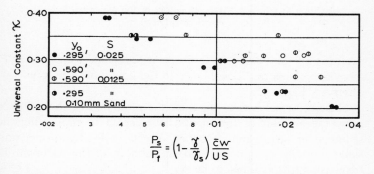

FIG. 8.4. Reduction of the von Karman constant in sediment-laden flow. (By permission of the American Society of Civil Engineers, ref. 8.)

load. The results showed that the von Karman constant κ is substantially reduced by the suspended sediment, Fig. 8.3.

Einstein and Chien[6] also reasoned that the work done on the sediment grains in keeping these in suspension must come from the vertical components of turbulence fluctuations and must result in the damping of turbulence. By plotting data as κ versus

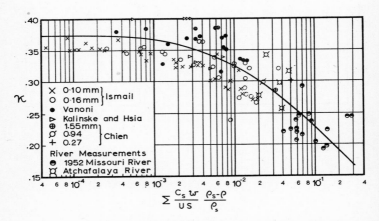

FIG. 8.5. Effect of suspended sediment on velocity distribution, according to Chien.[9] (By permission of the American Society of Civil Engineers.)

the ratio of the power P_s to suspend sediment to the power P_f to overcome hydraulic resistance to the flow a definite trend was observed, Fig. 8.4.

Their proposal was to measure the reduction of the value of κ by the amount of turbulent energy spent in supporting the sediment in suspension. The rate of energy dissipation per unit time and unit weight of fluid in supporting the sediment in suspension was assumed to be

$$\sum \frac{c_s w}{US} \frac{\rho_s - \rho}{\rho_s}.$$

Here c_s is the average concentration by weight of a given grain size with settling velocity w and the summation sign designates a summation over all the particles in suspension. This expression is correlated with κ in Fig. 8.5.

Chien[9] postulates that the main damping effect of the sediment on turbulence takes place near the bed where the concentration is highest. Vanoni and Nomicos[8] followed this idea and used P_s, the power to suspend the sediment in a thin layer near the bed, and found that data of Fig. 8.4 plotted with less scatter, Fig. 8.6.

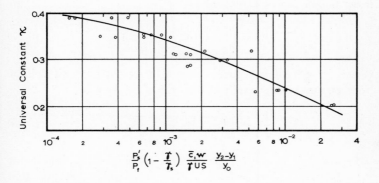

FIG. 8.6. Reduction of the von Karman constant in sediment laden flow. (By permission of the American Society of Civil Engineers, ref. 8.)

The power P_s to support sediment in a water column of unit horizontal area and height y_0, the depth of flow, is

$$P_s = \frac{\gamma_s - \gamma}{\gamma_s} \bar{c} w y_0, \qquad (8.24)$$

where γ and γ_s are the specific weights of water and sediment respectively, $\bar{c}$ is the mean concentration in weight per unit volume taken over the entire depth and w is the settling velocity of the sediment.

The power P_f to overcome the flow resistance for the same water column is

$$P_f = \gamma y_0 US. \tag{8.25}$$

Thus

$$\frac{P_s}{P_f} = \left(1 - \frac{\gamma}{\gamma_s}\right) \frac{\bar{c}w}{\gamma US}. \tag{8.26}$$

The power P_s' to support sediment in a similar column, but of lesser height can be expressed as

$$P_s' = \left(1 - \frac{\gamma}{\gamma_s}\right) \bar{c}_1 w (y_2 - y_1), \tag{8.27}$$

where $\bar{c}_1$ is the mean concentration in weight per unit volume between the levels y_1 and y_2. This yields for the ratio

$$\frac{P_s'}{P_f} = \left(1 - \frac{\gamma}{\gamma_s}\right) \frac{\bar{c}_1 w}{\gamma US} \frac{y_2 - y_1}{y_0}. \tag{8.28}$$

Figure 8.6 shows the same data as Fig. 8.4 plotted for $y_1 = 0 \cdot 001 y_0$ and $y_2 = 0 \cdot 01 y_0$. It is reasonable to suspect that the changes in velocity distribution and in turbulence structure take place mainly in a zone close to the bed where the concentration is high, and the sediment particles suspended in the main part of the flow are usually of small size and do not require much energy for suspension. The problem of the velocity distribution is still not well understood. In terms of the logarithmic velocity distribution a change of κ from 0·4 to 0·2 for example, would make the average velocity of such sediment-laden flow twice the corresponding sediment free flow.

According to this concept of variation of the von Karman constant with concentration of sediment, flows with suspensions of neutrally buoyant particles should remain unaffected because no energy is required to suspend these particles. Yet, Elata and

Ippen[10] showed experimentally that the von Karman constant of flow with suspensions of neutrally buoyant particles decreases with increasing concentration and that turbulence intensity increases.

This points to the necessity of studying the mechanics of sediment suspension in a much greater detail than is done by the simplified theories.

The basic problem of diffusion of particles in a turbulent flow is of great importance in many fields. The diffusion may be that of solids in liquid or of atomized liquids in gases. The applications range from sediment loads of rivers to coal washing, mineral dressing, liquid and pneumatic conveying, combustion of pulverized or atomized fuels to many chemical processes. One of the most quoted theoretical treatments is by Tchen, in a Ph.D. thesis (1947) of Delft, which is summarized by Hinze.[11] In Tchen's theory the following assumptions are made:

1. The turbulence of the fluid is homogeneous and steady.

2. The domain of turbulence is infinite in extent.

3. The particle is spherical and so small that its motion relative to the ambient fluid follows Stokes' law of resistance.

4. The particle is small compared with the smallest wavelength present in the turbulence.

5. During the motion of the particle the neighbourhood will be formed by the same fluid particles.

6. Any external force acting on the particle originates from a potential field, such as gravity field.

Here the assumption[5] is the critical one and is not likely to be satisfied in a turbulent flow. The fluid elements in turbulent motion do not retain their identity for any length of time or distance and it is unlikely that a particle could be surrounded by the same fluid particles. It is implied that the solid particles do not overshoot and this could only be a reasonable assumption if the densities of particles and fluid are about the same. For a

E*

large density ratio the results are suspect. The equation of motion is put into the following form:

$$\underbrace{\frac{\pi}{6} d^3 \rho_p \frac{dv_p}{dt}}_{\text{1.}} = \underbrace{3\pi\mu d(v_f - v_p)}_{\text{2.}} + \underbrace{\frac{\pi}{6} d^3 \rho_f \frac{dv_f}{dt}}_{\text{3.}} + \underbrace{\frac{1}{2} \frac{\pi}{6} d^3 \rho_f \left(\frac{dv_f}{dt} - \frac{dv_p}{dt} \right)}_{\text{4.}}$$

$$+ \underbrace{\frac{3}{2} d^2 \sqrt{(\pi\rho_f\mu)} \int_{t_0}^{t} dt^1 \frac{\frac{dv_f}{dt^1} - \frac{dv_p}{dt^1}}{\sqrt{(t - t^1)}}}_{\text{5.}} + \underbrace{F_e}_{\text{6.}} , \qquad (8.29)$$

where t_0 is the starting time, suffixes f and p refer to fluid and particle respectively, and the fluid velocity v_f is measured near the particle, but sufficiently far from it not to be disturbed by the relative motion of the particle. The meaning of the terms is as follows:

1. Force required to accelerate the particle.
2. Viscous resistance force according to Stokes' law.
3. Force due to pressure gradient in the fluid surrounding the particle, caused by the acceleration of the fluid.
4. Force to accelerate the added mass of the particle relative to the ambient fluid.
5. The "Basset" term, which takes into account the effect of the deviation of flow pattern from steady state.
6. External potential force.

The terms 3, 4 and 5 are important only if the particles are about the same density as the fluid or lighter. The instantaneous coefficient of resistance of the particle may become many times that for steady motion if the particle is accelerated at a high rate by an external force.

The complicated analysis shows that the ratio of particle diffusion coefficient to fluid diffusion coefficient $\varepsilon_s/\varepsilon$ is unity for infinitely long diffusion times and less than one for short diffusion times of heavy particles. However, for particles which are much lighter than fluid the intensity and amplitudes of the particle motion are greater than those of the fluid.

Mikio Hino[12] tackled the problem from the equations of motion of turbulent flow. Although several bold approximations are made the results are still interesting. The treatment predicts that the von Karman constant will always decrease and that the turbulence intensity will increase with increasing concentration of buoyant particles and decrease with increased density of particles. It also predicts a rather rapid decrease in the diffusion coefficient.

Momentum transfer in a two-phase stream, consisting of particles carried by a fluid, was studied by S. L. Soo[13] by applying the statistical theory of turbulence. It is implied in the method of treatment that the particles should follow the fluid motion as assumed by Tchen.

The general conclusions are:

1. In a two-phase stream the characteristics of turbulence of one phase can be determined from those of the other phase.

2. The fundamental parameters affecting the statistical properties of momentum transfer between the two phases are:

$$\left(\frac{d_p\sqrt{\overline{u'^2}}\rho}{\mu}\right), \left(\frac{d_p}{l_1}\right), \left(\frac{\rho_p}{\rho}\right), \tag{8.30}$$

where d_p is the diameter of particle, l_1 is the Lagrangian scale of turbulence of the stream, and ρ_p is the density of the particle.

3. When the effect of gravity on particles is significant, the turbulent motion of the particles is anisotropic, even though the stream turbulence is isotropic. The parameters affecting momentum transfer will then be:

$$\left(\frac{\sqrt{\overline{u'^2}}}{\sqrt{d_p g}}\right), \left(\frac{d_p\sqrt{\overline{u'^2}}\rho}{\mu}\right), \left(\frac{l_p}{l_1}\right), \left(\frac{\rho_p}{\rho}\right). \tag{8.31}$$

4. In general, the scale of turbulence of the particles is greater than that of the stream, and the diffusivity of the particles is greater than the eddy diffusivity of the stream, but tends towards it.

Although by theoretical reasoning Soo concludes that the diffusivity of the particles is slightly greater than the eddy diffusivity of the stream, his experimental results[14] show a distinctly smaller diffusivity of the particles.

The dispersion of fine particles in a turbulent flow is discussed by statistical methods by Liu[15] with emphasis on very low concentrations in air.

A number of papers treat this diffusion problem by similar theoretical approaches, but the results are contradictory and far too complex to be of practical use as yet. It should also be pointed out that the diffusion coefficient is fundamentally a second order tensor and is not symmetrical for non-isotropic turbulence.

Apart from the diffusion problem, it does appear that the suspended sediment causes changes in the structure of the turbulence which may be more important than its effect in damping of the turbulence.

When the sediment is very fine, 50μ or less in diameter, but still of mineral density and properties, observations show that the concentration may increase upwards instead of downwards as predicted by the theory based on kinematic reasoning. The kinematic approach neglects the cumulative dynamic effects on the fluid of the immersed weight of the solids.

A very interesting treatment based on energy considerations was proposed by Bagnold.[16]

A mass m per unit area of bed surface of the suspended solids of density ρ_s is assumed to be falling steadily downwards through the local eddies at the constant fall velocity w of its constituent grains. In steady motion the centre of gravity of the grain mass remains at a constant height above the bed. For equilibrium the turbulence must be lifting the mass upwards at velocity w relative to the general body of the fluid, against the immersed weight $[(\rho_s - \rho)/\rho_s]gm$. The rate of doing work, the power expended by the fluid in this lifting, is $[(\rho_s - \rho)/\rho_s]gm \cdot w$.

In the steady state the power spent by the fluid must be replenished from some external source in order to maintain turbulence. Some of this power input is supplied by the weight component $[(\rho_s - \rho)/\rho_s]gm \sin \beta$, which is transferred to the fluid surrounding each solid grain. With the symbols of Fig. 8.7 the

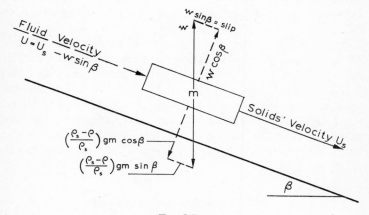

Fig. 8.7.

power input from the excess weight component is $[(\rho_s - \rho)/\rho_s] g \cdot mU_s \sin \beta$.

This yields the net power P_N spent by fluid in maintaining the suspension of solids

$$P_N = [(\rho_s - \rho)/\rho_s]gmU_s(w/U_s - \sin \beta). \qquad (8.32)$$

This becomes zero when the fall velocity of grains becomes

$$w = U_s \sin \beta \qquad (8.33)$$

regardless of the total mass m. If eqn. (8.33) is satisfied the sediment suspension is self-sustaining and requires no net energy supply by the fluid. A given stream under these conditions can transport an unlimited amount of sediment or one limited only by the availability of the sediment.

It follows that when the fall velocity of particles w is less than $U_s \sin \beta$, ($U_s \doteq U$), one could expect a reversal of concentration gradient or an "anomalously high" sediment discharge. The reversal of concentration gradient is due to the increasing velocity with distance from the stream-bed, because at constant values of w and $\sin \beta$ the subtractive term in net power input expression increases, implying increasing suspending power of the fluid.

A proportion of the suspended load of many streams consists of fine clays and colloids. These have characteristics which are different from granular material in the usual sense, and their behaviour is dominated by electro-chemical forces. For example, particles may have the same electric charge in fresh water and repel each other. Coming into salt water they may lose their charge through ion exchange and attract one another to form flocs. Such flocs may have much greater fall velocities than the single particles.

8.1. Suspended Sediment Load

If the concentration at a reference level a is known, the total suspended load transport may be obtained by integrating the product of velocity and concentration over the depth of flow as

$$G_s = \int_{y=a}^{y_0} cu\,dy. \tag{8.34}$$

Lane and Kalinske[17] suggested a simplified form for the integration by introducing a mean value of the diffusion coefficient ε_s. They took as their starting point

$$\ln (c/c_a) = -w \int_a^y dy/\varepsilon \tag{8.35}$$

and

$$u/u_* = 5{\cdot}75 \log y/k + 8{\cdot}5 \tag{8.36a}$$

$$U/u_* = 5{\cdot}75 \log y_0/k + 6. \tag{8.36b}$$

The last two equations lead to

$$(u - U)/u_* = 5 \cdot 75 \log y/y_0 + 2 \cdot 5 = (1/\kappa)(\ln y/y_0 + 1)$$

and

$$u/U = 1 + (u_*/\kappa U)(\ln y/y_0 + 1). \tag{8.37}$$

Then with $u_* = (gy_0 S)^{1/2}$ and the value of Karman's universal constant $\kappa = 0 \cdot 40$ and U expressed in terms of Manning's formula, the term $u_*/(\kappa U)$ becomes $1 \cdot 7 g^{1/2} n/y^{1/6}$.

The shear stress variation is taken to be

$$\tau = \tau_0(1 - y/y_0) = \rho \varepsilon du/dy. \tag{8.38}$$

With $du/dy = (\tau_0/\rho)^{1/2}/l = u_*/\kappa y$, eqn. (8.38) yields

$$\varepsilon = \kappa y_0 u_*(1 - r)r, \tag{8.39}$$

where $r = y/y_0$. This expression yields zero value of ε at the surface and at the bottom and maximum value in the middle.

To avoid evaluating the integral with this value of ε, it is assumed that ε is constant throughout the cross-section and the average value is taken

$$\varepsilon_{av} = y_0 u_*/15. \tag{8.40}$$

With this value eqn. (8.35) yields

$$c/c_a = e^{-15t(r-a)}. \tag{8.41}$$

where $t = w/u_* = w/(gy_0 S)^{1/2}$ for wide channels. Equation (8.41) plots as a straight line on semi-logarithmic paper and is a very convenient approximation (Fig. 8.8).

The total suspended load carried per unit time and width is obtained by introducing eqns. (8.37) and (8.41) into eqn. (8.34).

$$G_s = U y_0 c_a \int_1^0 (u/U) e^{-15t(r-a)} dr$$

$$= U y_0 c_a e^{15ta} \int_0^1 (u/U) e^{-15tr} dr. \tag{8.42}$$

Thus

$$G_s = qc_a e^{15ta}P, \qquad (8.43)$$

where q is the water flow, and $P = f(t, u_*/\kappa U)$. The second term in the bracket has been shown to equal $1.7g^{1/2}n/y_0^{1/6}$, so that P is a function of w/u_* and the relative roughness. The

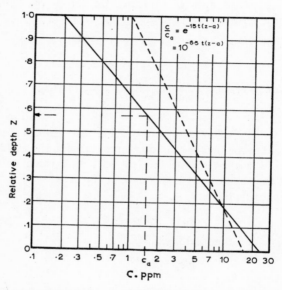

FIG. 8.8. Relative depth y/y_0 versus sediment concentration.

function P may be evaluated and plotted on log–log paper as P versus w/u_* with $n/y_0^{1/6}$ as parameter (Fig. 8.9).

The mean sediment concentration in any vertical cross-section is obtained by dividing G_s by the water discharge,

$$c_{av} = c_a e^{15ta}P. \qquad (8.44)$$

Apparently when $a = 0$ then $c_{av}/c_a = P$, or P is the ratio of average concentration in the vertical to the concentration at zero level, the latter approaching unity for very fine sediment.

R. A. Callander (University of Auckland, N.Z.) suggested a different approximation. For $z_1 \nless 0$ eqn. (8.23) may be approximated by

$$\frac{c}{c_a} \doteq \left(\frac{a}{y}\right)^{z_1}. \tag{8.45}$$

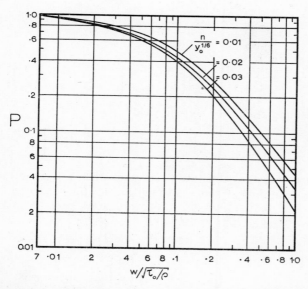

FIG. 8.9. Suspended sediment load function, according to Lane and Kalinske.[17]

This approximation is satisfactory for suspensions of sand, where most of the material is close to the bed and only small values of y need to be considered, so that $(y_0 - y)/(y_0 - a)$ approaches unity. The other limiting condition is when z_1 is very small. Then the bracketed term in eqn. (8.23) approaches one and is not sensitive to $(y_0 - y)$. How much error is caused by this approximation in the transition between the two limiting conditions has not been investigated. Thus

$$\frac{\bar{c}}{c_a} = \frac{1}{Uy_0} \int \frac{c}{c_a} u\, dy$$

$$= \frac{u_*}{Uy_0} \int_a^{y_0} \left(\frac{a}{y}\right)^{z_1} \frac{u}{u_*}\, dy$$

$$= \frac{u_*}{Uy_0} \int_a^{y_0} \frac{a^{z_1}}{1 - z_1} \frac{u}{u_*}\, d(y^{1 - z_1})$$

$$= \frac{u_*}{U} \frac{a^{z_1}}{y_0(1 - z_1)} \left\{ \left[\frac{u}{u_*} y^{1 - z_1} \right]_a^{y_0} - \int_a^{y_0} y^{1 - z_1} d\left(\frac{u}{u_*}\right) \right\}.$$

Substituting $d(u/u_*) = 1/\kappa y\ dy$ yields

$$\frac{\bar{c}}{c_a} = \frac{u_*}{U} \frac{a^{z_1}}{y_0(1 - z_1)} \left[\frac{u}{u_*} y^{1 - z_1} - \frac{1}{1 - z_1} \frac{1}{\kappa} y^{1 - z_1} \right]_a^{y_0}.$$

When $y = y_0$ the velocity $u = u_{max}$ and when $y = a$ the velocity $u = u_a$. Substituting and rearranging yields for $z_1 \neq 1$

$$\frac{\bar{c}}{c_a} = \frac{1}{1 - z_1} \frac{u_*}{U} \left\{ \left[\frac{u_{max}}{u_*} - \frac{1}{\kappa(1 - z_1)} \right] \left(\frac{a}{y_0}\right)^{z_1} \right.$$

$$\left. - \left[\frac{u_a}{u_*} - \frac{1}{\kappa(1 - z_1)} \right] \frac{a}{y_0} \right\}. \qquad (8.46)$$

For $z_1 = 1$ a similar integration would yield

$$\frac{\bar{c}}{c_a} = \frac{a}{y_0} \frac{u_*}{U} \ln \frac{y_0}{a} \left[\frac{u_{max}}{u_*} - \frac{1}{2\kappa} \ln \frac{y_0}{a} \right]. \qquad (8.47)$$

In case of the reversed concentration gradient and negative values of z_1

$$\frac{c}{c_a} \doteq \left(\frac{y_0 - y}{y_0 - a}\right)^{z_1}. \qquad (8.48)$$

Here the reference level $y = a$ is close to the surface. Assuming the velocity distribution to be approximated by the tangent at $y = 0.364 \, y_0$, where $u = U$

$$d\left(\frac{u}{u_*}\right) = \frac{2.72}{\kappa y_0} dy = -\frac{2.72}{\kappa y_0} d(y_0 - y)$$

and by analogy with eqn. (8.46) the following expressions can be derived:

(i) z_1 not equal to -1 or -2.

$$\frac{\bar{c}}{c_a} = \frac{1}{1+z_1} \frac{u_*}{U} \left\{ \frac{2.72}{\kappa(2+z_1)} \left[\left(1 - \frac{a}{y_0}\right)^{-z_1} - \left(1 - \frac{a}{y_0}\right)^2 \right] \right.$$
$$\left. - \frac{u_a}{u_*} \left(1 - \frac{a}{y_0}\right) \right\}. \qquad (8.49a)$$

(ii) $z_1 = -1$.

$$\frac{\bar{c}}{c_a} = \left(1 - \frac{a}{y_0}\right) \frac{u_*}{U} \left\{ \left[\frac{u_a}{u_*} + \frac{2.72}{\kappa} \left(1 - \frac{a}{y_0}\right) \right] \ln \left(\frac{1}{1 - a/y_0}\right) \right.$$
$$\left. - \frac{2.72}{\kappa} \frac{a}{y_0} \right\}. \qquad (8.49b)$$

(iii) $z_1 = -2$.

$$\frac{\bar{c}}{c_a} = \left(1 - \frac{a}{y_0}\right)^2 \frac{u_*}{U} \left\{ \frac{u_a}{u_*} \frac{1}{1 - a/y_0} + \frac{2.72}{\kappa} \ln \left(1 - \frac{a}{y_0}\right) \right\}.$$
$$(8.49c)$$

H. A. Einstein [18] expressed the suspended sediment transport as

$$G_s = \int_y^{y_0} c_y u_y dy$$

$$= \int_y^{y_0} c_a \left(\frac{y_0 - y}{y}\right) \left(\frac{a}{y_0 - a}\right)^z 5.75 u_* \log_{10}(30.2y/\Delta) dy \qquad (8.50)$$

using Keulegan's [19] velocity distribution formula. Here Δ is

k_s/x, where k_s is the roughness of the bed and x is a correction coefficient. Replacing a by a dimensionless value $A = d/y_0$ yields:

$$
\begin{aligned}
G_s &= \int_a^{y_0} c_y u_y dy = \int_A^1 y_0 c_y u_y dy \\
&= y_0 u_* c_a [A/(1-A)]^z 5 \cdot 75 \int_A^1 [(1-y)/y]^z \log_{10}[30 \cdot 2y/(\Delta/y_0)] dy \\
&= 5 \cdot 75 c_a y_0 u_* [A/(1-A)]^z \left\{ \log_{10}(30 \cdot 2 y_0/\Delta) \int_A^1 [(1-y)/y]^z dy + \right. \\
&\quad \left. + \int_A^1 [(1-y)/y]^z \log_{10} y\, dy \right\}.
\end{aligned}
\tag{8.51}
$$

Changing the logarithm to base e yields

$$
\begin{aligned}
G_s &= 5 \cdot 75 c_a y_0 u_* [A/(1-A)]^z \left\{ \log_{10}(30 \cdot 2 y_0/\Delta) \int_A^1 [(1-y)/y]^z dy + \right. \\
&\quad \left. + 0 \cdot 434 \int_A^1 [(1-y)/y]^z \ln y\, dy \right\},
\end{aligned}
\tag{8.52}
$$

where $z = w/(\kappa u_*)$ and $\kappa \doteq 0 \cdot 40$.

For practical application this is converted into

$$
G_s = 11 \cdot 6 u_* c_a a [2 \cdot 303 \log_{10}(30 \cdot 2 y_0/\Delta) I_1 + I_2],
\tag{8.53}
$$

where

$$
I_1 = 0 \cdot 216 A^{z-1}/(1-A)^z \int_A^1 [(1-y)/y]^z dy,
\tag{8.54}
$$

$$
I_2 = 0 \cdot 216 A^{z-1}/(1-A)^z \int_A^1 [(1-y)/y] \ln y\, dy.
\tag{8.55}
$$

Here $11 \cdot 6 u_*$ is the velocity at the interface of the laminar sublayer in the case of a hydraulically smooth bed, or the velocity in a distance of 3·68 roughness diameters from the wall in the case of rough boundaries. The values of I_1 and I_2 are given in graphical form in ref. 18.

There are very few published results of comparisons between the calculated and measured suspended sediment load of rivers, apart from those in support of particular methods. But concentration measurements seem to indicate a more uniform suspended sediment distribution than that given by the simple theory. Nordin and Dempster[20] report on vertical distribution of velocity and sediment. They also show that the measured exponent of sediment distribution, z, varies with about the 0·55 power of fall velocity. The fall velocity is shown to be appreciably reduced by a high concentration of suspended fine material. Their conclusion that "the ratio of the sediment transfer coefficient to the momentum transfer coefficient appears to be a direct function of particle size and bed configuration" is interesting when viewed against the general discussion of sediment movement in this chapter and of that of Chapter 13. Colby and Hembree[21] plotted z_1 against z_m, where

$$z_m = \frac{w}{0·4 u_*}$$

and

$$u_* = [gmS]^{1/2} = \frac{U}{5·75 \log_{10}(12·27\, Dx/k_s)}$$

(cf. ref. 18, 19). With the mean velocity U known from the stream gauging the shear velocity u_* can be calculated. At a given time and cross-section $0·4 u_*$ is a constant and the plot of z_1 is essentially against the fall velocity w. The average of all the results plotted shows that z_1 is proportional to the 0·7 power of the fall velocity w, when w is defined by Rubey's equation (Chapter 6, ref. 8). A detailed comparison of measured and calculated sediment transport was also made by Hubbell and Matejka.[22] The river on which their investigations were made is in sand dune country and not very typical, but the results are very interesting and generally in keeping with other reported comparisons. It appears that with experience in the use of the various formulae, results can be obtained which are of the same order of size as the measured suspended sediment discharge.

It could be mentioned here that for some streams suspended sediment rating curves have been established by measurement, giving the sediment load either in volume or weight against discharge. If the ordinates of the flow-duration curve of the same stream are replaced by the given values from the sediment rating curve, a "suspended sediment–duration curve" is obtained. The area under this curve is a measure of long period total suspended sediment quantity.[23]

References

1. LAURSEN, EMMETT M., The total sediment load of streams, *Proc. A.S.C.E.* **84**, No. HYI, Part 1 (February 1958).
2. HUNT, J. N., The turbulent transport of suspended sediment in open channels, *Proc. Roy. Soc.* (A) **224**, No. 1158, 322–35 (1954).
3. VANONI, V. A., Transportation of suspended sediment by water, *Trans. A.S.C.E.* **111**, 67 (1946).
4. VANONI, V. A., Some effects of suspended sediment on fluid characteristics, *Proc. Fifth Iowa Hydraulic Conference*, 1952, pp. 137–58.
5. ISMAIL, H. M., Turbulent transfer mechanism of suspended sediment in closed channels, *Trans. A.S.C.E.* **117** (1952).
6. EINSTEIN, H. A. and CHIEN, NING, *Second Approximation to the Solution of the Suspended Load Theory*, M.R.D. Sediment Series No. 3, Corps of Engineers, Missouri River Division, Omaha, Nebraska, Jan. 1954.
7. LANE, E. W., CARLSON, E. J. and MANSON, O. S., Low temperature increases sediment transportation in Colorado River, *Civil Engineering* (Sept. 1949).
8. VANONI, VITO A. and NOMICOS, GEORGE N., Resistance properties of sediment-laden streams, *Proc. A.S.C.E.* **85**, No. HY 5 (1959).
9. CHIEN, NING, The present status of research in sediment transport, *Proc. A.S.C.E.* **80**, Sep. No. 565 (December 1954).
10. ELATA, C. and IPPEN, A. T., *The Dynamics of Open Channel Flow with Suspensions of Neutrally Buoyant Particles*, Technical Report No. 45, Hydrodynamics Laboratory M.I.T., Cambridge, Mass., 1961.
11. HINZE, J. O., *Turbulence, An Introduction to Its Mechanism and Theory*, McGraw-Hill, 1957, p. 353.

12. HINO, MIKIO, Turbulent flow with suspended particles, *Proc. A.S.C.E.* **89,** No. HY 4 (July 1963).
13. SOO, S. L., Statistical properties of momentum transfer in two-phase flow, *Chemical Engineering Science,* **5,** No. 2 (April 1956).
14. SOO, S. L., IHRIG, H. K. and EL KOUH, A. F., Experimental determination of statistical properties of two-phase turbulent motion, *A.S.M.E. Trans.* **82**D (*Journal of Basic Engineering*), 3: 609–21 (Sept. 1960).
15. LIU, VI-CHANG, Turbulent dispersion of dynamic particles, *Journal of Meteorology,* **13,** 399 (Aug. 1956).
16. BAGNOLD, R. A., Auto-suspension of transported sediment; turbidity currents, *Proc. Roy. Soc.* (A) No. 1322, **265** (Jan. 1962).
17. LANE, E. W. and KALINSKE, A. A., Engineering calculations of suspended sediment, *Trans. Am. Geophysical Union,* **22,** 603–7 (1942).
18. EINSTEIN, H. A., *The Bed-load Function for Sediment Transportation in Open Channel Flows,* Tech. Bull. No. 1026, Sept. 1950, U.S. Dept. of Agriculture.
19. KEULEGAN, GARBIS H., Laws of turbulent flow in open channels, *Nat. Bureau of Standards, J. Res.* **21** (1938).
20. NORDIN, C. F. and DEMPSTER, G. R., *Vertical Distribution of Velocity and Suspended Sediment Middle Rio Grande New Mexico,* U.S. Geological Survey Professional Paper 462–B, 1963, 20 pp.
21. COLBY, B. R. and HEMBREE, C. H., *Computations of Total Sediment Discharge, Niobrara River near Cody, Nebr.,* U.S. Geological Survey Water-Supply Paper 1357, 1955, 187 pp.
22. HUBBELL, D. W. and MATEJKA, D. Q., *Investigations of Sediment Transportation Middle Long River at Dunning, Nebraska,* U.S. Geological Survey Water-Supply Paper 1476, 1959, 123 p.
23. —————— —————— ——————, *Analysis of Flow-Duration, Sediment Rating Curve Method of Computing Sediment Yield.* U.S. Bureau of Reclamation Sedimentation Section. Denver, Colorado, April 1951.

CHAPTER 9

The Empirical Approach to Stable Channel Design

THE so-called rational approach, which gave the Shields entrainment function and a large number of sediment transport formulae —most of which are of the same form as the Du Boys' formula and involve empirical constants—is of Continental origin. The entirely empirical, so-called regime theory, is mainly an Anglo-Indian approach. A channel in regime is defined as having zero net erosion or deposition over a hydrological cycle.

Here the Kennedy formula of 1895

$$V_0 = aD^b = 0.84D^{0.64} \tag{9.1}$$

is of historical importance, because of the empirical design laws which followed from both Egyptian and Indian schools.

Among the subsequent publications the best known contribution is by Lacey.[1] An interesting feature is that Lacey did not produce any unpublished information but rearranged the then existing field data in so clear and able a manner that these empirical rules have often been taken as basic laws.

Lacey wrote the Kennedy type formula in terms of the hydraulic mean radius as

$$V_0 = a_1 m^{b_1} \tag{9.2}$$

and found that Kennedy's data were satisfied by $b_1 = 0.5$ = constant and $a_1 = 1.17$, i.e.

$$V_0 = 1.17 m^{0.5}. \tag{9.3}$$

The relationship for regime for any type of sediment, other than "Kennedy's standard silt", was obtained by introducing a factor f, known as Lacey's silt factor.

The silt factor expresses the relationship to the "standard silts" for which $a_1 = 1 \cdot 17$ as

$$f = \left(\frac{a}{1 \cdot 17}\right)^2, \qquad (9.4)$$

where a is the value of a_1 for the particular material.

Thus the general formula is

$$V_0 = 1 \cdot 17 \sqrt{(fm)}. \qquad (9.5)$$

For various materials values of f were given by Lacey as follows:

	f
Massive boulders ($d \doteq 25$ in.)	39·60
Large stones	38·60
Large boulders, shingle and heavy sand	20·90
Medium boulders, shingle and heavy sand	9·75
Small boulders, shingle and heavy sand	6·12
Large pebbles and coarse gravel	4·68
Heavy sand	2·00
Coarse sand	1·56–1·44
Medium sand	1·31
Standard Kennedy silt (Upper Bari Doab)	1·00
Lower Mississippi silt	0·357

It follows from eqn. (9.5) that the product (fm) is constant in silt-stable canals with the same mean velocity and it was assumed that this also applies to the product (fP), where P is the length of wetted perimeter. Consequently, the product $f^2 A$ is a function of velocity alone. Available data plotted as V_0 versus Af^2 yielded

$$Af^2 = 3 \cdot 8 V_0^5. \qquad (9.6)$$

$$Qf^2 = 3 \cdot 8 V_0^6. \qquad (9.7)$$

It should be noted that the range of values plotted was

$$5 < Af^2 < 3000.$$

$$1 < V_0 < 4.$$

This is a relatively limited range, since for rivers the mean velocity may substantially exceed 10 ft/sec, and Af^2 may be 10^5 or more.

The mean velocity V_0 may be calculated from Manning's formula

$$V_0 = (1 \cdot 486/n)m^{2/3}S^{1/2}. \tag{9.8}$$

With n replaced from

$$n = 0 \cdot 022f^{0 \cdot 2} \tag{9.9}$$

a relationship suggested by Lacey, m and V_0 may be eliminated by means of eqns. (9.5) and (9.7) to give

$$S = f^{1 \cdot 51}/(2587Q^{1/9}) \doteqdot 0 \cdot 000387f^{3/2}/Q^{1/9}. \tag{9.10}$$

It is interesting that with known Q and f the designer can calculate the equilibrium slope without dimensioning the channel, and thus see whether or not an equilibrium slope is possible. However, in river work, Q, f and S are all given, and they may not satisfy eqn. (9.10).

Basically for a known discharge, and assumed shape of cross-section the dimensions of the channel can be calculated after assuming a suitable value of the silt factor f. With f and Q known eqn. (9.7) yields V_0, and Q/V_0 yields the area of cross-section A. Equation (9.5) yields the hydraulic mean radius

$$m = 0 \cdot 7305V_0^2/f. \tag{9.11}$$

Dividing eqn. (9.6) by eqn. (9.11) and rearranging yields

$$P = 3 \cdot 8V_0^3/(0 \cdot 7305f) \tag{9.12}$$

or

$$Pf = 5 \cdot 2V_0^3 \tag{9.13}$$

and

$$P/m = 7{\cdot}1V_0. \tag{9.14}$$

From eqn. (9.7)

$$V_0^3 = f(Q/3{\cdot}8)^{1/2} \tag{9.15}$$

and substituting in eqn. (9.13) yields

$$P = 2{\cdot}668Q^{1/2}. \tag{9.16}$$

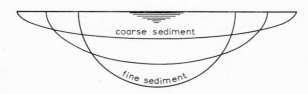

FIG. 9.1. Diagrammatic representation of the variation of cross-sectional shapes with the size of sediment for constant discharge and length of wetted perimeter.

The result given by eqn. (9.16) is remarkable since it shows that for a given discharge the wetted perimeter of a stable channel is constant and independent of the fineness of the silt. Equation (9.14) shows that the shape of the channel cross-section depends on the velocity alone. However, it is well known that the silt size influences the shape of the cross-section. This tendency is evident in nature and is diagrammatically illustrated in Fig. 9.1.

This observation is useful in determining required waterway openings. Lacey suggested that a stable cross-section of a watercourse is semi-elliptical. If the periphery is not composed of the same material the cross-sectional shape will not tend to be semi-elliptical. For example, where the banks are of stiffer material the bed is nearly horizontal.

Lacey also proposed a relationship between the particle size in inches and the silt factor as

$$d = f^2/64. \tag{9.17}$$

With eqn. (9.9) this yields

$$n = d^{1/10}/30$$

which could be compared with the Strickler formula

$$n = d^{1/6}/31\cdot3.$$

This relationship appears to be based on rather limited data.

In his reply to the discussions of this remarkable paper[1] Lacey altered eqn. (9.6) and (9.10) to

$$Af^2 = 4\cdot0V_0 \tag{9.18}$$

and

$$S = 0\cdot00055f^{5/3}/Q^{1/6} \tag{9.19}$$

and added

$$S = 0\cdot000383f^{3/2}/m^{1/2}, \tag{9.20}$$

$$n_a = 0\cdot0225f^{1/4}, \tag{9.21}$$

$$V_0 = (1\cdot3458/n_a)m^{3/4}S^{1/2}, \tag{9.22}$$

$$V_0 = 16\cdot116m^{2/3}S^{1/3}, \tag{9.23}$$

where n_a is the Lacey's absolute roughness factor.

Later Lacey[2] changed eqn. (9.5) to

$$V_0 = 1\cdot15(fm)^{1/2}, \tag{9.24}$$

whence for the silt factor

$$f = 0\cdot75V_0^2/m = f_{vm}. \tag{9.25}$$

These yield

$$P = (8/3)Q^{1/2} \tag{9.26}$$

$$A = 1\cdot26Q^{5/6}/f^{1/3} \tag{9.27}$$

$$m = 0\cdot4725Q^{1/3}/f^{1/3} \tag{9.28}$$

$$V_0 = 0\cdot794Q^{1/6}/f^{1/3} \tag{9.29}$$

$$S = \frac{f^{5/3}}{1750Q^{1/6}} = 0\cdot00055f^{5/3}/Q^{1/6} \tag{9.30}$$

$$P/m = 6\cdot9896V_0. \tag{9.31}$$

The last expression for S is based on $V \propto m^{3/4}S^{1/2}$, whereas eqn. (9.10) was based on Manning's formula. Lacey[3,4] later proposed a "general theory of flow in alluvium". By assuming similarity principles to be satisfied two additional parameters, VS^* and $y_0^n S^*$, were introduced. Dimensional reasoning and a number of assumptions were employed in the development. Here S^* is slope in parts per thousand and n is set equal to $\frac{1}{2}$. With these parameters the so-called normal equation

$$VS^* = K(m^n S^*)^r \qquad (9.32)$$

was proposed. By taking $n = \frac{1}{2}$ and plotting available data as VS^* versus $(m^{1/2}S^*)$ the following relationship was obtained:

$$VS^* = 1 \cdot 60(m^{1/2}S^*)^{4/3}. \qquad (9.33)$$

The upper limit of $VS^* = 253$ and $m^{1/2}S^* = 43 \cdot 5$ above which the flow is supercritical. These limits are obtained by putting V equal to the critical velocity $(gm)^{1/2}$ in eqn. (9.33). From here Lacey developed

$$V = 1 \cdot 42(VS^*)^{1/4}m^{1/2} \qquad (9.34)$$

from which by comparison with eqn. (9.24)

$$f = 48\sqrt{(SV)} = f_{sv}. \qquad (9.35)$$

Further Manning's n is expressed as

$$n_a = 0 \cdot 0251(VS^*)^{1/8} \qquad (9.36)$$

and the particle size in inches as

$$d = 0 \cdot 03(VS^*). \qquad (9.37)$$

Lacey's first paper was an outstanding achievement in systematic study of observational results. However, the attempts to make this into a theory have not been as successful and are open to criticism at many points.

Examining the equation

$$V = Cm^x S^y, \qquad (9.38$$

Liu and Hwang[5] showed that x and y vary with the bed formation and sediment size. See also Henderson.[6]

Writing for discharge

$$q = Vm = Cm^{1+x}S^y \qquad (9.39)$$

and assuming a canal along whose length the bed material is the same, then from the Einstein–Brown equation

$$q_s \propto m^3 S^3. \qquad (9.40)$$

Hence,

$$\frac{q_s}{q} \propto m^{2-x}S^{3-y}. \qquad (9.41)$$

For such a canal with d and q_s/q constant, $m^{2-x}S^{3-y}$ must be constant and $m^{1/2}S$ is constant if $(2-x)/(3-y) = \frac{1}{2}$. When $x = \frac{3}{4}$ and $y = \frac{1}{2}$ this condition is satisfied.

This relationship

$$m^{1/2}S = \text{constant} \qquad (9.42)$$

is well supported by observation.

Introduction of the relationship of eqn. (9.41) into eqn. (9.38) yields

$$V \propto m^{x-y[(2-x)/(3-y)]}. \qquad (9.43)$$

The exponent of m varies widely and approaches $\frac{1}{2}$ in a few cases only. This shows that Lacey's first equation $V \propto \sqrt{m}$ is not as well founded as eqn. (9.42). See also Fig. 13.1 and its discussion.

Criticism of Lacey's formulae centered on two points: that they took no account of the magnitude of sediment discharge, and that they were based on observations covering a narrow range of silt sizes only.

It may have been noticed that the sediment discharge q_s does not appear in any of these equations and it is reasonable to expect that the silt factor accounts for this.

From eqn. (9.5) for a two-dimensional case

$$V^2/m \doteq V_0^2/y_0 = 1 \cdot 37f = K \qquad (9.44)$$

and from Manning's equation

$$S^{1/2} = nV/(1\cdot 49y_0^{2/3}). \qquad (9.45)$$

Combining with a bed-load equation such as that of Shields

$$(S_s q_s/q)[(\gamma_s - \gamma)/\gamma S] = 10(\tau - \tau_c)/[(\gamma_s - \gamma)d] \qquad (9.46)$$

and substituting

$$\tau = \gamma y_0 S \quad \text{and} \quad \tau_c = \gamma y_0 S_c \qquad (9.47)$$

one obtains

$$(S_s q_s/q) = 10 y_0 S^2 (1 - S_c/S)/[(S_s - 1)^2 d]. \qquad (9.48)$$

Substituting for energy slopes from eqn. (9.45)

$$(S_s q_s/q) = \frac{10}{(S_s - 1)^2 d} y_0 \frac{n^4 V^4}{(1\cdot 49)^4 y_0^{8/3}} \left(1 - \frac{S_c}{S}\right) \qquad (9.49)$$

and rearrangement yields

$$V_0^2/y_0 = (S_s q_s/q)^{1/2} 0\cdot 7(S_s - 1)d^{1/2} / \left[n^2 y^{1/6} \left(1 - \frac{S_c}{S}\right)^{1/2} \right] = K. \qquad (9.50)$$

A comparison between eqns. (9.44) and (9.50) shows that f incorporates many important variables and its value from river to river may differ appreciably.

Observation has shown that the sediment load has appreciable effect on the wetted perimeter. With low sediment load and fine sediment P has been found to be $2\cdot 0Q^{1/2}$ or less and with high discharges of sand $P = 3\cdot 4Q^{1/2}$.

Inglis[7] reported on the range of departure from Lacey's mean values found by the Punjab Irrigation Research Institute. They made a statistical analysis of a mass of data obtained from the Lower Chenab canal and found that

P values varied from 0·82 to 1·45 $\bar{P}$; Stand. Dev. 0·178
V values varied from 0·89 to 1·21 $\bar{V}$; Stand. Dev. 0·095 $\qquad$ (9.51)
S values varied from 0·69 to 1·31 $\bar{S}$; Stand. Dev. 0·177

where the bar refers to mean values.

They further reported that "there was much evidence to show that the divergences were mainly caused by variations in the sand charge entering different channels."

Subsequently Inglis put forward formulae incorporating the sediment discharge. In discussion on the paper *Meanders and their Bearing on River Training* by Inglis,[8] White proposed dimensionless formulae of the kind

$$\frac{Bg^{1/5}}{Q^{2/5}} = \alpha_1 \left(\frac{Q}{d^{5/2}g^{1/2}}\right)^{n_1}\left[\frac{d(cg)^{1/3}}{v^{2/3}}\right]^{n_2}\left(\frac{Q_s}{Q}\right)^{n_3}. \qquad (9.52)$$

Given a certain fall velocity w for the sediment load, then the rate of deposition will be proportional to the concentration, or for given concentration it will be proportional to the fall velocity. Hence the rate of settling out is proportional to $(c \cdot w)$.

It was found from experiment[9] that this assumption was justified for quartz sands between 0·15 and 0·5 mm, that in here c varied inversely as w. For grains less than 0·08 mm approximately Stokes' law held with w proportional to d^2. For grains coarser than about 0·7 mm w was found to be proportional to $d^{1/2}$. It was concluded that the dimensionless term $cw/(gv)^{1/3}$ is an important parameter in the design of stable canals. Introduction of this parameter into the White's formula and utilizing Indian data a set of formulae was proposed.

$$B = \alpha_1 \frac{Q^{1/2}}{g^{1/3}v^{1/12}}\left(\frac{cw}{d}\right)^{1/4}$$

Lacey's equivalent $P = 2·67Q^{1/2}$.   (9.53)

$$A = \alpha_2 \frac{v^{1/36}Q^{5/6}}{g^{7/18}(cwd)^{1/12}}$$

Lacey's equivalent $A = \dfrac{1·26Q^{5/6}}{f^{1/3}}$.   (9.54)

$$V = \alpha_3 \frac{g^{7/18}}{v^{1/36}}\, Q^{1/6}(cwd)^{1/12}$$

Lacey's equivalent $V = 0·794Q^{1/6}f^{1/3}$.   (9.55)

$$y_0 = \alpha_4 \frac{v^{1/9}}{g^{1/18}} \frac{Q^{1/3}d^{1/6}}{(cw)^{1/3}}$$

$$\text{Lacey's equivalent } m = 0 \cdot 4725 \left(\frac{Q}{f}\right)^{1/3}. \quad (9.56)$$

$$S = \alpha_5 \frac{(cwd)^{5/16}}{v^{5/36}g^{1/18}Q^{1/6}}$$

$$\text{Lacey's equivalent } S = 0 \cdot 00055 \frac{f^{5/3}}{Q^{1/6}}. \quad (9.57)$$

Lane[10] introduced the observation that stability of the side slopes was also affected by the slope and recommended the separation of the study of stability into the side and bed components.

Subsequently, Blench[11] introduced a number of "factors" into the design of stable canals by the regime method as initiated by Lacey.

Thus

$$\text{Bed factor } \frac{V^2}{D} = F_b, \quad (9.58)$$

which is the same as eqn. (9.47).

$$\text{Side factor } \frac{V^3}{B} = F_s, \quad (9.59)$$

where B is defined as the breadth that multiplied by depth gives the area of the mean section. When multiplied by $\rho^2 v$ the term $(\rho^2 v V^3/B)$ is dimensionally $[F^2 L^{-4}]$ and it is suggested that F_s is a factor in the expression for the square of the mean tractive force intensity on the hydraulically smooth sides. This interpretation is open to question. The term $\rho \mu U^3/x$ is proportional to the square of the shear stress in a laminar boundary layer but in that case x is measured in the direction of the flow, whereas B is measured perpendicular to it. Thus, this shear stress could only be caused by the secondary currents.

F

A plot of data obtained from irrigation canals as gDS/V^2 versus VB/v on double logarithmic paper was found to have the slope of minus $\frac{1}{4}$. The plot of friction factor $2gDS/V^2$ for smooth pipes of diameter D versus VD/v yields the Blasius straight line of rigid boundary flow, which also has the slope of minus $\frac{1}{4}$. Thus it was concluded that the regime boundary is a smooth one. The Blasius equation for smooth circular pipes is modified to

$$\frac{V^2}{gDS} = 3.63 \left(\frac{VD}{v}\right)^{0.25}. \tag{9.60}$$

The equivalent for open-channel flow is written as

$$\frac{V^2}{gDS} = 3.63(1+aC)\left(\frac{VB}{v}\right)^{0.25}.$$

The term $(1+aC)$ is an empirical addition, by means of which it was found that the above equation could be made to satisfy the classic laboratory flume data of Gilbert[12] for dunes on the bed.

Here C is a bed-load charge in hundred-thousandths by weight and a is approximately $1/400$ for Gilbert's sands. A value of $1/233$ is recommended for non-uniform sands.

The regime equations for design purpose were rearranged as

$$B = (F_b Q/F_s)^{1/2} \tag{9.61}$$

$$D = (F_s Q/F_b^2)^{1/3} \tag{9.62}$$

$$S = \frac{F_b^{5/6} F_s^{1/2} v^{1/4}}{3.63(1+aC)gQ^{1/6}}. \tag{9.63}$$

The bed load was also introduced into the bed factor, the details are given in ref. 10.

Parallel with the development of the regime method by the engineers in India, similar work was going on in Egypt. Chaleb,[13] for example, published a formula for non-silting conditions:

$$V_0 = 0.39D^{0.73}. \tag{9.64}$$

In *Irrigation Practice in Egypt* by Molesworth and Yenidunia of 1922 one finds equations of the Kennedy type for Lower Egypt.

$$V_0 = 0 \cdot 39 D^{2/3}, \tag{9.65}$$

and for Upper Egypt

$$V_0 = 0 \cdot 475 D^{2/3}. \tag{9.66}$$

The authors recommended

$$D = (9060S + 0 \cdot 725)\sqrt{B} \tag{9.67}$$

which also included the channel slope and the bed width B. A more detailed account of these formulae is given by Leliavsky.[14]

However, no regime theory was accepted for application by canal designers in other countries than those where they were developed. For example, it was found in America that the Lacey method was in disagreement with local field data.

Generally, there can be considerable discrepancies between the results calculated from various equations. This was strikingly demonstrated by Lane,[15] Fig. 9.2 being reproduced from this paper.

In this paper Lane also deals with the shape of the cross-section of silt-stable canals. Lane introduced the term "form factor" which is the ratio of the flow cross-sectional area to that of the rectangle enclosing the channel cross-section below water level. This ratio would be $0 \cdot 50$ for a triangle, $0 \cdot 67$ for a parabola, $\pi/4$ for a semi-ellipse, and unity for a rectangle by definition. Lane's study yielded ratios from $0 \cdot 56$ to $0 \cdot 92$, the value depending on the size and grading of the boundary material. It appears that a parabola would be closer than an ellipse. However, the main point is that the assumption of a single type of cross-sectional shape, such as Lacey's semi-ellipse is not substantiated.

One can find local regime theories developed in every area where irrigation is practised. The fact that these regime rules have not "transplanted" is an indication that not all of the physical parameters defining the problem are correlated by the regime

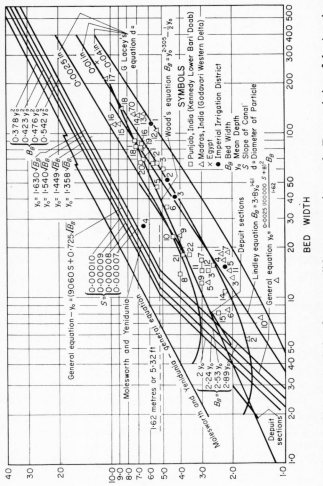

FIG. 9.2. Bed width–depth relation for a non-silting non-scouring canal. (By permission of the American Society of Civil Engineers, from ref. 15, p. 1314.)

method of design. The feature that Lacey's formulae had exponents in round numbers encouraged the belief that a deep physical meaning is behind these formulae. The success of the formulae in India (they were derived from Indian data) encouraged this belief and gave rise to a "regime theory". The fact that these formulae were empirical and based on a very limited number of physically significant parameters was lost sight of at times.

Note that nearly all of the numerical coefficients in the empirical relationships of this chapter *are not dimensionless*— as a check of dimensional homogenity will reveal—and therefore their magnitude depends on the units of measurements. In this chapter the ft-lbf-sec system of units has been used.

References

1. LACEY, G., Stable channels in alluvium, *Proc. Inst. of Civil Engineers*, **229** (1929).
2. LACEY, G., Uniform flow in alluvial rivers and canals, *Proc. Inst. of Civil Engineers*, **237**, 421 (1953).
3. LACEY, G., A general theory of flow in alluvium, *Inst. of Civil Engineers*, **27**, 16 (1946).
4. LACEY, G., Flow in alluvial channels with sandy mobile beds, *Proc. Inst. of Civil Engineers*, **9**, 145 (1958).
5. LIU, H. K. and HWANG, S. Y., Discharge formula for straight alluvial channels, *Proc. A.S.C.E.* **85**, No. HY 11, p. 65 (Nov. 1959).
6. HENDERSON, F. M., Stability of alluvial channels, *Proc. A.S.C.E.* **87**, No. HY 6, p. 109 (Nov. 1961).
7. INGLIS, SIR CLAUDE, *Divergence from regime in stable channels in alluvium*, Central Irrigation and Hydrodynamic Research Station, Poona, India, Annual Report (Technical), 1941–42 pp. 4–11.
8. INGLIS, SIR CLAUDE, *Meanders and their Bearing on River Training*, Maritime and Waterways Paper No. 7, Institution of Civil Engineers, London, Session, 1946–47.
9. INGLIS, SIR CLAUDE, Central Irrigation and Hydrodynamic Research Station, Poona, India, Annual Reports (Technical), 1940–41, p. 50, and 1941–42, p. 33.
10. LANE, E. W., Progress report on studies on the design of stable channels by the Bureau of Reclamation, *Proc. A.S.C.E.* Sep. No. 280 (September 1953).
11. BLENCH, T., *Regime Behaviour of Canals and Rivers*, Butterworths, London, 1957.
12. GILBERT, G. K., *The Transportation of Debris by Running Water*, U.S. Geological Survey Professional Paper 86, 1914.

13. CHALEB, K. O., *Minutes of Proc. Inst. of Civil Engineers, London*, **229**, Pt. 1, 260 (1929–30); **223**, 285.
14. LELIAVSKY, S., *An Introduction to Fluvial Hydraulics*, Constable, London, 1955.
15. LANE, E. W., Stable channels in erodible material, *Proc. A.S.C.E.* **61**, 1307–26 (1935).

CHAPTER 10

The Tractive Force Method of Stable Channel Design

10.1. Two-dimensional Channels

STABLE channel design is basically a problem of sediment transport equilibrium, whether the rate of sediment transport is zero or not. But the lack of a general sediment transport function has prevented a general theoretical solution of the problem of sediment transport equilibrium.

The earlier attempts make use of the simple bed-load functions of the Du Boys type, which in terms of slope and sediment discharge per unit width and unit time may be written as

$$q_s = C_s \tau (\tau - \tau_c), \tag{10.1}$$

where $\tau = \gamma y_0 S$ and $\tau_c = \gamma y_0 S_c$.

Hence,

$$q_s = C_s \gamma^2 y_0^2 S^2 \left(1 - \frac{S_c}{S}\right). \tag{10.2}$$

Empirical values for the sediment discharge coefficient C_s were quoted in Chapter 6. The water discharge is given by the Chézy equation. The ratio of these two relationships defines the relative intensity of sediment movement.

$$\frac{q_s}{q} = \frac{C_s \gamma^2}{C} y_0^{1/2} S^{3/2} \left(1 - \frac{S_c}{S}\right). \tag{10.3}$$

Using

$$C = \frac{1 \cdot 49}{n} y_0^{1/6} \quad \text{and} \quad C_s = \frac{0 \cdot 17}{d_{[mm]}^{3/4}}$$

as given by Straub (see ref. 2, Chapter 6) this becomes

$$\frac{q_s}{q} = \frac{0 \cdot 11 \gamma^2 n y_0^{1/3} S^{3/2}}{\bar{d}_{[mm]}^{3/4}} \left(1 - \frac{S_c}{S}\right). \tag{10.4}$$

Straub also gave

$$S_c = 0 \cdot 00025 \, (\bar{d}_{[mm]} + 0 \cdot 8)/y_0.$$

Expressing the slope in terms of Manning's formula and solving for the equilibrium velocity yields

$$V = 0 \cdot 2 \left(\frac{q_s}{q}\right)^{1/3} \frac{\bar{d}_{[mm]}^{1/4}}{n^{4/3}(1 - S_c/S)^{1/3}} \, y_0^{5/9} \tag{10.5}$$

or by using $A = By_0$ these relationships could be expressed in terms of Q and Q_s.

Any of the bed-load functions could be treated in similar fashion by using empirical coefficients. For example, the Shields bed-load equation

$$\frac{G}{\gamma q} \frac{S_s - 1}{S} = 10 \frac{\tau - \tau_c}{\gamma(S_s - 1)d} \tag{10.6}$$

could be written as

$$\frac{G}{\gamma q} - \frac{10}{(S_s - 1)^2 d} \, y_0 S^2 \left(1 - \frac{S_c}{S}\right) \tag{10.7}$$

or, since in the turbulent region

$$\frac{\tau_c}{\gamma(S_s - 1)d} = 0 \cdot 056 \tag{10.8}$$

$$\frac{G}{\gamma q} = \frac{10S}{(S_s - 1)} \left[\frac{y_0 S}{(S_s - 1)d} - 0 \cdot 056\right]. \tag{10.9}$$

For example, with $S_s = 2 \cdot 6$ this becomes

$$\frac{G}{\gamma q} = S \left(3 \cdot 91 \frac{y_0 S}{d} - 0 \cdot 35\right). \tag{10.10}$$

With the same value of 2·6 for specific gravity eqn. (10.8) gives for the critical conditions the particle size as

$$d = \frac{\tau_c}{0 \cdot 056(S_s - 1)\gamma} = \frac{\tau_c}{0 \cdot 09\gamma} \doteqdot 11 y_0 S. \qquad (10.11)$$

This is a very simple criterion for determination of the particle size which will be on the point of movement in the stream. This relationship is derived from theoretical reasoning and the constants involved are well supported by experimental results.

At threshold conditions the particle size d could be used for the mean roughness height. Then with $y' = k/30 \cdot 2$ in the logarithmic velocity distribution and $u = U \equiv V$ at $y = 0 \cdot 4 y_0$ the Chézy coefficient becomes

$$C = 32 \cdot 6 \log_{10} \frac{y_0}{d} + 35 \cdot 3 = 32 \cdot 6 \log \frac{12 \cdot 1 y_0}{d}. \qquad (10.12)$$

With

$$V = C\sqrt{(y_0 S)} \quad \text{and} \quad Q = BC y_0 \sqrt{(y_0 S)},$$

width, slope, depth, and sediment size are related to the discharge.

In the region where $y_0/d \doteqdot 30$ Manning's n is related to the median particle size by the Strickler formula

$$n = \frac{d^{1/6}}{31 \cdot 3}. \qquad (10.13)$$

Keulegan[1] gives $n = d_{50}^{1/6}/46 \cdot 9$ in terms of the median particles size, Lane and Carlson[2] give for their studies in San Luis Valley $n = d_{75}^{1/6}/30$, and Irmay[3] gives $n = d^{1/6}/49 \cdot 0$, where d is stated to be the maximum size, but has later been interpreted as the d_{90} size. It must be understood that these roughness relationships with the particle size imply a flat bed, i.e. threshold of particle movement. It will be shown in the chapter on channel roughness than when the bed is rippled or covered by dunes these relationships are not valid.

Combination of eqns. (10.11) and (10.13) yields

$$n = 0.048(y_0 S)^{1/6} \qquad (10.14)$$

$$V = 31 y_0^{1/2} S^{1/3} \qquad (10.15)$$

and

$$Q = 31 B y_0^{3/2} S^{1/3} = \frac{B d^{3/2}}{1.18 S^{7/6}}. \qquad (10.16)$$

Equation (10.15) could be compared to the Lacey's equation $V = 16 m^{2/3} S^{1/3}$ by plotting $V/S^{1/3}$ versus y_0.

10.2. Channels of Finite Width

10.2.1. *General background of the tractive force design method*

Tractive force design, a term coined for design in terms of boundary shear, became prominent after the publication by Professor Lane[4] of the work done by the U.S.A. Bureau of Reclamation under his direction.

Firstly, three classes of instability are defined:

  (i) channels subject to scour that do not silt;

  (ii) channels in which objectionable silt deposition occurs but, no scouring;

  (iii) channels in which objectionable silting and scouring both occur at various times.

The Lacey relationships apply to the third class, whereas Blench's equations are said to be valid for both the second and third classes.

Secondly, three important physical aspects are clearly brought to notice. These are:

  (i) the drag intensity over the wetted boundary is not constant;

  (ii) the resistance to displacement of a particle on the side slope is different from that of a particle on the flat part of the bed;

(iii) the capacity of soils to withstand drag forces differs greatly from soil type to soil type.

10.2.2. *Drag distribution and resistance to motion*

Generally the boundary shear varies from a maximum at the deepest point to zero just above the water's edge (Fig. 10.1).

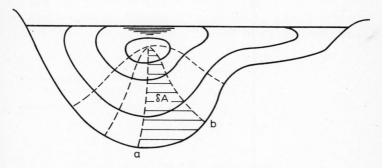

FIG. 10.1. Diagrammatic velocity distribution.

Drawing orthogonals to the isovels of a cross-section generally reveals the varying nature of the velocity gradient in the boundary region. From such an isovel pattern the boundary shear stress distribution could be calculated. It is generally assumed that the orthogonals to the isovels are surfaces of zero shear. This is true only on the average. At any instant, however, there is a turbulence shear stress on these orthogonals caused by the turbulent momentum transfer. If the orthogonals are assumed to be surfaces of zero shear, then the component of weight of the water contained between the orthogonals and the boundary $\delta W = \gamma \delta A S$ is balanced by the shear stress, so that

$$\tau_0 = \frac{\gamma \delta A S}{\overline{ab}}.$$

When the velocity distribution is not known, as in design,

determination of the boundary shear stress distribution becomes a major problem. The analytical results, which are mostly based on the logarithmic velocity distribution, are both unwieldy and often in poor agreement with observation, the latter probably due to the secondary currents.

Not only the shear stress, but also the resistance to displacement of a particle depends upon its location on the periphery of the cross-section. The following analytical treatment was marked out in principle by Forchheimer[5] and was introduced into the tractive force design by Lane.[4]

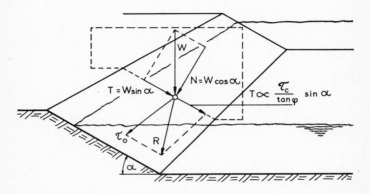

FIG. 10.2. Forces on a particle on the slope.

With ϕ being the angle of repose, the criterion for equilibrium in still water would be $W \sin \alpha = W \cos \alpha \tan \phi$

$$\therefore \ \tan \alpha = \tan \phi.$$

In flowing water (Fig. 10.2) the weight component of the particle down the slope, T, combines with the applied fluid shear stress τ_0. The resultant R of these forces is resisted by a force which cannot exceed the value of normal weight component times the friction factor, that is $W \cos \alpha \tan \phi$.

On the horizontal the critical shear stress is

$$\tau_c \propto W \tan \phi$$

or
$$W \propto \tau_c / \tan \phi, \tag{10.17}$$

where W is the weight of particle per unit area. On the slope the weight term is replaced by the normal load $N = W \cos \alpha$ and the limiting resisting force per unit area will be equal to the resultant force R. Hence,

$$R \propto \tau_c \cos \alpha \tag{10.18}$$

and
$$T = W \sin \alpha \propto \frac{\tau_c}{\tan \phi} \sin \alpha. \tag{10.19}$$

The constant of proportionality is assumed to remain constant throughout.

Hence,

$$\tau_c^2 \cos^2\alpha = \tau_0^2 + \tau_c^2 \frac{\sin^2\alpha}{\tan^2\phi}$$

$$\therefore \frac{\tau_0}{\tau_c} = \cos \alpha \sqrt{\left(1 - \frac{\tan^2\alpha}{\tan^2\phi}\right)} \tag{10.20}$$

This is the form given by Lane.

With

$$\cos^2\alpha - \frac{\sin^2\alpha}{\tan^2\phi} = 1 - \sin^2\alpha \left(1 + \frac{1}{\tan^2\phi}\right)$$

it becomes

$$\frac{\tau_0}{\tau_c} = \sqrt{\left(1 - \frac{\sin^2\alpha}{\sin^2\phi}\right)}. \tag{10.21}$$

Both of these expressions give the ratio of shear stress required to start motion on the slope to that required on the level surface of the same material.

10.2.3. *Design values for boundary shear*

Efforts have been made to relate the capacity of soils to withstand drag force to the type of soil, the aim being to provide

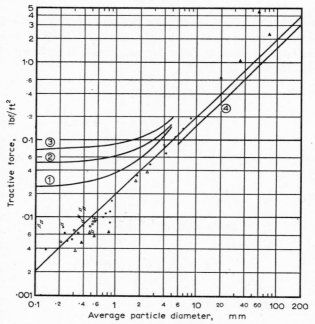

FIG. 10.3. Observed critical and recommended permissible tractive force values for non-cohesive material. Points indicate observed values from a number of sources. Lines 1 to 4 show permissible unit tractive force for non-cohesive material as recommended by U.S. Bureau of Reclamation. (1) Recommended values for canals with clear water. (2) Recommended values for canals with low content of fine sediment in the water. (3) Recommended values for canals with high content of fine sediment in the water.

tables or charts which would specify the permissible boundary shear for any kind of material.

These design values for non-cohesive material are classified according to particle size. The available information is not conclusive. There is no agreement about the particle size to be used when dealing with non-uniform materials. The U.S. Bureau of Reclamation recommends d_{75} for particles larger than about 5 mm diameter and the median size for finer non-cohesive materials. See Fig. 10.3.

A reduction from 10 to 40 per cent of these design values for shear stress is recommended with increasing horizontal curvature of the channel.

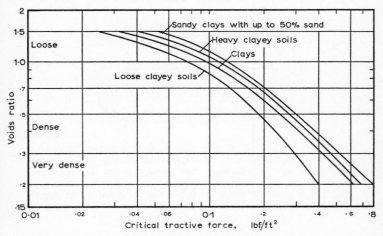

FIG. 10.4. Recommended design values for canals in cohesive material, according to Hydro-technical Construction, Moscow, May 1936.

Similar design values for cohesive soils are presented in terms of voids ratio, Fig. 10.4.

However, the results with cohesive soils are even less conclusive than with non-cohesive soils, because the factors involved in erosion resistance of cohesive material are not simply defined, nor explained. Experiments have shown that the critical tractive force can be correlated with the plasticity index, the dispersion ratio, the mean particle size and the proportion of clay.

10.2.4. *The stable cross-section*

The cross-sectional shape is largely dependent upon the soil type. For channels in non-cohesive material the weight component down the slope has to be combined with the applied fluid shear, whereas in cohesive materials the rolling-down effect of the particles is negligible.

One of the most widely used cross-sections is the trapezoidal one. In designing such a channel by the tractive force method the design value of the boundary shear occurs only over a small

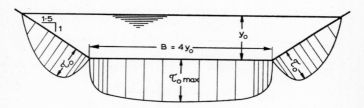

Fig. 10.5. Shear stress distribution over the periphery of a trapezoidal channel, ref. 4. $\tau_{0(max)}$ equals 0·89; 0·97 and 0·99 times $\gamma y_0 S$ for B equals 2; 4 and 8 times y_0 respectively. The maximum value on the sides, τ_0, equals 0·735; 0·750 and 0·760 times $\gamma y_0 S$ respectively and occur at 0·1 to 0·2 of the depth and varies slightly with the slope of the sides.

length of the wetted perimeter. When one considers the shear distribution over the periphery of a trapezoidal channel and the side slope correction (the tractive-force ratio) the above statement becomes clear.

The ideal stable hydraulic cross-section would have reached the stage of impending motion at all points of the cross-section at the same time. For a given soil and discharge this ideal section has the least excavation and least width, and maximum mean velocity. To arrive at such an ideal cross-section various approximations are used in the analytical treatment.

The derivation by the U.S. Bureau of Reclamation assumes that the shear stress on an element of the boundary is due to the weight of water vertically above it, that is the weight component down the slope of the channel. The lateral shear forces between the adjacent currents of different velocity are neglected by this assumption, but alternative studies by the Bureau of Reclamation have shown that this is not serious.

The force equilibrium yields (Fig. 10.6)

$$\gamma y \Delta x S = \tau_0 \frac{\Delta x}{\cos \alpha}$$

$$\therefore \; \tau_0 = \gamma y S \cos \alpha. \tag{10.22}$$

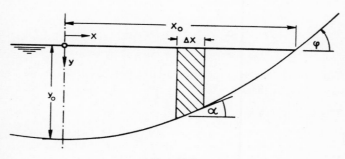

Fig. 10.6

If $\tau_{0(\text{max})}$ is the maximum shear stress at $y = y_0$, then

$$\frac{\tau_0}{\tau_{0\,(\text{max})}} = \frac{y}{y_0} \cos \alpha. \tag{10.23}$$

At the threshold of particle movement $\tau_{0(\text{max})} = \tau_c$ and by substitution for τ_0 / τ_c from eqn. (10.20)

$$\frac{y}{y_0} = \sqrt{\left(1 - \frac{\tan^2 \alpha}{\tan^2 \phi}\right)}.$$

From Fig. 10.6

$$\tan \alpha = \frac{dy}{dx}. \tag{10.24}$$

Substituting and rearranging yields

$$\left(\frac{dy}{dx}\right)^2 + \left(\frac{y}{y_0}\right)^2 \tan^2\phi = \tan^2\phi \qquad (10.25)$$

or

$$\frac{dy}{\sqrt{[1-(y/y_0)^2]}} = \tan\phi\, dx. \qquad (10.26)$$

This yields

$$y_0 \cos^{-1}\frac{y}{y_0} = x\tan\phi$$

or

$$\frac{y}{y_0} = \cos\left(\frac{x\tan\phi}{y_0}\right). \qquad (10.27)$$

Thus the above assumptions lead to a cosine curve for the stable cross-sectional shape.

The half-width is

$$x_0 = \frac{\pi y_0}{2\tan\phi}. \qquad (10.28)$$

The area of the cross-section is

$$A = 2y_0 \int_0^{\pi y_0/2\tan\phi} \cos\left(\frac{x\tan\phi}{y_0}\right) dx = \frac{2y_0^2}{\tan\phi}$$
$$\left[\sin\left(\frac{x\tan\phi}{y_0}\right)\right]_0^{\pi y_0/2\tan\phi}$$
$$= 2y_0^2/\tan\phi. \qquad (10.29)$$

The perimeter P is

$$P = 2\int_0^{x_0} \sqrt{\left[1 + \left(\frac{dy}{dx}\right)^2\right]} dx = 2\int_0^{x_0} \sqrt{\left\{1+\tan^2\phi\right.}$$
$$\left.\left[1-\cos^2\left(\frac{x\tan\phi}{y_0}\right)\right]\right\} dx. \qquad (10.30)$$

Substituting $\theta = x \tan \phi / y_0$ and transcribing the integrand as

$$\sqrt{(\sec^2 \phi - \tan^2 \phi \cos^2 \theta)} = \sec \phi \sqrt{(1 - \sin^2 \phi \cos^2 \theta)}$$

yields

$$P = \frac{2y_0}{\sin \phi} \int_0^{\pi/2} \sqrt{(1 - \sin^2 \phi \cos^2 \theta)} d\theta. \tag{10.31}$$

With limits from 0 to $\pi/2$, $\cos^2 \theta$ may be replaced by $\sin^2 \theta$ without changing the result. Hence,

$$P = \frac{2y_0}{\sin \phi} \int_0^{\pi/2} \sqrt{(1 - \sin^2 \phi \sin^2 \theta)} d\theta. \tag{10.32}$$

This is an elliptic integral of the second kind and is complete with the limits $\pi/2$ and 0. The value is readily obtained from tables for any given value of ϕ. Designating the integral by the symbol E yields

$$P = \frac{2y_0}{\sin \phi} E. \tag{10.33}$$

From known area and wetted perimeter

$$m = \frac{A}{P} = \frac{2y_0^2}{\tan \phi} \frac{\sin \phi}{2y_0 E} = \frac{y_0 \cos \phi}{E}. \tag{10.34}$$

Summarizing:

Surface width $\qquad\qquad 2x_0 = \dfrac{\pi y_0}{\tan \phi}.$ $\qquad\qquad$ (10.35a)

Area $\qquad\qquad\qquad A = \dfrac{2y_0^2}{\tan \phi}.$ $\qquad\qquad\qquad$ (10.35b)

Perimeter $\qquad\qquad P = \dfrac{2y_0}{\sin \phi} E.$ $\qquad\qquad$ (10.35c)

Hydraulic mean radius $\qquad m = \dfrac{y_0 \cos \phi}{E}.$ $\qquad\qquad$ (10.35d)

Leliavsky[6] gives a slightly different approach to the same problem.

Bretting[7] assumed that the shear stress is proportional to the distance between the bottom and water surface, measured perpendicular to the bed, whence

$$\frac{\tau_0}{\tau_{0\,(\text{max})}} = \frac{y}{y_0 \cos \alpha}. \tag{10.36}$$

Combined with logarithmic velocity distribution formulae, differential equations were set up and the boundary shape and isovel patterns calculated.

10.3. Design by Tractive Force Method

Watercourses which are very wide relative to their depth can be treated by the two-dimensional approach discussed in section 10.1.

Narrow watercourses have to be treated as stable in cross-section, and the simple expression of

$$d = 11y_0 S \tag{10.37}$$

obtained for two-dimensional approach must now be written in terms of the hydraulic mean radius.

The general discussion of this problem will be greatly simplified if the angle of repose is given a fixed value, which can be selected according to particular conditions. For example, the stable channel parameters for $\phi = 30°$ and $\phi = 35°$ become:

	$\phi = 30°$		$\phi = 35°$	
Surface width	$B = 2x_0 = 5\cdot45y_0$		$B = 4\cdot49y_0$	(10.38a)
Area	$A \quad\quad = 3\cdot45y_0^2$		$A = 2\cdot86y_0^2$	(10.38b)
Perimeter	$P \quad\quad = 5\cdot87y_0$		$P = 4\cdot99y_0$	(10.38c)
Hydraulic mean radius	$m \quad\quad = 0\cdot59y_0$		$m = 0\cdot57y_0$	(10.38d)
	$\dfrac{P}{m} = 10$		$\dfrac{P}{m} = 8\cdot75$	(10.38e)

Thus eqn. (10.37) is replaced by

$$d = \frac{11mS}{0\cdot59} \doteq 19mS \qquad (10.39)$$

and eqn. (10.15) modified by a factor $(\frac{11}{19})^{1/6}$, yields

$$V \doteq 28m^{1/2}S^{1/3}. \qquad (10.40a)$$

Eliminating S between eqns. (10.39) and (10.40) yields

$$V \doteq 10\cdot5d^{1/3}m^{1/6} \qquad (10.40b)$$

and would be an expression corresponding to Lacey's first equation

$$V = 1\cdot17\sqrt{(fm)}.$$

These relationships define the limiting minimum size of the channel for given discharge, slope and particle size. By the use of eqn. (10.40) it has been implied that the channel is not rippled or covered by dunes, etc., that is one is designing for the threshold of particle movement.

It has been pointed out that the Strickler formula is in terms of median particle size for uniform bed material. If the bed material is not uniform, the median size should be replaced by a dominant size with which the bed tends to become armoured. This size appears to be about the d_{80} to d_{90} size, depending on the grading. However, due to the one-sixth power relationship the effect of errors in estimating the particle size is not very great.

The coefficient of the mean velocity relationship could be raised by about 10–15 per cent.

Other necessary relationships for the design can be derived from those above.

Thus $VA = Q$ and $Pm = A$, yielding

$$Q = 28Pm^{3/2}S^{1/3} \qquad (10.41)$$

and

$$S^{1/3} = Q/[28 \times 10(d/19S)(d/19S)^{3/2}]$$
$$S = (0\cdot1785)^{6/13}[d^{5/2}/Q]^{6/13}$$
$$\therefore\ S = 0\cdot45d^{1\cdot15}Q^{-0\cdot46}. \qquad (10.42)$$

This could be compared with the Lacey expression

$$S = 0.00055f^{5/3}/Q^{1/6}.$$

The channel width for

$$\phi = 30° \quad B = 5.45y_0 = \frac{5.45d}{11S} \doteqdot 0.5\frac{d}{S} \qquad (10.43a)$$

$$\phi = 35° \quad B = 4.49y_0 = 0.41\frac{d}{S} \qquad (10.43b)$$

or

$$\phi = 30° \quad B = 1.1d^{-0.15}Q^{0.46} \qquad (10.44a)$$

$$\phi = 35° \quad B = 0.91d^{-0.15}Q^{0.46} \qquad (10.44b)$$

and

$$\phi = 30° \quad P = 1.18d^{-0.15}Q^{0.46} \qquad (10.45a)$$

$$\phi = 35° \quad P = 1.01d^{-0.15}Q^{0.46}. \qquad (10.45b)$$

This could be compared with the Lacey equation

$$P = 2.67Q^{1/2}.$$

These formulae have been worked for assumed values of specific gravity and angle of repose and are valid for sediment larger than $\frac{1}{4}$ in., that is where the plot of the Shields entrainment function versus particle Reynolds number, levels out to a value of about 0.056. However, the same treatment can be followed for any given conditions by introducing appropriate values and the coefficients are changed accordingly. General expressions can also be written, obviously more cumbersome, or correction factors could be worked out (see also ref. 6, Chapter 9).

If the slope is less than the value computed by eqn. (10.42), the channel will aggrade. Then equilibrium can be established only by increasing the slope.

In canal design this may mean re-siting, in river control work it would suggest a cut-off. However, it must be kept in mind that these relationships are based on a straight channel. Therefore, in river control work allowance must be made for bend losses.

It must also be stated that eqn. (10.42) for the minimum slope is as yet not firmly established. Although this analysis shows that the width to depth ratio depends only on the angle of repose and is about five, in natural rivers in coarse alluvium it is much greater and increases with discharge.

But eqn. (10.42) does provide the engineer with some guidance, when considering an aggrading river, as to whether it is because of lack of slope or because the river has been allowed to spread into too wide a channel.

In river work an added complication arises in defining the design discharge. It should be the discharge which at constant steady flow would have the same overall effect upon the river channel as the natural fluctuating discharge has. Such a discharge has been termed the dominant or bankfull discharge, but at the present time the definition of this discharge is still rather difficult.[8, 9]

The results of the foregoing analysis can be displayed for comparison as well as for design purposes for a given discharge on a B versus S plot with the particle size d as a parameter (Fig. 10.7).

For a given Q eqns. (10.42) and (10.44) define a line on the B versus S plane. This line defines the limiting conditions for the stable channel, that is the limiting narrow section.

Below this line the B–S relationship cannot be satisfied.

From eqn. (10.44)

$$d = (N_1/B)^{13/2} \tag{10.46}$$

and from eqn. (10.42)

$$d = (S/N_2)^{13/15}. \tag{10.47}$$

Whence,

$$S = N_2 \left(\frac{N_1}{B}\right)^{15/2}, \tag{10.48}$$

where N_1 and N_2 are numerical constants for the particular conditions.

For the wide section, the two-dimensional design, Q, B, d and S were related by eqn. (10.16), or in terms of B

$$B = P = \frac{1 \cdot 14 Q S^{7/6}}{d^{3/2}}. \qquad (10.49)$$

For a given Q this equation defines a family of straight lines on the log–log plane of B versus S. For the given discharge and particle size the narrowest channel with the minimum cross-sectional area

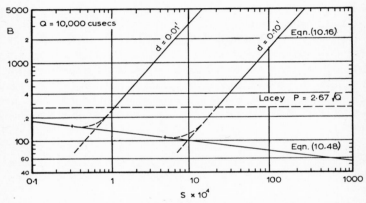

FIG. 10.7. Diagrammatic presentation of the threshold tractive force design.

is characterized by a point on the line defined by eqn. (10.48). Expressing it in other words, eqns. (10.42) and (10.44) define the point where the relationship between B and S for given d and Q lies on the line defined by eqn. (10.48). Between the eqn. (10.49) which defines the wide channel and eqn. (10.48) for the limiting narrow one there will be a transition. The foregoing treatment does not determine the transition region.

It is important to realize that the y–α relationship

$$\frac{y}{y_0} = \sqrt{\left(1 - \frac{\tan^2\alpha}{\tan^2\phi}\right)} \quad \text{or} \quad \frac{y}{y_0} = \cos\left(\frac{x \tan \phi}{y_0}\right)$$

will still be satisfied if a section of constant depth is inserted into
the centre of the cosine curve. This leads to the following cross-
section (Fig. 10.8) which is seen to correspond to the transition
in Fig. 10.7.

It is likely that, if an exact relationship is used instead of the
approximation $\tau \propto y \cos \alpha$, a continuous flat curve would result
instead of the straight centre part. Yet this is a small discrepancy
and could be overshadowed by the effects of the secondary
currents. The above cross-section could be considered to be the

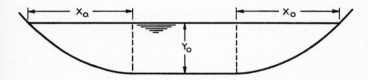

Fig. 10.8. Stable cross-section for threshold conditions, but larger
than the minimum size.

transition between the minimum one and the infinitely wide (two
dimensional) cross-section.

This also shows that there is an infinite number of cross-
sections which satisfy the tractive force design criteria, and
consequently with d and Q fixed an unlimited number of the
ratios of P/m. It should be recalled that the Lacey approach
postulates a unique relationship between P/m and the mean
velocity [eqn. (9.31) or eqn. (9.14)]

$$P/m = 6 \cdot 9896 V$$

It should be realized that the approach to the design of stable
channels put forward in sections 10.2.4 and 10.3—with the threshold of particle movement as the criterion—is based essentially on
theoretical reasoning and has as yet not been tested and proved
by field application. In particular it must be kept in mind that
these relationships are based on straight channels and no allowance has been made for secondary currents of a meandering

watercourse. However, these relationships should contribute to the general understanding of the stable channel design problem and should also provide the designer with a limit criterion. Additional aspects of the shear and velocity distribution problems are dealt with in refs. 10, 11 and 12. It appears that the secondary currents and the distribution of turbulence are the most important factors affecting the advance of theoretical design methods. Mathematical and experimental research into these aspects is required for further progress.

References

1. KEULEGAN, G. H., Laws of turbulent flow in open channels, *National Bureau of Standards Journal of Research*, **21,** 701 (1938).
2. LANE, E. W. and CARLSON, E. J., Some factors affecting the stability of canals constructed in coarse granular materials, *Proc. Minnesota International Hydraulics Convention*, Sept. 1953.
3. IRMAY, S., *On Steady Flow Formulae in Pipes and Channels*, Paper No. III–3, Third Meeting IAHR, Grenoble, France, 1949.
4. LANE, E. W., Progress report on studies on the design of stable channels by the Bureau of Reclamation, *Proc. A.S.C.E.* Sep. No. 280 (September 1953).
5. FORCHHEIMER, P., "*Hydraulik*" *Teubner Verlagsgesellschaft*, Leipzig and Berlin, 1924.
6. LELIAVSKY, S., *An Introduction to Fluvial Hydraulics*, Constable, London, 1955, pp. 83–84.
7. BRETTING, A. E., Stable channels, *Acta Polytechnica Scandinavica*, Ci 1 (1958).
8. NIXON, M., A study of the bankfull discharge of rivers in England and Wales, *Proc. I.C.E.* **12,** 157 (February 1959).
9. WOLMAN, M. G. and LEOPOLD, L. B., *River Flood Plains: Some Observations on their Formation*, U.S. Geol. Survey. Prof. Paper 282–C (1957).
10. LUNDGREN, H. and JONSSON, I. G., Shear and velocity distribution in shallow channels, *Proc. A.S.C.E.* **90,** HY1 (Jan. 1964).
11. ENGELUND, F., A practical approach to self-preserving turbulent flows, *Acta Polytechnica Scandinavica*, Ci 27 (1964).
12. ENGELUND, F., Flow resistance and hydraulic radius, *Acta Polytechnica Scandinavica*, Ci 24 (1964).

CHAPTER 11

Comparison of the Regime and Tractive Force Methods of Stable Channel Design

IT IS most important to realize fully the conditions for which these methods are applicable.

The regime method of design is for a channel with a live bed that may scour or deposit at times, but over a climatic cycle the net result of scour and deposition is zero. The regime type of channel is characterized by

$$m^{1/2}S = \text{constant.} \qquad (11.1)$$

The tractive force method of design was developed for threshold conditions of sediment transport. It assumes that threshold critical shear stress conditions exist along the channel and over the periphery. Since the shear stress is proportional to mS it follows that the tractive force method of channel design is characterized by

$$mS = \text{constant.} \qquad (11.2)$$

Therefore these are not just alternate methods for the same calculation, but are complementary to each other, the tractive force method marking the lower limiting case. Extension of the tractive force method of design to the "live bed" case would make these alternative methods. To do this it is necessary to define the relationship between the rate of transport and the shear stress and also to express the mean velocity of flow as a function of the sediment transport rate. The latter requires that the resistance coefficient or roughness height must be known as a function of the sediment transport rate. With sediment transport taking place the plane bed develops ripples, dunes, etc., depending on flow conditions, and the roughness height varies accordingly. The roughness height is no longer approximated by the diameter of the particles. Although much work has been done in this direction, these relationships in a general form are still outstanding.

The three Lacey equations

$$V = 1 \cdot 17 \sqrt{(fm)} \tag{11.3}$$

$$V = 16 m^{2/3} S^{1/3} \tag{11.4}$$

$$P = 2 \cdot 67 \sqrt{Q} \tag{11.5}$$

involve five variables, i.e. Q, P, m, S and f and therefore only two quantities may be fixed initially. But in river work for example, usually Q, S and f are given and cannot be altered to suit the design. In such a case the three Lacey equations can be satisfied simultaneously only if Q, S and f satisfy

$$S = \frac{f^{5/3}}{1750 Q^{1/6}}. \tag{11.6}$$

It was shown (9.50) that the silt factor f incorporates d and q_s/q, but d is given and the ratio q_s/q should be a quantity which could be fixed beforehand. Equation (11.4) expresses the velocity in terms of flow resistance and eqn. (11.3) the same velocity in terms of particle resistance. Therefore these could be looked upon as resistance equations expressed in terms of action or reaction, and between them the silt factor could be expressed in terms of S and m.

If the slope is greater than that given by eqn. (11.6), then the engineer requires a criterion by which the channel could be widened and thus its sediment transporting power reduced. For the tractive force method of design such a criterion was provided by eqns. (10.42), (10.44) and (10.45).

$$S = 0.45d^{1.15}Q^{-0.46} \qquad (11.7a)$$

$$B = 1.1d^{-0.15}Q^{0.46} \qquad (11.7b)$$

$$P = 1.18d^{-0.15}Q^{0.46} \qquad (11.7c)$$

It was pointed out that the slope given by eqn. (11.7a) is the minimum slope. If S is greater than this minimum value the channel can be widened by inserting a constant depth section between the banks. The criterion for bed movement in the tractive force method was $d = 19mS$ and in the regime method $m^{1/2}S = \text{constant}$. Introducing the flow resistance yielded $V = 28m^{1/2}S^{1/3}$ and $V = 16m^{2/3}S^{1/3}$ respectively. These expressions for the mean velocity have been developed without specific consideration of the channel shape. A third relationship, such as eqn. (11.7c) or eqn. (11.5) should also include or be augmented by a relationship between the slope, sediment size, and water discharge. For the tractive force method this additional criterion was given by eqn. (11.7a). It now appears reasonable to assume that eqn. (11.6), like (11.7a) for the tractive force method, gives such a criterion for the regime method. Equation (11.6) should then be interpreted as the minimum slope below which a regime channel cannot be formed, and should only be used as such for verification that the actual P and S are greater than these minimum values.

The P and S relationship in the Lacey stable channels with given d and q_s/q can be derived as follows:

The flow resistance is

$$V = Cm^xS^y \qquad (11.8)$$

and discharge

$$q = Vm = Cm^{1+x}S^y. \qquad (11.9)$$

The sediment discharge, in terms of the Einstein–Brown

formula (section 6.5), for example, for given conditions and sediment gives

$$q_s \propto m^3 S^3, \tag{11.10}$$

so that

$$\frac{q_s}{q} \propto m^{2-x} S^{3-y}. \tag{11.11}$$

Eliminating m with $Q = VPm$

$$P \propto QS^{(1+x)(3-y)/(2-x)-y} \tag{11.12}$$

and for $P \propto \sqrt{Q}$ one obtains

$$S \propto Q^{-1/[2(1+x)(3-y)/(2-x)-2y]}. \tag{11.13}$$

This exponent has been found[1,2] to be quite close to $(-\frac{1}{6})$ for a plane bed, but for a dune bed its value ranges between $(-\frac{1}{4})$ and $(-\frac{1}{6})$.

References

1. LIU, H. K. and HWANG, S. Y., Discharge formula for straight alluvial channels, *Proc. A.S.C.E.* **85,** No. HY 11, 65 (November 1959).
2. HENDERSON, F. M., Stability of alluvial channels, *Proc. A.S.C.E.* **87,** No. HY 6, 109 (November 1961).

CHAPTER 12

Ripples, Dunes and Antidunes

THE distinctive pattern into which an erodible granular bed forms under some conditions of water flow or wave action over it has intrigued observers for centuries. Why do these bed features grow and change from one form to another, yet remain stable in shape with a given set of conditions? What is the mechanism of their formation? Numerous attempts have been made to describe the formation and movement of these bed features, their height and spacing in terms of a few observable parameters, but they have proved to be unsatisfactory. Empirical relationships of the form

$$c = 0 \cdot 00013(u_s^2 - 0 \cdot 11) \text{ m/sec}, \qquad (12.1)$$

where c is the velocity of propagation of the bed features, u_s is the surface velocity of the water, appeared first.[1] This one was based on the observations in the River Loire and was proposed for velocities less than $1 \cdot 1$ m/sec. It does not include parameters such as water depth and particle size of the bed material, etc.

In 1883 G. H. Darwin[2] published in the Royal Society his results of experiments on the sand-ripple formation due to oscillatory motion. He compared the ripple marks to the vortex layer between two uniform streams, in this case the lower layer being sand. "The layer of transition between two currents of fluid is dynamically unstable, but if a series of vortices be interpolated, so as to form friction rollers as it were, it probably becomes stable." Hydrodynamic theory shows that a vortex sheet is unstable and will break up into vortices which tend to concentrate. Darwin discusses at some length the vortices he observed in his experimental apparatus, but failed to explain the mechanism of ripple formation any more closely.

Deacon[3] carried out experiments (1892) in a glass-sided flume. He observed the beginning of ripple formation at $u_s = 1 \cdot 3$ ft/sec. Deacon's results were:

$u_s = 1 \cdot 5$ ft/sec ripples moved at $c = 0 \cdot 0007$ ft/sec.

$u_s = 1 \cdot 75$ ft/sec ripples moved at $c = 0 \cdot 0017$ ft/sec.

$u_s = 2 \cdot 00$ ft/sec ripples moved at $c = 0 \cdot 042$ ft/sec.

$u_s = 2 \cdot 125$ ft/sec ripple form became irregular

$u_s = 2 \cdot 5$ ft/sec sand grains were carried at times over a number of ripple lengths.

$u_s = 2 \cdot 6$–$2 \cdot 8$ ft/sec showed fewer and less defined ripples.

$u_s = 2 \cdot 9$ ft/sec ripples disappeared.

Deacon gave a very good description of the mechanism of the ripple formation. His description of the various stages of ripple formation is not only one of the earliest, but also of a quality such that subsequent descriptions have added little to it.

An analytical approach to the problem was put forward by Exner.[4] Exner started from the assumption that the capacity of the flow to transport sediment depends on its velocity. Then, when the flow is saturated with sediment, that is when it is carrying the maximum amount of sediment for the given velocity, an acceleration of flow implies erosion and a deceleration implies deposition. Thus scour or deposition depends on $\partial u/\partial x$. If y and η denote the water surface and sand bed ordinates respectively, both measured above a common datum, then $\partial \eta/\partial t$ will represent the rate of scour, leading to Exner's first equation

$$\frac{\partial \eta}{\partial t} = -K \frac{\partial u}{\partial x}, \qquad (12.2)$$

where u is the velocity of flow near the bed and is a function of the distance x along the bed. K is the "erosion coefficient", a factor relating sediment discharge to flow velocity.

Continuity gives on assuming that $u = U$

$$u(y-\eta) = q \qquad (12.3)$$

and substituting yields

$$\frac{\partial \eta}{\partial t} = \frac{Kq}{(y-\eta)^2} \frac{\partial(y-\eta)}{\partial x}. \qquad (12.4)$$

Since the local water surface is approximated to horizontal, $\partial y/\partial x$ is of smaller order of magnitude than $\partial \eta/\partial x$. Thus

$$\frac{\partial \eta}{\partial t} + \frac{Kq}{(y-\eta)^2} \frac{\partial \eta}{\partial x} = 0. \qquad (12.5)$$

Here (qK) and y are now constants and the general solution is

$$y - \eta = f\left[\frac{Kq}{(y-\eta)^2} - x\right]. \qquad (12.6)$$

Assuming the original bottom shape to be sinusoidal with a wavelength λ and an amplitude a, Exner obtained a general solution in the form of

$$\eta = a \cos \frac{2\pi}{\lambda}\left[x - \frac{qK}{(y-\eta)^2} t\right] \qquad (12.7)$$

from which the speed of propagation of the ripple

$$c_r = \frac{qK}{(y-\eta)^2}. \qquad (12.8)$$

The results of this simple theory are in reasonable agreement with observation. Exner showed that the initial sinusoidal sand bed will transform gradually into an asymmetrical wave with a gentle upstream slope. The theory does not show how the original sinusoidal form is obtained from an initially plane bed.

Exner further considered the case when the water surface slope and friction are taken into account. In a further extension the variation of the channel width was considered. However, these refinements add little to an understanding of the general problem. Leliavsky[5] gives a good account in English of these treatments.

G

Experimental work done by Blasius[6] about 1910 was limited in range. The depth only slightly exceeded 2 in. (5·5 cm) and the maximum velocity was 2 ft/sec. But Blasius was the first to introduce the ratio of stream velocity to wave celerity into the description of ripple and dune formation, that is the Froude number in present-day nomenclature.

Very extensive experimental investigations were carried out by Gilbert and Murphy[7] and the published results are still widely used by research workers. The primary aim of the investigation was to learn the laws which control the movement of bed load, and especially to determine how the quantity of load is related to the stream's slope and to the discharge of water and sediment. The flume length and width as well as the discharge were varied over a wide range. The grains, of seven different shapes, varied between 0·34 and 5·2 mm in diameter. The flow covered a range from low velocities and no sediment movement up to very agitated flows at supercritical velocities and high rate of sediment transport. The tests covered all stages of development of bed forms from their appearance and growth to erosion at increasing velocity, and the appearance of a new form—the antidune—at supercritical velocity.

Similar, but not as extensive experiments were carried out at Dresden and a summary is most readily available in *Proc. Am. Soc. Civ. Eng.* by Kramer,[8] which also included references to the earlier European experimental work. Kramer makes use of the wave celerity in the analysis of the results. In the discussion of Kramer's paper, Straub[9] presents results, obtained at the University of Minnesota, as a function of the bed load. Straub concludes that the parameter important in determining the initial movement of the sand and the appearance and development of bed forms is the Froude number, in conjunction with the grading of the sediment and the magnitude of the tractive force (Fig. 12.1).

Shields[10] discussed the development of bed forms in terms of $\tau_c/(\rho_s-\rho)gd$ and the particle Reynolds number u_*d/v or d/δ', where τ_c is the critical bed shear stress, ρ_s and ρ are the densities of grains and water respectively, d is the particle size, u_* is the shear velocity, and δ' the laminar sublayer thickness.

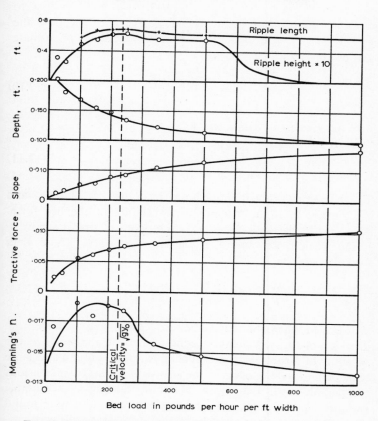

FIG. 12.1. Dependence of various parameters on bed load, according to Straub (ref. 9). (By permission of the American Society of Civil Engineers.)

The earlier Russian work by Goncharov and others defined the various stages of bed formation in terms of non-transporting velocity V_{non} and the ratio of the depth of flow to the roughness height. This work suggested that bed forms appear, V', at velocity ratios

$$\frac{V'}{V_{\text{non}}} = 2 \cdot 5 \left(\frac{k}{y_0}\right)^{1/12} \qquad (12.9)$$

and disappear, V''',

$$\frac{V'''}{V_{\text{non}}} = 2 \cdot 5 \left(\frac{y_0}{k}\right)^{1/12} \qquad (12.10)$$

with the greatest development, V'', when

$$\frac{V''}{V_{\text{non}}} = \frac{0 \cdot 75 V''' + 0 \cdot 25 V'}{V_{\text{non}}} . \qquad (12.11)$$

The subsequent investigations are in terms of $V^2/(gy_0)$ and c_r/V, where c_r is the velocity of translation of the bed form. Also $(gd)/V^2$ is used. Here y_0 is the depth of uniform flow, d is the particle size and V is the mean velocity. These yield formulae such as

$$\frac{c_r}{V} = 0 \cdot 0188 \frac{V^2}{gy_0} - 0 \cdot 0292 \frac{gd}{V^2} . \qquad (12.12)$$

The next phase of the studies in Russia, mainly under the direction of M. A. Velikanov, concentrated on the study of the structure of turbulent open-channel flow. It was found that large scale periodic eddies occur in the flow with transverse dimensions comparable with the depth of flow. Similarly, measurable variations in the suspended sediment concentration were found along the stream. It was concluded that these large-scale perturbations possess the greatest amount of fluctuating energy and are directly related to the formation of ridge-type bottom deposits. Velikanov[11] put forward a mathematical model showing that turbulence could cause erosion and deposition along the bed. Velikanov started from Exner's treatment, which did not show how the initially flat sand bed becomes wavy, and proceeded to show that turbulence could lead to this deformation of the flat surface. Writing

$$\bar{d} \operatorname{div} (m v_g) + \frac{\partial \eta}{\partial t} = 0, \qquad (12.13)$$

where $\bar{d}$ is the mean grain diameter, v_g is the mean velocity vector of all moving grains, m is "coefficient of continuity" for sand grains in motion and is the ratio of the volume of sand grains moving over a unit of bed area to the volume at a layer of thickness d, and assuming that m is constant, and v_g is proportional to the mean stream velocity

$$v_g = Au. \qquad (12.14)$$

A depends on the mean grain diameter only and

$$Amd = K.$$

Velikanov obtains Exner's first equation

$$\frac{\partial \eta}{\partial t} + K \frac{\partial u}{\partial x} = 0. \qquad (12.15)$$

This approach shows the weakness of the implicit assumptions, because m clearly depends on velocity; the greater the velocity the more particles are moving. Neither would the grain velocity bear a constant relation to the stream velocity. The increase in the flow of solids along δx in unit time δt equals the change of volume within this unit

$$(q_s + \delta q_s)\delta t - q_s \delta t = -\delta \eta \, \delta x$$

or

$$\frac{\partial q_s}{\partial x} + \frac{\partial \eta}{\partial t} = 0. \qquad (12.16)$$

The total transport of solids—with the grain size assumed to remain constant—is divided into groups according to the intervals of stream velocities from u to $u + du$

$$(dq_s) = \bar{d}mu(du). \qquad (12.17)$$

Allowing the flow to vary between 0 and ∞ yields

$$q_s = d \int_0^\infty mu\,du. \tag{12.18}$$

Here m is considered to be a function of u (proportional to the number of sand grains moving at the velocity u) and to be proportional to the frequency of the fluctuation of the transporting velocity u.

It is now assumed that this frequency depends on x only, that is that there is a definite space correlation and the shape of the correlation function approximates

$$R_{(x)} = \left(1 - \frac{x^2}{l^2}\right)^2, \tag{12.19}$$

where $l = x$ when $R = 0$. The coefficient m is then expressed in terms of the velocity fluctuations in the vicinity of the point $x = 0$. The distribution of instantaneous velocity values at any point along the x-direction is assumed to follow the normal Gaussian distribution

$$f(u) = \frac{1}{\sigma\sqrt{(2\pi)}}\, e^{-(u-\bar{u})^2/2\sigma^2}, \tag{12.20}$$

where the $\bar{u}$ is the average value of u and σ is the standard deviation of the velocity fluctuations. Thus for correlation between two points with $u_0' = u_0 - \bar{u}$ and $u' = u - \bar{u}$, the distribution function is

$$f(u_0, u) = \frac{1}{2\pi\sigma^2\sqrt{(1-R^2)}}\, e^{-[u_0'^2 - 2Ru_0'u' + u'^2]/2\sigma^2(1-R^2)}. \tag{12.21}$$

Writing

$$b = \frac{u' - Ru_0'}{\sigma\sqrt{(1-R^2)}} \tag{12.22}$$

$$a = \frac{u_0'}{\sigma} \tag{12.23}$$

and substituting one obtains

$$f(a, b) = \frac{1}{\sqrt{(2\pi)}} e^{-a^2/2} \frac{1}{\sqrt{(2\pi)}} e^{-b^2/2}. \qquad (12.24)$$

Here the first factor is the probability density for a, the second the probability density for b at a given value of a. Velikanov then approximates the velocity of sand grains by the positive values of

$$v_g = u - u_c, \qquad (12.25)$$

where u_c is the threshold velocity of sand grain movement.

Thus

$$u = \bar{u} + u' = v_g + u_c \quad \text{or} \quad u' = v_g + u_c - \bar{u}$$

and

$$b = \frac{v_g + u_c - \bar{u} - Ru_0'}{\sigma\sqrt{(1-R^2)}}. \qquad (12.26)$$

The sediment transport now becomes proportional to

$$q_s = k\bar{d} \int_{b_0}^{\infty} f(b) v_g db, \qquad (12.27)$$

where b_0 is the value of b when $v_g = 0$, and

$$v_g = b\sigma\sqrt{(1-R^2)} + (u_c - \bar{u}) + Ru_0'. \qquad (12.28)$$

Putting

$$\sigma\sqrt{(1-R^2)} = \alpha \quad \text{and} \quad u_c - \bar{u} - Ru_0' = \beta$$

yields

$$q_a = k\bar{d} \int_{b_0}^{\infty} \frac{1}{\sqrt{(2\pi)}} e^{-b^2/2} (\alpha b - \beta) db$$

$$= \frac{k\bar{d}}{\sqrt{(2\pi)}} \left[\alpha e^{-b^2/2} - \beta \int_{b_0}^{\infty} e^{-b^2/2} db \right] \qquad (12.29)$$

and q_a is defined by

$$q_s = \int_{-\infty}^{\infty} q_a da. \qquad (12.30)$$

The variation of bed profile now becomes

$$\frac{\partial \eta}{\partial t} = \frac{dq_a}{dx} = \frac{k\bar{d}}{l} f(\xi, \varepsilon, a), \qquad (12.31)$$

where

$$\xi = \frac{x}{l}, \quad \varepsilon = \frac{u_c - \bar{u}}{\sigma}, \quad R = (1 - \xi^2)^2$$

$$f = \frac{dR}{d\xi}\left[\frac{R}{\sqrt{(1-R^2)}}\frac{1}{\sqrt{(2\pi)}}e^{-b^2/2} - a\frac{1}{\sqrt{(2\pi)}}\int_{b_0}^{\infty}e^{-b^2/2}db\right]$$
$$(12.32)$$

This function was analysed numerically and it was found that over the length l the bed could both erode and build up or only erode or build up depending on the combination of the variables ε and a.

Similar observations were made by Tison.[12] Tison also demonstrated with highly viscous fluids that periodic ripples do not form when the flow is laminar.

A number of writers have reasoned that in the case of shallow flow the surface waves and bed forms are related. This approach has been quite successful in describing the ripples caused by waves on the sea bed.[13,14] But when flow takes place over a smooth bed this approach does not describe the formation of ripples. Anderson[15] proposed an analytical potential flow model by using Exner's equation of erosion and obtained a relationship between the Froude number Fr and the depth–wavelength ratio

$$\mathrm{Fr}^2 = \frac{\sinh 2ky_0}{ky_0(\tanh ky_0 \sinh 2ky_0 - 2)}, \qquad (12.32)$$

where k is the wave number $2\pi/L$, L is the wavelength, and y_0 is the depth of flow.

Kondrat'ev[16] proposed in 1953 a solution in terms of a velocity potential ϕ and a stream function ψ. The free surface and the erodible bed profiles are assumed to be streamlines and are given by a simple harmonic function. It is further assumed that the flow is critical, that is the Froude number is unity.

A. N. Lyapin[16] calculated the velocity, acceleration and stream profile by assuming that the stream velocity slows down and speeds up along the stream. Considering a fluid element of cross-sectional area A and thickness dx in the direction of flow and the friction over the perimeter to be given by $f(U)\,dx$ then

$$\rho A dx \frac{dU}{dt} + \rho dp + f(U)dx = 0,$$

$$\frac{dU}{dt} + \frac{1}{\rho}\frac{dp}{dx} + f_1(U) = 0. \tag{12.33}$$

The flow is now assumed to be composed of a uniform stream with U_0 and a variable mean velocity U. Thus the difference between the distance traversed by the element in question during a time interval t at velocities U and U_0 is

$$s = dx - x = Ut - U_0 t$$

and it is assumed that

$$\frac{dp}{dx} = k_0 S,$$

so that

$$\frac{d^2 s}{dt^2} + \frac{k_0}{\rho} S + f_1(U) = 0. \tag{12.34}$$

J. F. Kennedy[17] treated the problem of antidunes by also assuming potential flow. He later extended this treatment to dunes and antidunes.[18] The analytical model considers a two-dimensional irrotational incompressible flow. With the co-ordinate origin in the undisturbed surface and y positive upwards the profiles of the free surface and bed are given by $y = \zeta(x, t)$ and $y = -y_0 + \eta(x, t)$ respectively. The amplitudes of surface waves ζ and of bed waves η are considered to be small in comparison with the wavelength and $\partial\zeta/\partial x$ and $\partial\eta/\partial x$ are limited to

G*

values very much smaller than unity, so that the non-linear terms in the boundary conditions can be neglected.

The velocity $\mathbf{q}$ is expressed in terms of a velocity potential ϕ

$$\mathbf{q} = (U+u,v) = \nabla\phi, \qquad (12.35)$$

where u and v are the x and y components of the perturbation velocity due to the waviness of the bed.

Thus

$$\nabla^2\phi = 0 \qquad (12.36)$$

is satisfied.

The kinematic boundary condition at the surface requires the velocity to be tangent to the surface, so that

$$U\,\frac{\partial\xi}{\partial x}+\frac{\partial\xi}{\partial t} = \frac{\partial\phi}{\partial y}, \quad \text{on } y = 0 \qquad (12.37)$$

and the dynamic condition that the pressure is constant on the free surface is expressed by Bernoulli equation

$$g\xi+\tfrac{1}{2}U\,\frac{\partial\phi}{\partial x}+\frac{\partial\phi}{\partial t} = 0, \quad \text{on } y = 0. \qquad (12.38)$$

At the interface between the fluid and the bed the velocity normal to the bed must vanish

$$U\,\frac{\partial\eta}{\partial x}+\frac{\partial\eta}{\partial t} = \frac{\partial\phi}{\partial y}, \quad \text{on } y = -y_0, \qquad (12.39)$$

where y_0 is the depth of flow over the wavy bed, Fig. 12.2.

At the interface also the continuity of sediment movement must be satisfied

$$\frac{\partial G}{\partial x}+B\,\frac{\partial\eta}{\partial t} = 0, \qquad (12.40)$$

where $G(x, t)$ is the local rate of sediment transport per unit width in terms of weight and B is the bulk specific weight of the sediment in the bed.

The bed is assumed to be a sinusoidal wave with varying amplitude

$$\eta_{(x,t)} = a_{(t)} \sin k(x - U_b t), \qquad (12.41)$$

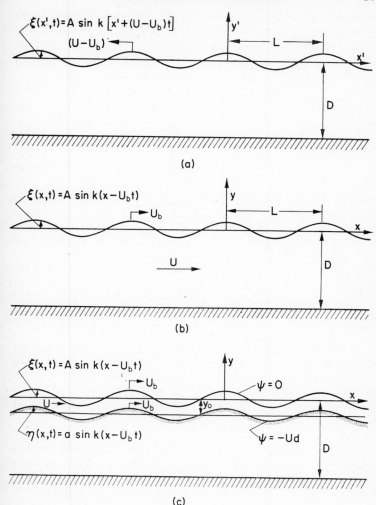

FIG. 12.2. Steps in the development of equations for flow over a moving wavy bed. (a) Translational gravity waves moving with velocity $-(U-U_b)$ in a fluid at rest with mean depth D. (b) Gravity waves moving with velocity U_b in a fluid with a flow velocity U; a velocity U has been superposed on the fluid of figure (a). (c) Flow over a moving wavy bed. A streamline of the flow shown in figure (b) has been replaced by a moving boundary. (From ref. 18, by permission of the *Journal of Fluid Mechanics*.)

where $a_{(t)}$ is the amplitude of the bed features, $k = 2\pi/L$ is the wave number, L is the wavelength, and U_b is the velocity of the bed form in the x-direction and is assumed to be constant.

A simple harmonic surface wave is considered, moving on water of depth D over a horizontal bed with celerity

$$U^2 = \left(\frac{g}{g}\right) \tanh kD \qquad (12.42)$$

and being described by the surface profile

$$\zeta_0 = A_0 \sin k(x - U_b t). \qquad (12.43)$$

The potential and stream functions are derived which satisfy the boundary conditions:

$$\phi_0 = Ux + A_0 U \frac{\cosh k(y+D)}{\sinh kD} \cos k(x - U_b t),$$
$$(12.44)$$

$$\psi_0 = Uy + A_0 U \frac{\sinh k(y+D)}{\sinh kD} \sin k(x - U_b t). $$
$$(12.45)$$

The bed corresponds to the streamline $\psi_0 = -Uy_0$ and its position is $y = -y_0 + \eta_0(x, t)$. Substituting these values above and neglecting higher order terms yields for the bed

$$\eta_0 = A_0 \frac{\sinh k(D - y_0)}{\sinh kD} \sin k(x - U_b t). \qquad (12.46)$$

If the fixed amplitude of the bed waves is replaced by $A_{(t)}$, where $A_{(t)}$ is a slowly varying function of time so that $A_t \ll UkA$, then the boundary conditions are still satisfied. Thus for flow over a wavy bed with slowly varying amplitude

$$\phi = Ux + UA_{(t)} \frac{\cosh k(y+D)}{\sinh kD} \cos k(x - U_b t) \qquad (12.47)$$

provided $U_b \ll U$.

Comparison of the expression for η_0 with that of $\eta_{(x,\,t)}$ shows that the amplitude of the bed profile is related to that of the surface waves by

$$a_{(t)} = A_{(t)} \frac{\sinh k(D - y_0)}{\sinh kD}$$

$$= A_{(t)} \left[1 - \frac{g}{kU^2} \tanh ky_0 \right] \cosh ky_0. \qquad (12.48)$$

This implies that the bed and water surface profiles are in phase or out of phase according to whether U^2 is greater than or less than $(g/k) \tanh ky_0$ or y_0 is less than or greater than D.

Next, use is made of a transport relationship of the form

$$G_{(x,\,t)} = m \left[\frac{\partial \phi}{\partial x} (x - \delta, -y_0, t) \right]^n, \qquad (12.49)$$

where m, n and δ are constants that depend on the depth and velocity of flow and the properties of fluid and sediment. The quantity δ is the distance by which the local sediment transport lags behind the local velocity at the bed. It is supposed to account for all the real fluid effects and the effects of turbulence. However, until such a function can be physically established the following treatment adds little to the understanding of the physics of the phenomenon. The occurrence and effects of the wake, formed when dunes and ripples are formed, should also be accounted for.

Introducing the ϕ value into the sediment transport relationship finally yields

$$U_b = -\frac{n\bar{G}k}{B} \coth k(D - y_0) \cos k\delta \qquad (12.50)$$

and

$$a_{(t)} = A_{(0)} \frac{\sinh k(D - y_0)}{\sinh kD}$$

$$\exp \left[t \frac{n\bar{G}k^2}{B} \coth k(D - y_0) \sin k\delta \right]. \qquad (12.51)$$

This relationship implies that the amplitude of an arbitrary disturbance on the flat bed will increase exponentially with time if the values of k and δ make the exponential term positive, i.e. the flat bed will be unstable.

Between eqns. (12.48), (12.50) and (12.51) with the values of $(D-y_0)$, $k\delta$, $\sin k\delta$, and $\cos k\delta$ different bed configurations can be distinguished.

It has been assumed that U, D and k are related by eqn. (12.42) and the wavelength L can have any value greater than the minimum

$$L_m = \frac{2\pi U^2}{g} \qquad (12.52)$$

which is obtained from eqn. (12.42) for $D \to \infty$. Observations show, however, that for a given velocity depth and material there is a dominant wavelength. It is assumed now that this dominant wavelength is that for which the initial rate of growth, given by the linearized formulation, is the greatest. This means finding the value of k for which a_t is a maximum at $t = 0$. From eqn. (12.51) the initial rate of growth is

$$a_t(0) = A(0) \frac{n\overline{G}k^2 \cosh k(D-y_0)}{\sinh kD} \sin ky_0. \qquad (12.53)$$

The wave number of the dominant wavelength is obtained by differentiating (12.53) with respect to k and equating the resulting expression to zero, D being eliminated by (12.42)

$$\frac{da_t(0)}{dk} = A(0) \frac{n\overline{G}}{B} \left\{ \left[2k \sin k\delta + k^2\delta \cos k\delta \right] \right.$$
$$\left[\frac{g}{kU^2} \cosh ky_0 - \sinh ky_0 \right] + k^2 \sin k\delta \left[-\frac{g}{k^2U^2} \right.$$
$$\left. \left. \cosh ky_0 + \frac{gy_0}{kU^2} \sinh ky_0 - y_0 \cosh ky_0 \right] \right\} = 0$$

which rearranged yields

$$\mathrm{Fr}^2 = \frac{U^2}{gy_0} = \frac{1 + ky_0 \tanh ky_0 + k\delta \cot k\delta}{(ky_0)^2 + (2 + k\delta \cot k\delta)ky_0 \tanh ky_0} . \qquad (12.54)$$

Bed and surface profiles		$D - y_0$	$k\delta$	$\sin k\delta$	$\cos k\delta$	Movement of bed features	Bed configuration
1	In phase	Pos	$0 < k\delta < \frac{\pi}{2}$	Pos	Pos	Upstream	Anti-dunes
2	In phase	Pos	$\frac{\pi}{2}$	Pos	Zero	None	Anti-dunes
3	In phase	Pos	$\frac{\pi}{2} < k\delta < \pi$	Pos	Neg	Downstream	Anti-dunes
4a	No bed waves	Neg	$\pi < k\delta \leqq \frac{3\pi}{2}$	Neg	Pos	—	Flat bed
4b	No bed waves	Neg	$0 < k\delta < \pi$	Pos	—	—	Flat bed
4c		Pos	$\pi < k\delta < 2\pi$	Neg	—	—	Flat bed
5	Out of phase	Neg	$\frac{3}{2}\pi < k\delta < 2\pi$	Neg	Pos	Downstream	Dunes

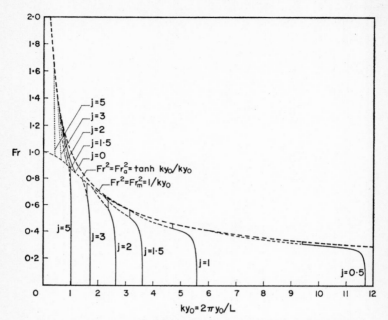

FIG. 12.3. Regions of occurrence of different bed configurations for several values of j. $Fr = Fr_a$ is the minimum Froude number for the occurrence of antidunes, and the maximum Froude number for the occurrence of dunes. $Fr = Fr_m$ is the maximum Froude number for the occurrence of long-crested features. The different configurations are denoted by the character of the lines representing eqn. (12.54) (except for $j = 0$) as follows:

— · —, antidunes moving upstream;

· · · ·, antidunes moving downstream;

————, dunes;

— — — —, region in which flat bed is predicted by the table.

The short vertical line segments show for each j the range of Fr over which the regime of transition from dunes to flat bed occurs. The flat bed is the configuration for Froude numbers between the transition regime and antidune regime. (From ref. 18 by permission of the *Journal of Fluid Mechanics*.)

By putting $\delta = jy_0$, where j is a dimensionless quantity depending on depth and velocity of the flow, and the fluid and sediment properties, eqn. (12.54) can be written as

$$Fr^2 = \frac{1 + ky_0 \tanh ky_0 + jky_0 \cot jky_0}{(ky_0)^2 + (2 + jky_0 \cot jky_0)ky_0 \tanh ky_0} \qquad (12.55)$$

and

$$\lim_{j \to 0} Fr^2 = \frac{2 + ky_0 \tanh ky_0}{(ky_0)^2 + 3ky_0 \tanh ky_0}. \qquad (12.56)$$

For the velocity U_b of these bed waves of dominant wavelength the following expressions are derived:

$$U_b = \frac{n\bar{G}k}{2B} \left[\frac{\sinh 2ky_0 + 2ky_0}{\sinh^2 ky_0 - jky_0 \cot jky_0 - 1} \right] \cos jky_0 \qquad (12.57)$$

and

$$\lim_{j \to 0} U_b = \frac{n\bar{G}k}{2B} \left[\frac{\sinh 2ky_0 + 2ky_0}{\sinh^2 ky_0 - 2} \right]. \qquad (12.58)$$

Kennedy gives a very detailed discussion of these analytical results, which are graphically displayed on Figs. 12.3 and 12.4.

The linearized analysis presented by Kennedy predicts a continuously growing amplitude (12.51), whereas observation shows maximum heights for both dunes and antidunes for given depth, velocity, and sediment. Qualitative explanations are given for the limiting heights of the various bed forms.

Generally the analytical treatment is neat and informative, but it does not add much more to the knowledge of the physics of the problem. It could be looked upon as an extension of Exner's and Anderson's work. Much of the result depends on this parameter δ or j about which nothing is known. With a different combination of parameters the same potential flow problem could yield answers of different form.

The problem has also been approached as an instability problem of the water–sand interface. The simplest form of this approach is the classical Helmholtz instability. In increasing order of complexity follow the treatments by Taylor,[19]

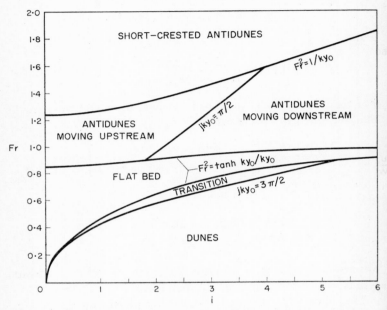

Fig. 12.4. Conditions for occurrence of difference bed configurations. (From ref. 18 by permission of the *Journal of Fluid Mechanics*.)

Goldstein,[20] Jeffreys,[21] Keulegan.[22,23] To this group could also be added the approach proposed by Bagnold.[24]

Dimensional reasoning was employed by Liu[25] leading to the relationship between u_*/w and $u_* d/v$ (Fig. 12.5).

Much of the more recent experimental information is plotted as a function of the Froude number. The abscissa could be the particle size (with the first movement, commencement of ripple formation and washing away of the ripples as parameters). It could be the stream depth, a velocity, the ratio of ripple height to particle size, etc. The Froude number also appears as a product with other dimensionless terms.[26] An example of recent presentation is Fig. 12.6 taken from the paper by Simons and Richardson.[27]

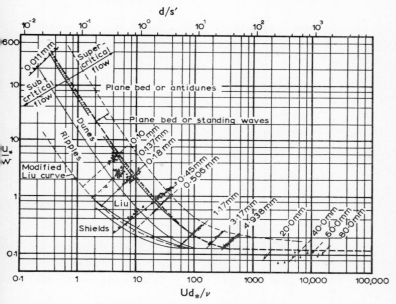

FIG. 12.5. Criteria for bed roughness in alluvial channels. (From ref. 29, by permission of the U.S. Geological Survey.)

A widely accepted classification of the various stages of sand movement is as follows: (Fig. 12.7)

(1) threshold flat bed,
(2) ripples,
(3) dunes,
(4) transitional wavy and flat bed,
(5) antidunes.

Among these the distinction between the ripples and dunes is often difficult. Kramer[8] based his ripple classification on the ratio of the height of a ripple to the depth of water in which it formed.

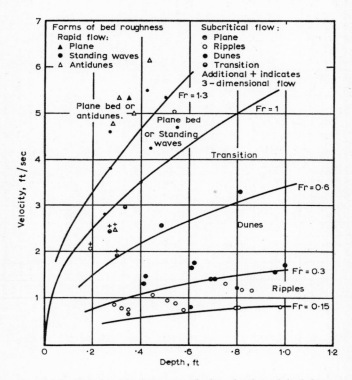

FIG. 12.6. Relationship between velocity, depth and bed forms. (By permission of the American Society of Civil Engineers, ref. 27, p. 92.)

Accordingly, if ripple height h_r was less than 3 per cent of depth of flow, these were classed as weak; h_r between 3 to 5 per cent belonged to medium ripples and excessive ripples when h_r was greater than 8 per cent of the depth of flow. However, this classification has been found to be unsatisfactory, particularly in laboratory flumes with shallow water over the sand bed.

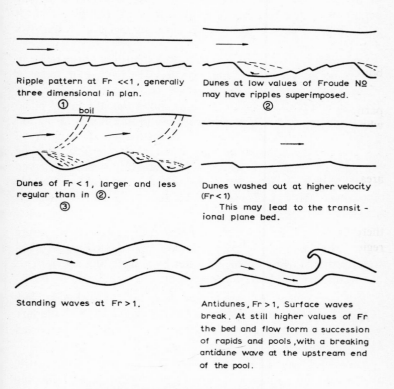

Ripple pattern at Fr << 1 , generally three dimensional in plan.
①

Dunes at low values of Froude № may have ripples superimposed.
②

Dunes of Fr < 1 , larger and less regular than in ②.
③

Dunes washed out at higher velocity (Fr < 1)
   This may lead to the transit-ional plane bed.

Standing waves at Fr > 1.

Antidunes, Fr > 1, Surface waves break. At still higher values of Fr the bed and flow form a succession of rapids and pools, with a breaking antidune wave at the upstream end of the pool.

FIG. 12.7. Bed forms in an alluvial channel.

Inglis[28] gives a classification according to the pattern:

Ripples form irregularly, whereas the crest of a dune stretches across a considerable width of the bed. In the case of a ripple there are no secondary ripples on the upstream slope, whereas small secondary ripples appear at times on the upstream slope of dunes.

However, this definition is still difficult to apply, particularly in narrow laboratory flumes. A more definite classification is obtained by naming the bed features according to the location of the point on the (u_*/w) versus $(u_* d/v)$ plane and using the definitions given for the various regions on the plane.[25,29] Another possibility is the classification in terms of Kennedy's Fig. 12.4.

Bogardi[30] classified the bed features according to the position on the gd/u_*^2 versus d plane, and $u_* \sqrt{[1 \cdot 65\gamma/(\gamma_s - \gamma)]}$ versus d plane.

Observation in a glass-sided flume shows that the initial plane boundary begins to deform at some point, and this deformation gradually spreads out, generally downstream. The point of initiation of the ripple seems to be by chance. A tendency for the particles to "pile up" and move intermittently can be observed when the flow is only slightly beyond the threshold of particle movement. This tendency could be due to a number of causes, such as:

1. *Sheltering*. Particles do not move uniformly over the entire area. The fast-moving particles close in on slower particles, thus further slowing down the latter by a sheltering effect. This can lead to a small local piling up.

2. *Intermittency*. Measurements show that in turbulent flow there is an intermittent system of strong eddies in the boundary region. These eddies excavate material that cannot be supported by the mean flow and will settle out again.

3. *Non-uniform material*. With non-uniform particle size, the larger more resistant grains cause a piling up of moving grains.

A local piling up will affect the flow. The streamlines will become curved and this will cause dynamic pressure changes and accelerations that affect the apparent weight of the grains. Changes in the slope of the bed surface will also change the normal component of the weight of the particles.

The quantity of particles eroded, when the threshold of particle movement has been passed, will be governed by the necessary equilibrium between the applied and resisting forces. When the number of grains in motion is large, the momentum exchange of moving grains, in collisions among themselves and with the stationary bed layer, can exert an additional normal load on the bed and an additional shear stress on the flow. However, ripples form when the flow is only slightly beyond the threshold of the particle movement and the number of grains in motion is observed to be small. Thus, the normal grain load should be of secondary importance. Once an inclined face has formed, the ripples appear with remarkable regularity. The particles can be observed to "slide up" the upstream inclined faces and roll over the crests of the ripples. There they come to rest forming a leeward slope at the angle of repose. This leads to the continuous downstream translation of the form. An occasional grain is caught in the interface between the main stream and the wake downstream of the ripple crest and is carried over the top of the wake. These grains land approximately six ripple heights downstream and either continue up the next slope or displace other grains where they land. The total rate of sediment transport is composed of the grains that move as the ripple form translates downstream, and of the few grains that move at approximately the local velocity of flow. The most prominent feature is the wake downstream of the ripple crest.

Separation patterns which are well known in hydraulics are associated with abrupt expansions, contractions and bends formed by fixed boundaries. The overall picture is characterized by an eddy or wake and the mean flow pattern past this wake. With dye, for example, the mean streamline pattern of the main flow and the standing eddy motion in the wake can be clearly seen as well as the approximate boundary between these two parts of flow. The shape of the wake is a fundamental part of the flow problem. The fluid outside the wake behaves as if the wake boundary were that of a fixed body around which the primary flow passes. The eddy motion in the wake is maintained by the primary flow and is subject to the same dynamic conditions as the primary flow all along the boundary zone between them.

There is a temptation to analyse the separation pattern by the Helmholtz free-streamline method as is done for cavitation pockets. But in the separation problem the two zones are mutually dependent and therefore this problem will be more difficult. The Helmholtz free-streamline, which extends to infinity,

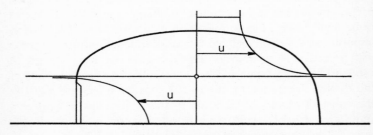

FIG. 12.8. Separation zone with irrotational vortex.

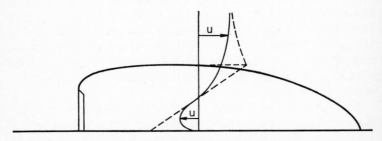

FIG. 12.9. Separation zone with forced (rotational) vortex of variable strength distribution.

can be closed in by assumptions of symmetry or by imposing re-entrant flow. However, it still yields a constant pressure wake which is far different from that observed. The conformal super-position of a free vortex upon the flow in the wake, including both main and wake flow in the transformation function, could overcome the constant pressure objections (Fig. 12.8). In turn this requires the velocity in the centre of the wake to go to infinity rather than to zero as observed.

No solution is known to this problem with a distribution of vorticity which satisfies the condition of no discontinuity in velocity and velocity gradient, no slip along the solid boundary, and zero velocity at the centre of the wake (Fig. 12.9). However, the solid boundary shear appears to be a second order term.

Any such solution would still lack the turbulence features of the flow. The boundary between the main stream and the wake is a highly turbulent "mixing zone" which expands with distance downstream. Also the eddy zone itself is turbulent and appears to consist mainly of a time variable pattern of large scale eddies.

Of all these separation patterns, the wake downstream of a negative step (an abrupt expansion) is most similar to that in the lee of a ripple. This particular wake was studied by Walker.[31] Walker's investigation was experimental in nature and was carried out in a rectangular conduit carrying water, with the abrupt expansion in the horizontal plane. The quantities measured were distribution of mean static pressure, mean velocity at a point and distribution of longitudinal and transverse components of turbulence intensity and turbulent shear. The turbulence measurements were made with a Lintronic hot-film anemometer. Figure 12.10 shows the measured velocity profiles and the mean streamline pattern developed from these. The streamline pattern shows three regions of flow: the main stream, the backflow region, and a region of pronounced shear flow separating these two. A separate small eddy can be observed in the bottom corner but this was not mapped. The backflow or ground roller actually consists of a number of large intermittent eddies. In the lee of the step, the pressure drops to approximately $(p-p_0)/\frac{1}{2}\rho U^2 = -0.06$, and along the downstream boundary at a value of x/h between three and four it drops to -0.07 and thereafter rises again. The lowest pressure is within the ground roller at $x/h \doteq 2$ with $(p-p_0)/\frac{1}{2}\rho U^2 = -0.09$ approximately.

The results obtained from the turbulence measurements are shown in Fig. 12.11.

The location of $[(\overline{u'^2})^{1/2}/U]_{max}$ in the region just downstream of the step is slightly above the $y = 0$ line, a result similar to that

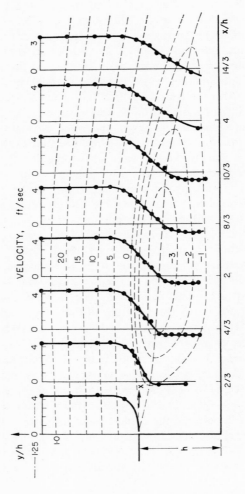

FIG. 12.10. Distribution of mean velocity and mean streamline pattern. (From ref. 34, p. 21, by permission of the American Society of Civil Engineers.)

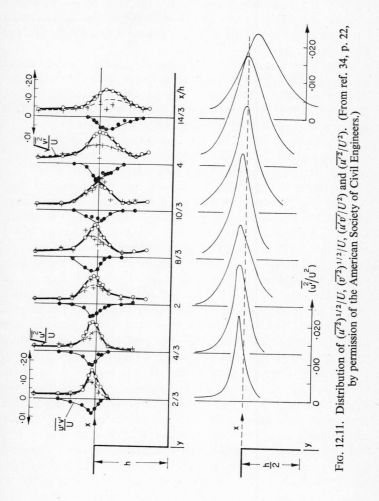

FIG. 12.11. Distribution of $(\overline{u'^2})^{1/2}/U$, $(\overline{v'^2})^{1/2}/U$, $(\overline{u'v'}/U^2)$ and $(\overline{u'^2}/U^2)$. (From ref. 34, p. 22, by permission of the American Society of Civil Engineers.)

of Tani[32] and Arie and Rouse.[33] However, the value of $[(\overline{u'^2})^{1/2}/U]_{max}$ did not show any definite increase with distance downstream. This is at variance with the results of Tani who found that the value of $[(\overline{u'^2})^{1/2}/U]_{max}$ increased with distance from the step.

Because of the number of operations involved in obtaining the value of $(\overline{v'^2})^{1/2}/U$, there is appreciable scatter in the results. The results indicate that the transverse component of turbulence is approximately two-thirds of the longitudinal component. This agrees with the results obtained by Arie and Rouse.

An interesting feature of the turbulence shear measurements was that outside the interface region the turbulence shear tended to have an opposite sign to that within the interface.

The function $\overline{u'^2}/U^2$ is plotted at a number of stations, and inspection of the areas under these curves shows that the energy of turbulence increases with the passage downstream. However, theoretical reasoning suggests a maximum value at about $x/h = 4$ and a steady decrease to an asymptotic value thereafter.

The definition of the outer boundaries of the interface is necessarily arbitrary. The boundaries could be taken to be where the value of $(\overline{u'^2})^{1/2}/U$ is one or two per cent larger than that of the main stream. This boundary was found to meet the solid boundary at the offset side slightly more than five step heights downstream. This compares well with the observation in the lee of a ripple in which there is a much stronger agitation on the sand surface at five to eight ripple heights downstream from the crest.[34] At six ripple heights downstream from the ripple crest there is a "hesitancy" in the grain movement in that some grains are moving forward and others backward. Closer to the step there is a bottom roller and the flow is toward the step, but the upstream velocities are small and only an occasional grain is moved; this area is marked in Fig. 12.12. It should be noted that on Fig. 12.12 the temporal mean shear stress at the re-attachment point must be zero. The small positive value shown must have resulted from the difficulty of measuring the fluctuating shear stress of changing sign.

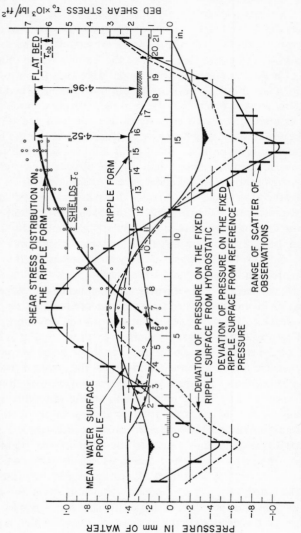

Fig. 12.12. Ripple form. Water surface profile, and distribution of pressure deviations and bed shear stress. (From ref. 34, p. 23, by permission of the American Society of Civil Engineers.)

The general flow pattern in the lee of a ripple can be studied by injecting small particles or droplets of zero immersed weight into the flow at the ripple crest. Visual observation and study of cine pictures will show that all the features observed in the wake downstream of a negative step occur in the lee of a ripple. Small droplets of a fluid immiscible with water were injected into the flow through small holes at various locations in the sand bed and filmed. This showed again that the back eddy downstream from the crest is intermittent and consists of a number of short-lived eddies, the resultant of which creates a return flow along the bed. There is also an intermittent exchange of fluid between the eddy and the main stream. About half of the droplets ejected at the crest were entrained in the eddy system and made at least one loop, the others were carried directly downstream by the main flow. The direction of the droplets in the back eddy region was quite unpredictable, whereas at distances greater than 1 in. above the bed reversed or large vertical movement was uncommon. The vertical motions were very large near the bed in the region of 3 to 6 in. downstream of the crest.

Sheen[35] carried out measurements of turbulence components $\overline{u^2}$, $\overline{v^2}$ and $\overline{uv}$ in the flow over this fixed and sand-coated rippled bed. Figure 12.13 shows the results at various stations along the ripple. The results are strikingly similar to those of Fig. 12.11 in the lee of the step. The velocity profiles show in the lee of the ripple a reverse flow, an eddy known as the ground roller. Between this eddy and the downstream crest the profiles show a region of retarded flow at the bed, initially of the same thickness as the back eddy and tapering to a boundary layer of about 0·25 in. thickness at the downstream crest of the ripple. The peak value of $\overline{u^2}$ is greatest just downstream of the point of separation—the ripple crest—and decreases rapidly with distance downstream. Over the length of the eddy region the rate of generation of turbulence is at a greater rate than spreading and dissipation. Beyond the eddy, to the crest of the next ripple, the total energy of turbulence decreases again to a level which is the same over all crests. From the reattachment point to the ripple crest the peak of $\overline{u^2}$ decreases and spreading and dissipation of the energy of turbulence dominates. From the point where the main flow reattaches a boundary layer starts and there is no longer a turbulence producing vortex layer separating streams of fluid at different velocities.

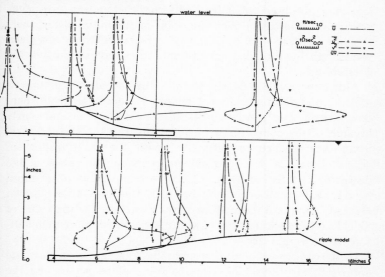

FIG. 12.13. Profiles of mean velocity, longitudinal and transverse components of velocity fluctuations, and turbulent shear measured on the ripple model described in ref. 34.

From the observations described, the mechanism of ripple formation can be deduced. When the threshold of grain movement is passed a disturbance in the plane grain boundary is created by a chance piling-up. This surface disturbance establishes an interface or surface of discontinuity in the flow, similar to that in flow past a negative step. In the shear flow of the interface zone the turbulence intensity is high and the grains are stirred up by the turbulent agitation where the interface reattaches itself to the grain boundary. From the reattachment point downstream the turbulent agitation decreases and also a boundary layer develops. Because of the reduced agitation some of the material made mobile at the reattachment point cannot be supported and settles out as it passes downstream. This leads to the formation of a second disturbance, and so on. Here it is important to observe that the bed-form development propagates gradually downstream from the point of the initial disturbance. It is not a process of amplification of a bed disturbance of a given wavelength, but a gradual growth until the steady state condition is established.

Along the established ripple form the turbulent agitation is maximum at the reattachment region and decreases from there downstream, partly because of diffusion and decay and partly because of the convergence of flow (Fig. 12.13). The temporal mean shear—which provides the power for the transport of grains—is zero at the reattachment point and increases in the downstream direction (Fig. 12.12). An important observation here is that entrainment and bed-load transport take place at values of temporal mean shear stress τ_0 well below the value of Shields' critical shear stress τ_c, which is reached at more than halfway up the ripple face.

In the subcritical flow the streamlines of the main flow are approximately sinusoidal with the tops of the wakes and the ripple crests forming the lower boundary, which is approximately in phase with the streamlines and out of phase with the grain boundary, cf. Kennedy.[18] The ripple form travels by erosion of sand on the upstream face and by deposition in the lee of the ripple, so that each grain travels intermittently and is buried for periods. In the lee of each perturbation of the flat bed the forward transport of sediment stops and material accumulates until the fluid drag over the crests limits the growth in height. Then the surface drag over the crest is approximately equal to that over a flat bed of this given grain roughness, mean velocity, and depth of flow. Approximate, because the turbulence of flow over a rippled bed is greater than over the flat one; by agitation the grains are made more mobile and the given surface drag can transport more grains. In principle, the surface drag governs the quantity of sediment transported.

Applying the continuity requirement to a control volume (Fig. 12.14), enclosing a part of the ripple and moving with the ripple form (discussion of ref. 34 by Dr. A. G. Mercer) shows that the bed load q_b is given by

$$\Delta q_b = c\Delta y, \tag{12.59}$$

so that the bed-load movement along the ripple face is proportional to the height y of the ripple. Here c is the velocity of the ripple form.

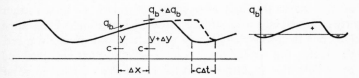

Fig. 12.14. Bed-load transport and ripple form.

The addition of the wake (form) drag causes the total drag on the flow to be substantially higher than the drag required for equilibrium over a plane boundary of sand grain roughness.

The ground roller at the lee of a ripple is maintained by the turbulence shear stress along the interface. It could be looked upon as a concentrated vortex filament. In a narrow laboratory flume this filament extends from wall to wall—connecting to the viscous sublayers on the side walls—and straight crested ripples are formed. However, the ripples formed in a wider flume have an irregular crest pattern, tending to a triangular pattern or tetrahedral form. The reason for this may be either that the vortex filaments join together and cover the bed by a net pattern of vortex filaments, or that short lengths of vortex filaments bind to the ground like loops or horse-shoes.

The formation of ripples takes place at relatively low values of particle Reynolds number—Re$_*$ less than 10 to 70, depending on the size of the watercourse. On the upstream face of the ripple form studied the roughness Reynolds number $u_* k/\nu$ varied from

3·9 at the trough to 7·0 at the crest or in terms of k/δ' from 0·58 to 1·06 respectively. Thus viscous effects are still fairly prominent, the intensity of the concentrated vortices low and the mean eddy size of the turbulence small.

With increasing velocity the intensity and spacing of the vortices increases. The transverse parts of filaments are less subject to small disturbances and longer straight crests are formed. The sequence of events is best illustrated with the aid of Fig. 13.2 (see also Fig. 6.19), which shows the variation of the Darcy–Weisbach friction factor f with velocity U and shear velocity u_*. The bed features grow larger until the peak value of f is reached. This also marks the limit of steepness of dunes (h/L). A further increase in velocity may still be associated with increasing dune height but their wavelength will increase proportionately more. With increasing velocity the dunes steadily flatten, the bed becomes undulating, a transition flat bed and on further increase it returns to a wavy form, the antidunes. The flattening of the bed forms is associated with rapid decrease of form drag (see Fig. 6.19, section 6.5) and even the total drag may decrease. However, the surface drag increases steadily, more material is moved and the wakes become smaller.

The size of the bed forms depends on the size of the flow system. The relatively small ripple shown on Fig. 12.12 has a height of about one-fifth of the depth of flow. A corresponding bed form in a deeper flow would be of larger size, but as yet no satisfactory explanation of this size effect exists. The regularity of the bed forms in plan and wavelength depends also largely on the intensity of turbulence and on the large perturbations of the flow. Here the sand waves observed under low-turbulence tidal flows in deep water, where large-scale perturbations from banks, etc., are not present, are an extreme example. These have long straight crests (up to 40 miles have been reported) and are quite enormous in size, with heights up to 60 ft and wavelengths up to 3000 ft. However, relative to the depth of flow (50–100 fathoms) the maximum height to depth ratio is one-fifth to one-tenth. In terms of the Liu diagram these could be ripples.

It appears too that the hitherto-unexplained phenomenon of ripples superimposed on the dune forms can be linked with the development of the boundary layer starting at the reattachment point. On the long dune face the flow conditions in the boundary layer become such that ripples are formed.

Reverting to the analytical models of bed features it should be observed that these assume the rate of sediment (bed load) movement to vary with distance in the same way as the velocity of flow, that is q_s is assumed to be proportional to the mean velocity U. However, the local velocity and temporal mean shear actually reverse direction over a substantial portion of the granular surface in the lee of each bed feature.

This means that the transport of grains is discontinuous with respect to distance along the flow and an oscillating tangential force acts at the lower boundary to the flow which is not included in the analytical models.

If a shear stress of varying magnitude is introduced then, with the x-axis in the average bed surface, the momentum equation for one-dimensional problem

$$\frac{\partial u}{\partial t} + u\frac{\partial u}{\partial x} = -\frac{1}{\rho}\frac{\partial}{\partial x}(p + \gamma z) - \frac{\tau}{\rho m} \qquad (12.60)$$

approximates to

$$u\frac{\partial u}{\partial x} = -\frac{1}{\rho}\frac{\partial}{\partial x}(\gamma m + \gamma\eta) - \frac{\tau}{\rho m}, \qquad (12.61)$$

where m is now the local depth of flow. Substituting from continuity $um = q$

$$\frac{\partial m}{\partial x} = -\frac{m}{u}\frac{\partial u}{\partial x} \qquad (12.62)$$

yields after an algebraic rearrangement and substitution of Fr^2 for u^2/gm

$$\frac{\partial u}{\partial x} = \frac{u}{m(1-\mathrm{Fr}^2)}\frac{\partial\eta}{\partial x} + \frac{\tau}{\gamma m^2}\frac{u}{1-\mathrm{Fr}^2}. \qquad (12.63)$$

Expressing the varying quantities as $u = u_0 + u'$, $m = m_0 + m'$, $\tau = \tau_0 + \tau'$ and neglecting higher order terms yields

$$\left(\frac{m_0}{u_0} - 2\frac{m_0 u'}{u_0^2}\right)\left(1 - \mathrm{Fr}_0^2 - 3\mathrm{Fr}_0^2\frac{u'}{u_0}\right)\frac{\partial u'}{\partial x}$$

$$= \frac{\partial \eta'}{\partial x} + \frac{\tau'}{\gamma m_0} + \frac{\tau_0}{\gamma m_0 u_0} u'.$$

A further approximation gives

$$\frac{m_0}{u_0}(1 - \mathrm{Fr}^2)\frac{\partial u'}{\partial x} = \frac{\partial \eta'}{\partial x} + \frac{\tau'}{\gamma m_0} + \frac{S_0}{u_0}u'. \qquad (12.64)$$

Let it now be assumed that the fluctuation of bed shear is proportional to the ordinate of the bed wave, i.e. $\tau = K\eta$, and that

$$\eta' = Ae^{ik(x - ct)},$$
$$u' = Bu_0 e^{ik(x - ct)}, \qquad (12.65)$$

where $B = \alpha + i\beta$ and A is a real quantity.

Substituting, separating the real and imaginary parts and expressing the phase shift θ between the bed and velocity wave, yields

$$\tan \theta = \frac{\beta}{\alpha} = \frac{Km_0(1 - \mathrm{Fr}_0^2) + S_0\gamma m_0}{KS_0/k - km_0^2\gamma(1 - \mathrm{Fr}_0^2)}$$

$$= \frac{K(1 - \mathrm{Fr}_0^2)/\gamma S_0 + 1}{K/k\gamma m_0 - km_0(1 - \mathrm{Fr}_0^2)/S_0}$$

$$= \frac{-K(\mathrm{Fr}_0^2 - 1)/\gamma S_0 + 1}{K/k\gamma m_0 + km_0(\mathrm{Fr}_0^2 - 1)/S_0}. \qquad (12.66)$$

This shows that in subcritical flow the phase shift θ between the bed and the velocity wave may be in the first or second quadrant depending on the relative size of the terms in the denominator. In all cases β is positive, but α may be positive or negative. Thus for long waves k is small, $K/k\gamma m_0$ dominates, and the phase shift is in the first quadrant. The velocity wave and depth wave are related by continuity as $m' = -(m_0/u_0)u'$, so that the depth wave leads the bed wave by a phase angle $(\pi + \theta)$. The surface wave is given by the vector addition of the bed and depth waves. In this case the surface wave angle would be in the third or fourth quadrant depending on the size of the two vectors and on angle θ.

For short waves and subcritical flow α is negative and the velocity wave is in the second quadrant. The depth wave will lead the bed wave by an angle greater than $3\pi/2$ and the surface wave will always be in the fourth quadrant or close behind the bed wave.

In supercritical flow (Fr > 1) the denominator, α, is always positive. The numerator, β, may be positive or negative depending on the value of Fr. At values of Fr only slightly more than one the numerator may still be positive and the depth wave will lead the bed wave by a phase angle $(\pi + \theta)$. The surface wave may be in third or fourth quadrant. This is in keeping with the observation that at the limit of stability the surface waves break upstream of the crest of bed waves. For large values of Fr the numerator becomes negative and the surface wave will be in the first or second quadrant if not modified by the breaking of the surface waves. Such a situation may occur with long waves of very small amplitude.

The second term in the denominator also embodies the overall resistance effect. When resistance is very high, $\tan \theta$ tends to $\pi/2$. With very low resistance and Froude number less than one $\tan \theta$ tends to zero and the surface becomes flat. For Fr > 1, θ tends to π and the bed and surface waves are in phase.

Substituting values pertaining to Fig. 12.12 in eqn. (12.66) yields a phase lag θ close to 180°, i.e. the surface and bed waves are nearly in phase with the surface wave a little behind the bed wave. It is surprising that—in terms of eqn. (12.66)—this bed wave should still rate as a short one. The observation that the surface and bed waves are nearly in phase supports experimental results—discussed earlier—that the lower boundary to the flow is not the sand boundary, but the top of the wake and the crest region of the sand wave.

The problem of phase shift has to be considered relative to the actual lower boundary to the flow. If the top of the wake is taken to be the boundary to the main stream, then it is seen that the two boundaries are nearly in phase. With increasing velocity the wake is "filled in" by the rapidly moving sediment and the nearly in phase picture emerges again. With long and flat bed waves the wake formation is insignificant, tan θ as well as the surface wave amplitude are nearly zero. Also at supercritical flow the wake is absent. At large values of Fr the crest of surface wave is slightly upstream of the bed wave and the convergent flow on the downstream side of the bed wave suppresses the development of a wake.

The predicted tendency of the surface wave to be slightly upstream of the bed wave—the lower boundary—at subcritical flows is quite noticeable in experiment. It is also in keeping with the shift of maximum shear stress in flow over a wavy bed calculated by Benjamin.

In terms of the analytical model used in this work the varying shear stress has to be expressed in terms of the actual boundary to flow, which in case of a strong wake will include only a little of the sand bed. It is seen from Fig. 12.13 that the turbulence shear over the wake is of greater magnitude than the temporal mean boundary shear over the crest region of the bed form; still in keeping with the oscillating shear stress concept. The variation of $\partial u/\partial y$ with x in the main flow is also seen to be appreciable.[34]

The next step towards the solution of this sand wave problem depends on linking of the shear stress distribution over the wake part of the main fluid flow boundary, and the shape of this wake, with flow parameters. There are essentially three problems involved simultaneously: the relationship between the particle size and flow parameters for conditions leading to wake formation, the contribution of form drag to sediment transport, and the distribution of shear stress over the lower boundary of the main fluid stream. It should be observed that with ripples and dunes the trough region of the shear stress wave acts upon the sand bed, the peaks being over the wakes. With rapid sediment movement, near and beyond the transition flat bed condition, a wavy sand boundary results and the oscillating departures from the hydrostatic pressure distribution together with the variation of shear stress over it maintains the form. The large wave length at subcritical velocities is similar to that of very low resistance and the water surface becomes flat. A very low amplitude surface wave could exist which would be in the fourth quadrant.

The size of the bed features can be estimated with the aid of available empirical information. By dimensional reasoning one could expect that the ratio of ripple or dune height h to the mean depth of the flow y_0 would depend on the ratio $(\tau_0 - \tau_c)/\tau_0$, where τ_c is the critical boundary shear for entrainment. Thus

$$\frac{h}{y_0} = f\left(\frac{\tau_0 - \tau_c}{\tau_0}\right). \tag{12.67}$$

Yalin[36] plotted experimental results as h/y_{0c} versus y_0/y_{0c}, where y_{0c} is the uniform flow depth corresponding to τ_c, and found that the experimental results were satisfied by

$$\frac{h}{y_0} = \frac{1}{6}\left(\frac{\tau_0 - \tau_c}{\tau_0}\right) = \frac{1}{6}\left(\frac{y_0 - y_{0c}}{y_0}\right). \tag{12.68}$$

The average value of τ_0/τ_c at which transitional flat bed is observed varies from observer to observer and from flume data to field data. Yalin quotes τ_0/τ_c equal to or less than 17·63. However, values of τ_0/τ_c up to 40 have been recorded in flume experiments and 90 or more in the field. From the ratio of τ_0/τ_c of approximately 17 it follows that the height of bed features will always be less than about one-sixth of the depth of flow. Ratios of the order of $\frac{1}{6}$ to $\frac{1}{10}$ appear to be fairly common in nature, but are by no means limited to these values. Ratios as high as $\frac{1}{2}$ have been reported [27,37] and the ratio $\frac{1}{3}$ is not uncommon. Here it must also be noted that the highest value of relative roughness occurs at flow conditions which are well away from those yielding the transitional flat bed. Figure 13.2 clearly illustrates that the maximum relative roughness—maximum value of friction factor f—is closer to the threshold limit than to that of transitional flat bed. The average shear can actually decrease from a peak near f_{max} as the transitional flat bed conditions are approached.

Since the ratio of $(\tau_0 - \tau_c)/\tau_0$ becomes asymptotic to unity, plotting in terms of it suppresses variations in experimental data into what appears to be a single function for larger values of τ_0. Plotting experimental data[38] in terms of $(\tau_0 - \tau_c)/\tau_c$ avoids this limitation, but the plot shows only weak correlation between h/y_0 and $(\tau_0 - \tau_c)/\tau_c$. However, this may be caused by the data. The height h of the bed feature is represented by a statistical value—mean or median—of all the heights of the bed features over a suitably wide and long stretch of a watercourse. But for any value of the resistance coefficient, for flow at constant depth, at least two values of U or u_* are possible, cf. Fig. 13.2. Thus, if resistance is assumed to be a function of (y/h) only, there will be two values of $(\tau_0 - \tau_c)/\tau_c$ for any value of h/y_0 in the subcritical region, that is there could be two lines. However, the bed features are steeper on the rising part of the f versus U curve than they are on the falling—eroding—part, and resistance is a function of not only depth and roughness height, but also of the spacing and shape of the roughness elements. Therefore, different h/y_0 ratios could be expected at the two different values of total shear, f being constant. The plot of the data[38] appears to support the above argument, but more information is necessary before any conclusions can be drawn. The scatter pattern of plotted points on the log h/y_0 versus log $(\tau_0 - \tau_c)/\tau_c$ plane suggests an average slope between $45°$ and $60°$.

Allen[38] linked observed data with the following relationship

$$\log y_0 = 0.8271 \log h + 0.8901, \qquad (12.69)$$

where both depth y_0 and dune height h are measured in metres.

By dimensional reasoning one can also conclude that the wavelength L of the features is primarily a function of ρ, ρ_s, g, u_*, v, d and y_0 leading to

$$\frac{L}{d} = f\left(\frac{u_* d}{v}, \frac{y_0}{d}, \frac{\rho u_*^2}{\gamma_s^* d}\right). \qquad (12.70)$$

The team $\rho u_*^2 / \gamma_s^* d$ defines the rate of sediment transport and could thus be assumed to be related to the height and celerity of the bed features and may be omitted here. Hence,

$$\frac{L}{d} = f\left(\frac{u_* d}{v}, \frac{y_0}{d}\right). \qquad (12.71)$$

If the flow is turbulent and over a hydraulically rough boundary then the viscous effects are not important and it follows that

$$\frac{L}{d} = f(y_0/d). \qquad (12.72)$$

If the flow takes place over a hydraulically smooth boundary, the relative roughness term vanishes and

$$\frac{L}{d} = f\left(\frac{u_* d}{v}\right). \qquad (12.73)$$

Yalin[36] plotted experimental data as $(y_0/d)\sqrt{(L/d)}$ versus y_0/d. However, in this method of plotting the effect of L/y_0 is overshadowed by $(y_0/d)^3$, that is the ordinate is identical to $\sqrt{[(y_0/d)^3 L/y_0]}$ and $(y_0/d)^3$ swamps L/y_0. Plots of L/d versus y_0/d indicate a very weak relation between L and d. The proposed relationship

$$L \doteq 1000d \qquad (12.74)$$

is a reasonable approximation for ripples and implies that at small values of Re* , ripple length depends on particle size only. However, the relationship

$$L \propto y_0 \qquad (12.75)$$

for dunes—at larger values of Re_*—is not as good an approximation. Average dune length has been found to increase with decreasing particle size,[40] for example,

$$d : \quad 0{\cdot}8 \quad 0{\cdot}6 \quad 0{\cdot}4 \quad 0{\cdot}3 \quad 0{\cdot}2$$
$$L : \quad 6{\cdot}5 \quad 7{\cdot}1 \quad 8{\cdot}1 \quad 9{\cdot}3 \quad 11{\cdot}3,$$

where d is medium diameter of bed material (in millimetres) and L is the average dune length (in feet). However, for a wide range of conditions the relationship

$$L = 5y_0 \qquad (12.76)$$

appears to be reasonable approximation, but more information is needed to define the limits of this range. Nordin[41] gives 4·2 for the constant of proportionality in eqn. (12.76).

It must also be borne in mind that in three-dimensional flow—in all but the very narrow laboratory flumes—the ripples and dunes are not identical for a given flow. The plot of observed data as the ratio of wavelength to amplitude yields a distinctly skew frequency distribution with the peak at the low values of L/h. It is also apparent from Fig. 13.2 that during the erosion phase a large range of L/h values are to be expected for a given value of $\tau_0/\gamma_s^* d$.

Combining eqn. (12.68) and eqn. (12.74) yields for ripples

$$\frac{h}{L} = \frac{1}{6000} \frac{y_0}{d} \frac{\tau_0 - \tau_c}{\tau_0} \qquad (12.77)$$

or

$$\frac{h}{L} \leqq \frac{y_0}{6000d} \qquad (12.78)$$

and eqn. (12.68) and eqn. (12.76) give for dunes

$$\frac{h}{L} \doteqdot \frac{1}{30} \frac{\tau_0 - \tau_c}{\tau_0} \doteqdot \frac{1}{30} \qquad (12.79)$$

if $\tau_c \ll \tau_0$. The latter ratio is about twice that at which the observed peak of the frequency distribution curve appears to be.

The ripple shown on Fig. 12.12 has a ratio of $h/L = 0.055$ and eqn. (12.77) yields $h/L = 0.05$. Allen[38] gave for small ripples ($h < 0.15$ m)

$$\log h = 0.9508 \log L - 1.0867 \qquad (12.80)$$

and for large ripples

$$\log h = 0.7384 \log L - 1.0746. \qquad (12.81)$$

This leads to yet another classification of ripples and dunes. Thus it follows that

ripples are bed features whose wavelength is proportional to the particle size and is independent of the depth of flow,

and that

dunes are bed features whose wavelength is proportional to the depth of flow and only slightly dependent on the particle size.

References

1. PARTIOT, H. L., *Ann. d. Ponts et Chauss.* 273 (1871).
2. DARWIN, G. H., On the formation of ripple-marks, *Proc. Roy. Soc., London* (1883–84).
3. DEACON, G. F., In discussion of paper on "Estuaries" by H. L. Partiot, *Proc. Institution of Civil Engineers*, Vol. CXVIII (1894), pp. 47–189.
4. EXNER, F. M., Über die Wechselwirkung Zwischen Wasser und Geschiebe in Flüssen, *Sitzungsberichte der Akademie der Wissenschaften*, Wien, Heft 3–4, 1925.
5. LELIAVSKY, S., *An Introduction to Fluvial Hydraulics*, Constable, 1955.
6. BLASIUS, H., Über die Abhängigkeit der Formen der R iffeln und Geschie-bebänke vom Gefälle, Zeitschrift für Bauwesen, 1912.
7. GILBERT, G. K. and MURPHY, E. C., The transportation of debris by running water, U.S. Geological Survey Professional Paper 86, 1914.
8. KRAMER, H., Sand mixtures and sand movement in fluvial models, *Proc. A.S.C.E.* **60**, 443 (1934).
9. STRAUB, L. G., Discussion on sand mixtures and sand movement in fluvial models, *Proc. A.S.C.E.* **61**, 101 (1935).
10. SHIELDS, A., Anwendung der Ähnlichkeits Mechanik und der Turbulenz-forschung auf die Geschiebe Bewegung, Preussische Versuchsanstalt für Wasserbau und Schiffbau, Berlin, 1936.

11. VELIKANOV, M. A., *Formation of sand ripples on the stream bottom*, Commission de Potamologie, Sec. 3, Rapport 13, International Association of Scientific Hydrology, 1936.

12. TISON, L. J., Origine des Ondes de Sable et des Bancs de sable sous l'action des Courants. International Association for Hydraulic Structures Research, Third Meeting, Sept. 1949, Grenoble, France.

13. BAGNOLD, R. A., Motion of waves in shallow water. Interation between waves and sand bottoms, *Proc. Roy. Soc., London* (A), **187** (October 1946).

14. MANOHAR, M., *Mechanics of bottom sediment movement due to wave action*, Beach Erosion Board Tech. Memo No. 75, 1955.

15. ANDERSON, A. G., The characteristics of sediment waves formed by flow in open channels, *Proceedings of the Third Midwestern Conference in Fluid Mechanics*, Minneapolis, March 1953, pp. 379–95.

16. KONDRAT'EV, N. E., a.o. *River Flow and River Channel Formation*. Translation published for the National Science Foundation, Washington, D.C., 1962.

17. KENNEDY, J. F., *Stationary waves and anti-dunes in alluvial channels*, Report No. KH–R–2 January, 1961, W. M. Keck Laboratory, California Institute of Technology.

18. KENNEDY, J. F., The mechanics of dunes and anti-dunes in erodible-bed channels, *Journal of Fluid Mechanics*, **16,** Part 4, 521 (Aug. 1963).

19. TAYLOR, G. I., Effect of variation in density on the stability of superposed streams of fluids, *Proc. Roy. Soc. London* (A) **132** (1931).

20. GOLDSTEIN, S., On the stability of superposed streams of fluids of different densities, *Proc. Roy. Soc. London* (A) **132** (1931).

21. JEFFREYS, H., On the formation of water waves by wind, *Proc. Roy. Soc., London* (A) **107** (1925).

22. KEULEGAN, G. H., *Interfacial stability and mixing in stratified flows*, National Bureau of Standards, Research Paper No. 2040, 1948.

23. KEULEGAN, G. H., *Laminar flow at the interface of two liquids*, National Bureau of Standards Research Paper No. 1591, 1944.

24. BAGNOLD, R. A., The flow of cohesionless grains in fluid, *Philosophical Trans. Roy. Soc., London* (A) **249**, No. 964, 235–97 (Dec. 1956).

25. LIU, H. K., Mechanics of sediment-ripple formation, *Proc. A.S.C.E.* **83,** No. HY2 (April 1957).

26. SIMONS, D. B. and RICHARDSON, F. V., Forms of bed roughness in alluvial channels, *Proc. A.S.C.E.* **87,** No. HY3 (May 1961).

27. SIMONS, D. B. and RICHARDSON, F. V., Resistance to flow in alluvial channels, *Proc. A.S.C.E.* **86,** No. HY5 (May 1960).

28. INGLIS, SIR CLAUDE C., *The behaviour and control of rivers and canals (with the aid of models)*, Research Publication No. 13 (1949) Central Water-Power, Irrigation and Navigation Research Station, Poona, India, Part II, p. 462.

29. SIMONS, D. B., RICHARDSON, F. V. and ALBERTSON, M. L., *Flume studies using medium sand* (0·45 mm). U.S. Geol. Survey Water-Supply Paper 1948–A, 1961.

30. BOGARDI, J., Some aspects of the application of the theory of sediment transportation to engineering problems, *Journal of Geophysical Research*, **66**, No. 10, 3337–46 (Oct. 1961).

BOGARDI, J., Hydraulic similarity of river models with movable bed, *Acta Technica* (*Hungaricae*), **24**, No. 3–4 (1959).

BOGARDI, J., European concepts of sediment transportation, *Proc. A.S.C.E.* **91**, HY 1 (Jan. 1965).

31. WALKER, G. R., A study of the two-dimensional flow of turbulent fluid past a step. Thesis presented to the University of Auckland, at Auckland, New Zealand, in 1961, in partial fulfilment of the requirements for the degree of Master of Engineering.

32. TANI, I., Experimental investigation of flow separation over a step, *International Union of Theoretical and Applied Mechanics, Proceedings Boundary Layer Research*, Symposium Freiburg/Br., 1957, pp. 377–86.

33. ARIE, M. and ROUSE, H., Experiments on two-dimensional flow over a normal wall, *Journal of Fluid Mechanics*, **1**, 129–42 (1956).

34. RAUDKIVI, A. J., Study of sediment ripple formation, *Proc. A.S.C.E.* **89**, No. HY6, Part 1, 15–33 (Nov. 1963).

35. SHEEN, S. J., Turbulence over a sand ripple. Thesis submitted as part requirement for the degree of Master of Engineering, at the Univ. of Auckland, New Zealand, 1964.

36. YALIN, M. S., Geometrical properties of sand waves, *Proc. A.S.C.E.* **90**, HY5 (Sept. 1964).

37. CAREY, W. C. and KELLER, M. C., Systematic changes in the beds of alluvial rivers, *Proc. A.S.C.E.* **83**, No. HY4 (1957).

38. ALLEN, J. R. L., Asymmetrical ripple marks and the origin of water-laid cosets of cross-strata, *Liverpool and Manchester Geological Journal*, **3**, 187–236 (1963).

39. GUY, H. P., SIMONS, D. B. and RICHARDSON, F. V., *Summary of alluvial channel data from flume experiments*, 1956–61, U.S. Geological Survey, Professional Paper 462L, 1965.

40. SIMONS, D. B., RICHARDSON, F. V. and NORDIN, C. F. Jr., *Sedimentary structures generated by flow in alluvial channels*, Report CER64DBS–EVR–CFN15 Colorado State Univ., Fort Collins, Colorado 1964.

41. NORDIN, C. F., *Aspects of flow resistance on sediment transport, Rio Grande near Bernalillo, New Mexico*, Water Supply Paper 1498–H, U.S. Geological Survey, 1964.

CHAPTER 13

Channel Roughness and Resistance to Flow

THE resistance to flow in alluvial channels, or in closed conduits carrying solids, is a problem of great practical importance and a complex one. The resistance to flow in a channel of fixed geometry carrying clear water in steady uniform flow can be predicted quite accurately. But when the same channel carries clear water in non-uniform state of flow the resistance problem becomes very complex. The methods of calculating varied flow problems are as yet all based on the assumption that the resistance approximates that of steady uniform flow at the same depth. It hardly needs to be emphasized that in a channel with erodible boundaries the resistance problem is very much more involved. The shape of the channel in alluvium changes with flow conditions; bed features may form and the cross-section of the channel may become displaced laterally. These changes affect the drag caused by surface roughness and introduce form drag caused by the bed features, as well as energy losses due to secondary currents. The problem is further complicated by the movement of sediment along the bed and in suspension, since the mixture of water and sediment does not behave as clear water.

The discussion of the resistance problem in alluvial channels will be aided by a brief survey of the problem in channels of fixed geometry.

The familiar Chézy formula $V = C\sqrt{(mS)}$ may be compared with the velocity distribution function,

$$u = 5.75u_* \log \frac{30.2y}{k} \qquad (13.1)$$

obtained from the boundary layer theory.

Here y' has been taken to be equal to $k/30.2$, where k is the Nikuradse sand roughness. This integrated over the depth of flow yields the discharge per unit width and upon division by the depth of flow y_0, the mean velocity. It will be found that the velocity at $y = 0.368y_0$ is equal to the mean velocity, leading to the approximation that mean velocity occurs at 0·4 depth or at 0·6 depth measured from the surface downwards. Replacing u_* by $\sqrt{(gy_0S)}$ and with $u = U$ at $y \doteq 0.4y_0$ the mean velocity $U = V$ is

$$U = 5.75 \sqrt{(gy_0S)} \log \frac{12.1y_0}{k}. \qquad (13.2)$$

Upon comparison with the Chézy formula

$$C = 32.6 \log (y_0/k) + 35.3. \qquad (13.3)$$

This relationship (Fig. 13.1) displays the dependence of resistance on the ratio of depth to the mean equivalent roughness height. At about $y_0/k = 30$ the slope is about $\tan^{-1} (\frac{1}{6})$ and at this point

$$C \propto (y_0/k)^{1/6} = K(y_0/k)^{1/6}.$$

Substituting into the Chézy formula

$$V = K(y_0/k)^{1/6}\sqrt{(y_0S)} = \frac{K}{k^{1/6}} y_0^{2/3}S^{1/2}$$

which leads to the Manning formula

$$V = \frac{1.49}{n} y_0^{2/3}S^{1/2}. \qquad (13.4)$$

It also shows that the Manning formula is consistent with the logarithmic velocity distribution in the neighbourhood of

$y_0/k = 30$. Again, in the region of $y_0/k = 10$ the Chézy co-efficient $C \propto (y_0/k)^{1/4}$ yielding $V \propto y_0^{3/4} S^{1/2}$ which is a form of mean velocity equation proposed by Lacey (1929).

The Chézy coefficient is related to the Manning n by

$$C = \frac{1 \cdot 49}{n} y_0^{1/6} \qquad (13.5)$$

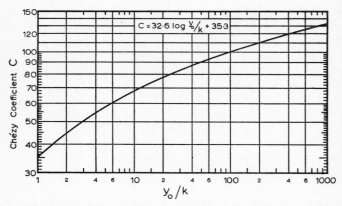

FIG. 13.1. Variation of Chézy C with relative roughness height.

and the Manning n is also related to the roughness height or particle size, when no movement of the bed material takes place, by the Strickler formula

$$n \doteqdot \frac{d^{1/6}}{31} = 0 \cdot 032 d^{1/6} \qquad (13.6)$$

(see section 10.1), with d measured in feet. Also frequently quoted in the form

$$n = 0 \cdot 0132 d^{1/6}, \qquad (13.7)$$

where d is in millimetres and taken as d_{65}. In passing it may be noted that the Fig. 13.1 is useful for selecting roughness heights in fixed bed hydraulic models.

The Chézy coefficient can also be related to the Darcy–Weisbach friction factor f. For pipe flow problems the general drag relationship is written as

$$\tau_0 = c_f \frac{\rho U^2}{2} = \frac{f}{4} \frac{\rho U^2}{2}, \qquad (13.8)$$

so that

$$u_* = \sqrt{(\tau_0/\rho)} = U\sqrt{(f/8)}. \qquad (13.9)$$

Writing for head loss

$$h_f = f \frac{L}{4m} \frac{U^2}{2g} \qquad (13.10)$$

and rearranging yields

$$U = \sqrt{\left(\frac{8g}{f}\right)} \sqrt{(mS)} = C\sqrt{(mS)}$$

or

$$C = \sqrt{(8g/f)}.$$

$$\therefore \frac{C}{\sqrt{(8g)}} = \frac{1}{\sqrt{f}}. \qquad (13.11)$$

Inserting $y' = k/30 \cdot 2$ into $u = 5 \cdot 75 u_* \log (y/y')$ yields the Karman–Prandtl equation for velocity distribution for turbulent flow over rough boundaries,

$$\frac{u}{u_*} = 5 \cdot 75 \log (y/k) + 8 \cdot 5. \qquad (13.12)$$

Integrating this over the depth and dividing by the depth y_0, as described above, yields the mean velocity

$$\frac{U}{u_*} = 5 \cdot 75 \log (y_0/k) + 6 \qquad (13.13)$$

and

$$\frac{u - U}{u_*} = 5 \cdot 75 \log (y/y_0) + 2 \cdot 5. \qquad (13.14)$$

Replacing u_* by $U\sqrt{(f/8)}$ yields for two-dimensional channel flow

$$\frac{u-U}{U\sqrt{f}} = 2 \cdot 03 \log \frac{y}{y_0} + 0 \cdot 88 = \frac{(u-U)C}{U\sqrt{(8g)}} .$$ (13.15)

The type of roughness found in the fixed boundaries of open channels can be represented quite adequately by means of the Nikuradse roughness height, which is not dependent on flow. This roughness can be determined experimentally and for the majority of boundary materials can be found in the technical literature. Using a development similar to that of the Karman–Prandtl resistance equations for pipe flow, resistance equations for the two-dimensional open channel flow can be derived.

These are:

(i) for smooth boundary: $\left(\dfrac{u_* k}{v} < 3\right)$, Re $= 4mU/v$

$$\frac{1}{\sqrt{f}} = 2 \cdot 03 \log (\text{Re} \sqrt{f}) - 0 \cdot 47;$$ (13.16)

(ii) and for rough boundaries $\left(\dfrac{u_* k}{v} > 70\right)$

$$\frac{1}{\sqrt{f}} = 2 \cdot 03 \log \frac{4m}{k} + 0 \cdot 91$$ (13.17)

or

$$\frac{1}{\sqrt{f}} = 2 \cdot 03 \log \frac{y_0}{k} + 2 \cdot 12.$$ (13.18)

These formulae for $1/\sqrt{f}$ appear in literature in very many forms and could be summarized as

$$\frac{1}{\sqrt{f}} = -c \log \left(\frac{k}{am} + \frac{b}{\text{Re}\sqrt{f}}\right)$$ (13.19)

in which the constants are in the following range: $c = 2$ to $2 \cdot 03$, $a = 11 \cdot 55$ to $12 \cdot 2$, b up to 3.

For the usual fixed boundary materials the roughness elements are spaced closely together, so that the wake of one roughness element interferes with the flow around the next element downstream, and with the formation of its wake.

In an alluvial channel with plane boundaries the same concepts of roughness height apply only when the flow remains below the threshold of particle movement. If the grain size is uniform, the roughness height will be equal to the grain diameter. In natural beds of non-uniform material the bed becomes armoured with larger particles, and again by experience one can select the proper particle size, such as $k = d_{65}$ or d_{90} or whatever is appropriate. However, in an alluvial channel with movable sand or gravel bed, the roughness elements depend on the flow as well as on the bed material. Such natural channels seldom have plane boundaries. In the appropriate circumstances they develop ripples, dunes, sandwaves or antidunes. These bed features have much greater spacing than the Nikuradse sand roughness and have appreciable form drag which can overshadow the surface roughness of the bed forms. Evaluated without regard to this, the equivalent roughness height k could be found to be greater than the depth of flow.

Many research programmes have been devoted to the study of the friction factor in channels with regularly spaced roughness elements of various shapes, including strips fastened to the bottom perpendicular to the flow.[1,2] A discussion of these is to be found in the Report of the Task Force on Friction Factors.[3]

The effect of waviness $\bar{w}$ was introduced by Bretting[4] yielding for smooth boundary

$$\frac{1}{\sqrt{f}} = 2 \log \left(\frac{\mathrm{Re}\sqrt{f}}{2 \cdot 512} \right) - 2 \log \bar{w} \qquad (13.20)$$

and for rough boundary a relationship of the form

$$\frac{1}{\sqrt{f}} = -2 \log (k/am). \qquad (13.21)$$

The latter was given as three exponential equations each approximating a range of relative roughness values.

If the height and length of the bed features could be expressed explicitly for any flow conditions, then the form loss caused by these bed features could be approximated as for expansion loss, that is $h_L = K(V_1 - V_2)^2/2g$ and included separately. However, known attempts have not been very successful as yet. Yalin[5] proposed a formula—similar to formulae given for fixed boundary channels[1]—which depends on the height h and length L of the bed features as follows

$$\frac{C}{\sqrt{g}} = \frac{2 \cdot 5 \ln (11y_0/k)}{\sqrt{(1 - h/L)\sigma}}, \qquad (13.22)$$

where

$$\sigma = \cot \phi - \tfrac{1}{2}h/y_0[2 \cdot 5 \ln (11y_0/k)]^2$$

and ϕ is the angle of repose.

The variation of resistance to flow with the changes in bed forms has been studied in laboratory flumes. In Fig. 13.2, from ref. 6, the bed friction factor f_b is plotted versus the mean velocity U, bed shear velocity u_{*b} and, as a check, versus u_{*b}/U. By definition of f, viz. $f = 8(u_*/U)^2$, this last set of points should lie on a parabola (see also Fig. 6.19, section 6.5).

It is seen that with the formation of the bed features the friction factor increases and then decreases as dunes give place to sand waves. The peak value is nearly 6 times the value at the threshold of particle movement. The friction factor is nearly as low for the transition flat bed as for the flat bed at the threshold conditions of sand movement. The plot of f_b against U or u_{*b} for the experiment with 0·40 mm sand, which was run at approximately constant mean depth and constant temperature, is analogous to a plot of f versus Reynolds number. The experiment with 0·14 mm sand was run at constant discharge and variable depth. Yet a common line could be drawn through the plotted points for f_b versus u_{*b} or U for both experiments. It appears that the form drag is so dominant that changes in drag due to changes in surface texture (sand size) are not easily distinguished.

Figure 13.2 also shows that for one value of u_{*b} there may be two values of f_b. This demonstrates that the shear velocity alone is not sufficient for description of the flow when sediment transport occurs.

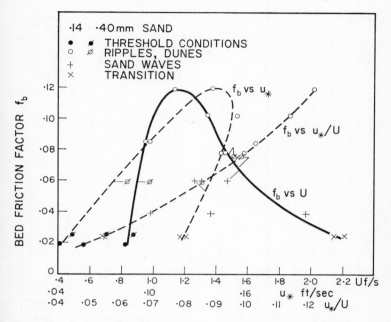

FIG. 13.2. Bed friction factor versus u_*, U and u_*/U. (From ref. 6, p. 18, by permission of the American Society of Civil Engineers.)

The results of flume experiments by Vanoni, Brooks, Nomicos[7] and Kennedy[8] are plotted as friction factor, slope and shear velocity against the mean velocity of flow (Fig. 13.3).

It is interesting that experimental points, obtained with various sands and flow conditions, indicate a relationship between friction factor and mean velocity. This plot does not show the rise of the friction factor from threshold conditions as indicated on Fig. 13.2. The relationship between the slope and mean velocity is seen to be much more involved.

Firstly, it is seen that more than one value of mean velocity is possible at some slopes. This is brought about by the changing

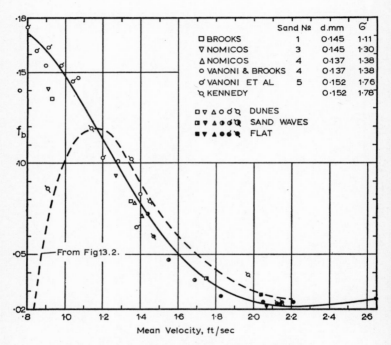

FIG. 13.3a. Bed friction factor f_b versus mean velocity.

roughness as the bed features change with flow conditions. Furthermore, it is not a unique relationship as seen from the curves for different depth of flow. Like the slope, the shear velocity shows that for a given shear velocity more than one mean velocity is possible and that the depth of flow, or the size of the watercourse, affects the problem. Similar changes have been

observed on natural watercourses.[9] Figure 13.4 illustrates one
such observation. It shows that roughness is not a unique
function of discharge. This is likely to be the reason for discontinuous rating curves observed on many rivers.

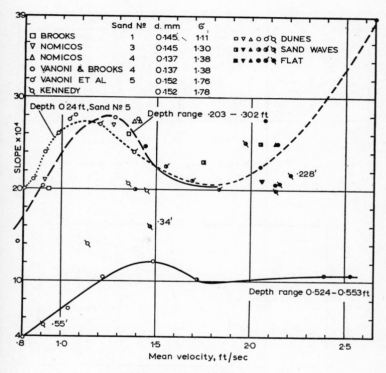

FIG. 13.3b. Slope versus mean velocity.

Einstein and Barbarossa[10] proposed a method for calculating
the form drag (bar resistance) in a stream. They postulated that
the bed shear τ_0 may be subdivided as

$$\tau_0 = \tau_0' + \tau_0'',\qquad(13.23)$$

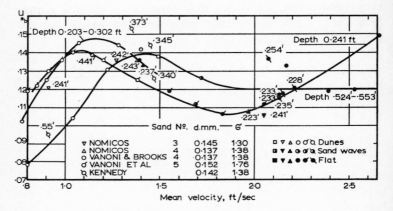

FIG. 13.3c. Bed shear velocity u_{*b} (ft/sec) versus mean velocity.

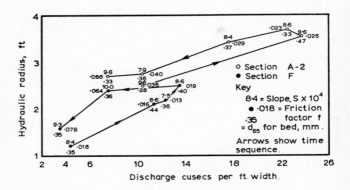

FIG. 13.4. Variation of hydraulic mean radius, slope, friction factor and bed material size with changing discharge for Rio Grande River at Bernalillo, New Mexico, April–July 1952. (With permission from ref. 7, data in U.S. Geological Survey Water-supply paper 1498–F, 1964.)

where τ_0' is the shear on a flat bed of the given grain roughness and τ_0'' is the contribution of form drag caused by the bed features. Similarly, the hydraulic mean radius is subdivided as

$$\tau_0 = \gamma m S = \gamma S(m' + m'') \qquad (13.24)$$

and the shear velocities are defined as

$$\left.\begin{aligned}
u_*' &= \sqrt{(g\, m'S)} \\
u_*'' &= \sqrt{(gm''S)} \\
u_*^2 &= u_*'^2 + u_*''^2.
\end{aligned}\right\} \qquad (13.25)$$

A channel without resistance from bed features and having the hydraulic mean radius m' will have the same velocity and slope as the actual channel. The velocity and m' are related by the logarithmic velocity distribution with constants as given by Keulegan

$$\frac{U}{u_*'} = 5.75\, log\left(12.27\, \frac{m'}{k_s}\, x\right), \qquad (13.26)$$

where $k_s = d_{65}$ is taken to be the grain roughness of the bed and x is a correction factor which compensates for conditions where the plane channel is not completely rough in the hydrodynamic sense. It is expressed as

$$x = f\left(\frac{k_s}{\delta'}\right) = f\left(\frac{k_s u_*'}{11.6v}\right), \qquad (13.27)$$

where δ' is the thickness of the laminar sublayer. For $k_s/\delta' > 5$ the factor is close to unity. From these equations m' and u_*' can be determined by trial and error and u_*'' can be found with known u_* and u_*'. The resistance is then related to the sediment transport along the bed and expressed in terms of U/u_*'' as a function of the parameter ψ of the Einstein bed-load function

$$\psi' = \frac{\rho_s - \rho}{\rho}\, \frac{d_{35}}{m'S}. \qquad (13.28)$$

Here d_{35} is taken to be the representative grain size.

A graphical procedure was evolved which avoids the trial and error solutions.

COMPARISON OF FRICTION FACTORS FOR SEDIMENT-LADEN FLOWS WITH THOSE FOR CLEAR WATER FLOWS OVER STABILIZED SAND BEDS OF THE SAME CONFIGURATION

Run no.	Set	Depth (ft)	Bed cond.	Sed. disch. concent. C (g/litre)	Friction factors		Decrease	
					mean f	for bed f_b	Δf_b	%
1	I	0·284	Dunes	3·64	0·074	0·106	0·006	5
2		0·284	Dunes	0	0·077	0·112		
3	II	0·244	Small dunes	4·60	0·0198	0·0211	0·0072	25
4		0·244	Small dunes	0	0·0246	0·0283		
5A	III	0·255	Flat	8·08	0·0165	0·0165	0·0064	28
6		0·255	Flat	0	0·0203	0·0229		
7	IV	0·255	Flat	3·61	0·0207	0·0227	0·0035	13·5
8		0·253	Flat	0	0·0230	0·0262		

The sands used were as follows:

Experiments set no.	Geom. mean diameter d_g (mm)	Geom. stand deviation	Mean sed. diam. (mm)	Mean fall vel. at 25°C (ft/sec)
I, II, III	0·091	1·16	0·105	0·031
IV	0·148	1·16	0·161	0·062

The graph of U/u_*'' against ψ' shows data from a number of rivers. There is a consistent trend but the scatter is also appreciable. Nor do observed results always follow this particular mean line. Experimental results from Vanoni and Brooks,[7] for example, cross the mean line of Einstein and Barbarossa at a considerable angle.

The effect of sediment on flow resistance has been one of the most controversial topics. Late last century it was reasoned that the loss of energy between any two sections on a stream was given by the difference in elevation of the total head. This headloss was

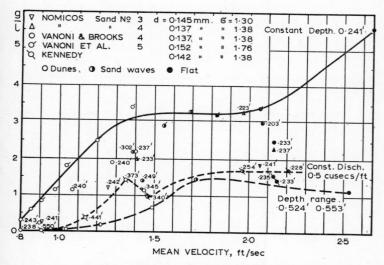

FIG. 13.5. Sediment discharge concentration $\overline{C}$ (g/litre) versus mean velocity (ft/sec).

taken to consist of hydraulic friction and of energy required to transport the sediment. Accordingly, the more energy is used on sediment the less is available to overcome friction and the mean velocity will be reduced to a value corresponding to the reduced friction gradient.

At the time when these ideas were put forward the concepts of turbulence were in their infancy. With present-day knowledge it is apparent that much of the energy to transport sediment comes from the turbulence and that this does not necessarily draw on the main energy head. Vanoni[11,12] carried out experiments in a flume with a fixed, artificially roughened bed and showed that flow with suspended load had a smaller friction factor than

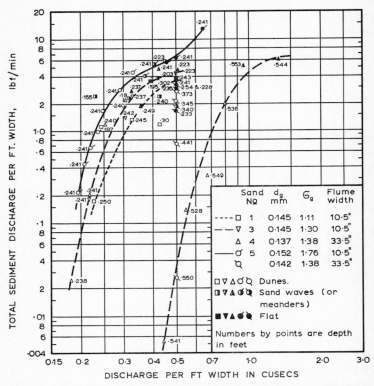

Fig. 13.6. Relation of depth to water and sediment discharge for various sands. (By permission from ref. 7.)

clear water flow of the same depth in the same channel. Figure 8.3 shows the effect of suspended sediment load on the velocity distribution and the Karman universal constant κ.

The results of Vanoni's experiments are summarized in the table on p. 234.

It was seen from Fig. 13.3 that the mean velocity is not uniquely determined by depth and slope and for a given value of u_{*b} more than one value of mean velocity may exist. From Fig. 13.5 it is seen that this also implies more than one value of sediment discharge concentration. The higher values of $\bar{C}$ for the constant depth run, 0·241 ft, which are inside the depth range 0·233–0·250 ft,

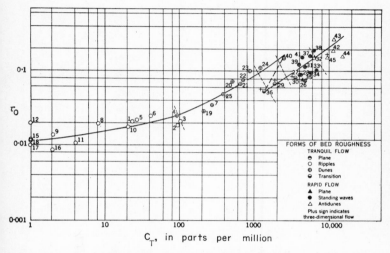

FIG. 13.7. Variation of shear τ_0 and concentration of total load C_T, in parts per million. (From ref. 13, by permission of the U.S. Geological Survey.)

are due to the larger standard deviation of this particular sand; that is there is more fine material available. Therefore it is necessary to know accurately the size distribution of the bed material if comparisons are to be made or when interpreting and analysing transport data of sediment laden flows. However, when laboratory data[7] are plotted as sediment discharge q_s against water discharge q a family of curves is obtained with the depth of flow as the third variable (Fig. 13.6).

It is shown by this information that for a given discharge an increase in sediment discharge requires a decrease in the water

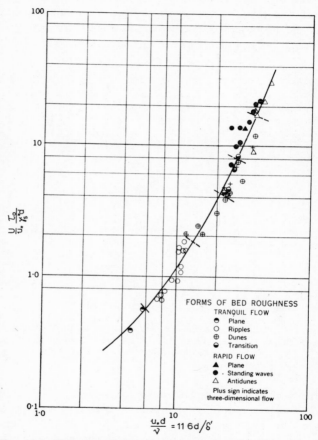

FIG. 13.8. Variation of (U/u_*) $(\tau_0/\gamma_s{}^*d)$ with u_*d/ν. (From ref. 13 by permission of the U.S. Geological Survey.)

depth, an observation which is also embodied in the relationships of Chapter 10.

Simons, Richardson and Albertson[13] propose the plotting of the bed shear stress $\tau_0 = \gamma y_0 S$ against concentration of the

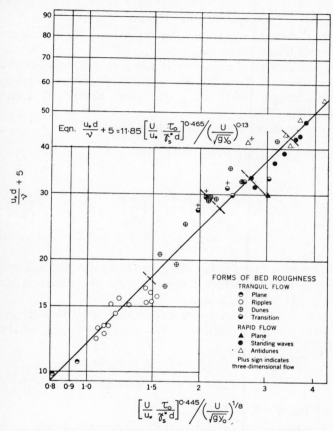

Eqn. $\dfrac{u_* d}{\nu} + 5 = 11 \cdot 85 \left[\dfrac{U}{u_*} \dfrac{\tau_0}{\gamma_s^* d} \right]^{0 \cdot 465} \Big/ \left(\dfrac{U}{\sqrt{g y_0}} \right)^{0 \cdot 13}$

$\dfrac{u_* d}{\nu} + 5$

FORMS OF BED ROUGHNESS
TRANQUIL FLOW
◐ Plane
○ Ripples
⊕ Dunes
◔ Transition
RAPID FLOW
▲ Plane
● Standing waves
△ Antidunes
Plus sign indicates
three-dimensional flow

$\left[\dfrac{U}{u_*} \dfrac{\tau_0}{\gamma_s^* d} \right]^{0 \cdot 445} \Big/ \left(\dfrac{U}{\sqrt{g y_0}} \right)^{1/8}$

FIG. 13.9. (From ref. 13 by permission of the U.S. Geological Survey.)

total load C_T in parts per million (Fig. 13.7). However, data of Vanoni and Brooks[7] plotted on the same graph do not follow the same trend as well.

The data of Fig. 13.7 plotted as

$$\frac{U}{u_*}\frac{\tau_0}{\gamma_s^*} = f\left(\frac{u_*d}{\nu}\right) \qquad (13.29)$$

on Fig. 13.8 show in a very interesting manner the sequence of the various forms of bed roughness.

The addition of a numerical constant to the ordinate term yields two straight lines. These straight lines are then combined into one straight line by using the Froude number as a third variable (Fig. 13.9).

By further manipulation the authors obtain

$$U = \tfrac{1}{2}S^{1/6}(C_D)^{2/3}\left(\frac{wd}{\nu}\right)^{4/3}\left(\frac{\gamma}{\gamma_s^*}\right)^{2/3}\sqrt{(gy_0S)} \qquad (13.30)$$

and

$$\frac{C}{\sqrt{g}} = \tfrac{1}{2}S^{1/6}(C_D)^{2/3}\left(\frac{wd}{\nu}\right)^{4/3}\left(\frac{\gamma}{\gamma_s^*}\right)^{2/3}, \qquad (13.31)$$

where C_D is the drag coefficient of the particle and equals $\gamma_s^*d/(\rho w^2)$.

It will need a great amount of data and checking under various conditions to verify whether this approach yields relationships which are generally applicable.

Equation (13.31) can be compared with Fig. 13.2 by first transcribing it into a relationship between f and Froude number as follows:

$$U/u_* = \sqrt{(8/f)} \quad \text{and} \quad U = C\sqrt{(y_0S)}$$

$$\gamma_s^*(\pi/6)d^3 = C_D\tfrac{1}{2}\rho w^2(\pi/4)d^2.$$

Substituting into eqn. (13.31)

$$\frac{U}{u_*} = \frac{1}{2}\left(\frac{f^{1/6}}{1\cdot414}\,\text{Fr}^{1/3}\right)\left(\frac{1\cdot21\gamma_s^{*2/3}d^{2/3}}{\rho^{2/3}w^{4/3}}\right)\left(\frac{w^{4/3}d^{4/3}}{\nu^{4/3}}\right)\left(\frac{\rho^{2/3}g^{2/3}}{\gamma_s^{*2/3}}\right)$$

and rearranging yields

$$f = \frac{17}{\sqrt{\text{Fr}}}\frac{\nu^2}{gd^3}. \qquad (13.32)$$

For a particular problem the friction factor is seen to be proportional to $y_0^{1/4}/U^{1/2}$. When plotted on the f versus U coordinate plane a family of curves is obtained which are of the same shape as the falling part of f versus U line on Figs. 13.2 and 6.19. Observed data plotted as Fig. 13.2 generally show a steeper downward slope near the peak of the f versus U curve than that defined by eqn. (13.32), but with increasing velocities there is

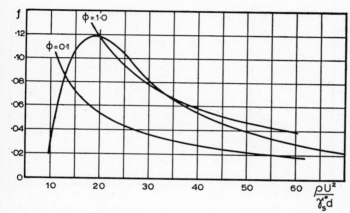

Fig. 13.10. The resistance relationship of Fig. 13.2 and the Einstein–Brown bed-load function superimposed.

usually a region over which the slopes are equal. Thus it could be expected that eqn. (13.31) yields best results for flow over a bed with eroding dunes and over transitional wavy and flat bed.

The resistance problem can also be approached from Fig. 13.2 where f is plotted against the mean velocity U. The abscissa can be made dimensionless to yield a plot of f versus $\rho U^2/\gamma_s^* d$. A bed-load function, such as the Einstein–Brown formula, can also be plotted on the same graph, after an algebraic rearrangement, yielding

$$f = (12 \cdot 8\phi)^{1/3} \left(\frac{\rho U^2}{\gamma_s^* d} \right)^{-1}.$$

This is a family of curves with the bed-load ϕ as the parameter (Fig. 13.10). For given values of ϕ the intersection points with the f versus $\rho U^2/\gamma_s^* d$ curve define values of f and U which provide a solution to the design problem. Note that in certain regions more than one solution is possible and that ϕ may remain nearly constant for large changes in the value $\rho U^2/\gamma_s^* d$. Thus, if the total shear is used in the bed-load formula, it would appear that

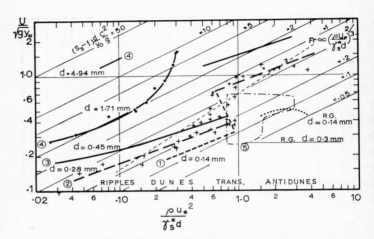

FIG. 13.11. The entrainment function and Froude number relationship. 1. Data by Vanoni, Brooks, Kennedy, refs. 2 and 3. 2. Data by Simons and Richardson, ref. 26, Chapter 12. 3. Data by Simons and Richardson, ref. 27, Chapter 12. 4. Data by Gilbert, ref. 7, Chapter 12. 5. Data from Rio Grande (ref. 9) are scattered inside this line.

the sediment transport in terms of bed-load does not change much while the bed features are eroded. This is not in keeping with laboratory observations and signifies only that the total drag is not a satisfactory parameter for definition of bed-load transport. The general shape of the f versus U function of Figs. 13.2 and 6.19 is evident in all the data from different sources that have been analysed, but there is evidently no unique line relating f and U.

Another form of presentation is obtained when the data are rearranged as $U/\sqrt{(gy)}$ versus $\rho u_*^2/\gamma_s^* d$. An alternate coordinate $(S_s-1)(d/y_0)(C^2/g)$ can be plotted on this graph, since

$$U^2/gy_0 = \rho u_*^2/\gamma_s^* d \left[(S_s-1) \frac{d}{y_0} \frac{C^2}{g} \right].$$

Figure 13.11 shows the resulting graph; individual observations have been omitted for sake of clarity, except for 0·28 mm and 1·71 mm sand. This figure displays the behaviour of flow in an alluvial channel. It shows the sequence of ripples, dunes, transition, and antidunes and the associated variation of resistance. The sediment load can be expressed in terms of the value of the abscissa, which is $1/\psi$ of the Einstein bed-load transport function. The graph also shows a lower and upper regime of the flow. For sands less than 1·5 mm in diameter (from data analysed), the transition region is approximately in the range of $\rho u_*^2/\gamma_s^* d$ between 0·4 and 1. Fine sediments show a pronounced step back in terms of the abscissa at the change from lower to upper regime, whereas with coarse sediments the change over is more gradual. However, the function indicated on this plane appears to vary with both the particle size and the d/y_0 ratio.

The bed forms and the rate of sediment transport in an alluvial channel are governed by the excess of shear stress above the threshold value. It has been shown in Chapter 12 that the relative height of the bed features is also approximately a function of the excess shear stress. The effect of transport and bed forms appears as a variation of the resistance coefficient $C/\sqrt{g} = U/u_*$. The mobility of the grains, or resistance to motion, is as a first approximation characterized by the value of $\rho u_*^2/\gamma_s^* d$.

It was found that plotting of the data in terms of $U/\sqrt{(u_*^2 - u_{*c}^2)}$ (instead of U/u_*) versus $\rho u_*^2/\gamma_s^* d$ condensed the data appreciably (Fig. 3.12), and the resulting function is consistent with physical reasoning. It should be noted that the plotted data have been observed on streams which range from large rivers to laboratory flumes and cover a particle size range from 0·09 to 4·9 mm.

Although there is appreciable scatter the trends are unmistak-

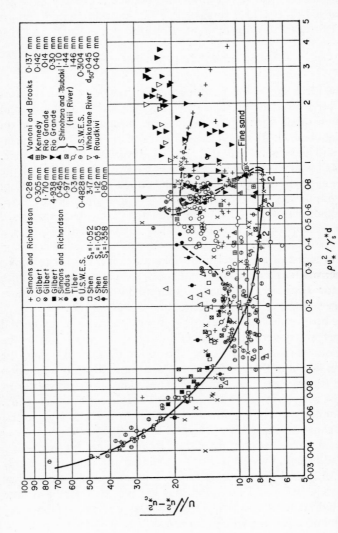

FIG. 13.12. Resistance in an alluvial channel as a function of the entrainment function.

able. The scatter is probably caused—at least partly—by the data not being interpreted on a uniform basis; for example, the effects of grading of the bed material should be allowed for. The abscissa values depend directly on the particle size and any inconsistencies in size definition will have large effects on the results. The data obtained by the author, as well as those by Simons and Richardson, show relatively small scatter in themselves. River data can further be influenced by survival of bed features from preceding river flows.

In general terms the data define a lower and an upper region with a transition between these. The lower region, on the left of the figure, corresponds to the steeply rising resistance curve on Fig. 13.2. The transition in the middle of the figure corresponds to the erosion phase with falling resistance factor f. The upper region applies to flow conditions beyond the transition flat bed where the resistance factor f increases again.

Several features on this graph are worthy of additional comment. Thus it is seen that the points corresponding to data by Shen[15] start deviating from the line defined by the general trend at very low values of $\rho u_*^2 / \gamma_s^* d$. Shen used lightweight materials with specific gravities of 1·052, 1·055 and 1·358. However, the same path is followed by data for coarse sands and gravels. This is in keeping with the argument put forward that the mobility of the grain is related to both the local temporal mean drag and turbulent agitation. With low values of specific gravity impulsive forces resulting from fluid turbulence are important in the same way as with gravel beds where the turbulence intensity is so high that impulsive forces are very important.

With smaller grain sizes the path through the transition region is as indicated by the dashed line—a doubling back—and three ordinate values are possible for one value on the abscissa. The smaller particles are sheltered by the viscous sublayer and higher values of $\rho u_*^2 / \gamma_s^* d$ are reached before the turbulent agitation becomes prominent. It should also be noticed that a larger range of resistance factor values is possible with fine grained sediment than with coarse ones.

It is apparent that the effect of turbulence and hence the size of the system play an important role. For example, the data from the Rio Grande[16] show a transition at higher values of $\rho u_*^2 / \gamma_s^* d$ than those from flume experiments for similar particle size, as well as larger values of $U/\sqrt{(u_*^2 - u_{*c}^2)}$ for the upper region. However, there does not appear to be a consistent trend in terms of d/y_0. Similarly, the values of Froude numbers appear to be scattered in a random fashion. For the 4·9 mm diameter grains the Froude number is 1·18–1·67 in the lower region, whereas for fine sands—such as in Rio Grande—the Froude number is about 0·6 in the upper region.

Figure 13.12 is presented mainly for discussion of trends, but it is apparent that it holds out promise for presentation of resistance data in a simple form. The resistance, bed load and suspended load—except for reference concentration—are generally defined in terms of u_* or $y_0 S$, u_* defines $u_* d/\nu$ and then u_{*c} is known and U can be calculated. Here S is the energy slope. In these coordinates the resistance becomes indeterminate at the threshold of sediment movement. As u_*^2 approaches u_{*c}^2 the ordinate value approaches infinity with the critical value of the entrainment function as an asymptote. However, since

$$U = K\sqrt{(u_*^2 - u_{*c}^2)} = K\sqrt{(1 - u_{*c}^2/u_*^2)}u_*,$$

the product $K\sqrt{[1 - (u_{*c}/u_*)^2]}$ must approach K_c, that is, the velocity at the limit is

$$U = K_c u_{*c}.$$

This value of the resistance coefficient, and those below the threshold value, can be determined by the methods applicable to fixed rough boundaries.

The adjustment of data in terms of the abscissa—$\rho(u_*^2 - u_{*c}^2)/\gamma_s^* d$—was investigated and abandoned as it had little effect on the pattern, except in the vicinity of the threshold limit.

It is believed that Fig. 13.12 contributes to understanding of the resistance problem. However, extensive systematic investigation, involving a wide range of particle sizes and flows, is necessary before it is of any practical value. In particular the transition region needs a much better definition, and this for two important reasons. Firstly, here the apparent scatter is greatest, because of the different paths of the transition function for different grain sizes and specific gravities. Secondly, many fluvial channels function in this transition region, so that it is a most important region for practical application.

In addition to the surface roughness, bed features and the sediment load, the geometrical features of the watercourse in plan and cross-section further complicate the resistance problem. It has been observed in model studies, where the surface roughness can be controlled,[17] that the resistance to flow in a winding channel can be much greater than the resistance in a uniform straight channel of the same roughness and size. The resistance to fully developed turbulent flow at constant depth in an open sinusoidal channel was investigated by Leopold, Bagnold, Wolman and Brush[18] in a laboratory flume. The overall resistance τ to flow is subdivided into the component parts attributable to specific causes. Of these the resistance due to skin friction τ_f is best understood. If τ is plotted against the mean velocity U^2 in a sinusoidal channel, then for a given roughness the resistance is proportional to the square of mean velocity up to some particular value of U (Fig. 13.13).

The component τ_i is due to the internal distortion of the flow, secondary currents and eddies. In experimental work τ_f and τ_i can be compared only if the curved and straight channels have the same flow cross-section and the same surface roughness all along the channel.

The third component has been called the spill resistance τ_s. This stress is not an actual boundary shear but represents the energy dissipation associated with a hydraulic jump (cf. also abrupt expansion in a closed pipeline). In open channel flow such discontinuous expansion is possible only when the on-coming flow is supercritical. At subcritical velocities the flow can adjust its area without a discontinuity taking place, cf. Bernoulli equation. In natural rivers local hydraulic jumps can

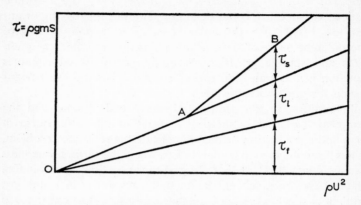

Fig. 13.13. Diagrammatic presentation of the stress components.

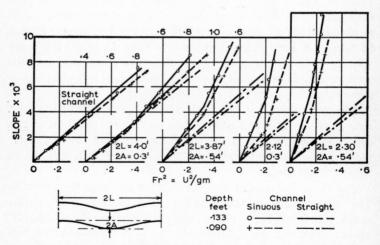

Fig. 13.14. Channel slope versus mean Froude number Fr^2 for straight and sinuous channels of trapezoidal cross-section; 0.385 ft base width and $4:3$ side slopes (horizontal to vertical). (By permission of the U.S. Geological Survey, ref. 18.)

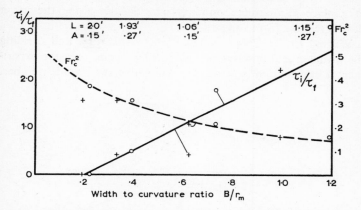

FIG. 13.15. Experimental relation of the ratio of internal distortion
resistance τ_i to skin friction resistance τ_f and the square of the
critical Froude number Fr_c^2 plotted against the channel width to
curvature ratio. (From ref. 18 by permission of the U.S. Geological
Survey.)

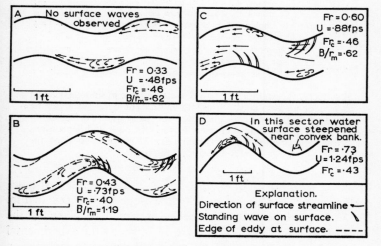

FIG. 13.16. General features of flow at various values of B/r_m.
(From ref. 18, by permission of the U.S. Geological Survey.)

take place at discrete boundary irregularities while the mean flow is still far from supercritical.

Writing $\mathrm{Fr}^2 = U^2/gm$, whence $\rho U^2 = \rho gm \mathrm{Fr}^2$, and dividing the ordinate and abscissa of Fig. 13.13 by ρgm, then the experimental information is presented as slope versus Froude number.

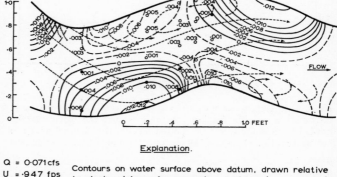

Explanation.

$Q = 0.071\,\mathrm{cfs}$
$U = .947\,\mathrm{fps}$
$\mathrm{Fr}^2 = .27$
$\mathrm{Fr}_c^2 = .21$
$s = .0078$
$2L = 2.22\,\mathrm{ft}$
$2A = .30\,\mathrm{ft}$
$B/r_m = .73$

Contours on water surface above datum, drawn relative to sloping datum of mean water surface (——————)
Contours on water surface below datum, drawn relative to sloping datum of mean water surface (— — — —)
Observed elevation in feet above datum (●)
Observed elevation in feet below datum (○)
Path of surface floats (- - - ➤)
Small standing surface ripples (～～～)

FIG. 13.17. Topographical map of water surface in sinuous channel at Froude number above threshold value. The datum is a sloping plane parallel to and coinciding with the mean water surface elevation. The contour lines represent elevations above and depressions below that sloping plane. (From ref. 18, by permission of the U.S. Geological Survey.)

From $\tau_0 = (f/4)\rho U^2/2 = (2g/C^2)\rho U^2/2$ the overall resistance coefficient $C^* = g/C^2$ is equal to the slope of line OA in Fig. 13.13. Beyond point A this coefficient would be given by the slope of a straight line OB. Figure 13.14 shows the experimental results. It is clearly seen that channel curvature can introduce a resistance loss which may be greater than that caused by skin friction.

The ratio of τ_i/τ_f plotted against the ratio of the surface width to the radius of curvature seems to define a relationship (Fig. 13.15). Here r_m is the radius of a circle which passes through the centre line of the channel at points of inflection and maximum amplitude.

If the Froude number at which the spill resistance appears (point A in Fig. 13.13) is called Fr_c and these values are plotted against B/r_m, the $\mathrm{Fr}_c - B/r_m$ relationship of Fig. 13.15 is obtained.

The general features of the flow at various values of B/r_m and Fr_c are displayed on Figs. 13.16 and 13.17.

The present state of knowledge of the mechanism of resistance to flow resulting from cross-sectional and plan geometry of the watercourse is still far from complete. The experimental work is limited to fixed boundary bends. Of the more recent work, that of A. T. Ippen et al.[19,20] is a very thorough study of velocity and shear distribution in a circular bend of a trapezoidal channel.

The theoretical and experimental work done in Russia is summarized by Rozovskii.[21] This work includes many details of interest.

References

1. SAYRE, W. W. and ALBERTSON, M. L., Roughness spacing in rigid open channels, *Proc. A.S.C.E.* **87**, No. HY3, 121–50 (May 1961).

2. CHITHAMBARAN, V. K. and MIRAJGAOKER, A. G., *Flume Studies of Natural Roughness in Rigid Open Channels*, The Institution of Engineers (India), 1964, pp. 571–85.

3. Friction factor in open channels, Progress Report of the Task Force on Friction Factors in Open Channels of the Committee on Hydromechanics of the Hydraulics Division, *Proc. A.S.C.E.* **89**, No. HY2 (March 1963).

4. BRETTING, A. E., A set of practical hydraulic formulae based on recent experimental research, Internat. Assoc. for Hydraulic Research, 2nd Meeting, 1948, No. 24, pp. 399–418.

5. YALIN, S., On the average velocity of flow over a movable bed, *La Houille Blanche*, No. 1, 45–50 (1964).

6. RAUDKIVI, A. J., Study of sediment ripple formation, *Proc. A.S.C.E.* **89**, No. HY6, 15–33 (Nov. 1963).

7. VANONI, V. A. and BROOKS, N. H., *Laboratory studies of the roughness and suspended load of alluvial streams*, Sedimentation Laboratory, California Institute of Technology, Pasadena, Report No. E–68, Dec. 1957.

8. KENNEDY, J. F., Further laboratory studies of the roughness and suspended load of alluvial streams, W. M. Leck Laboratory of Hydraulics and Water Resources, Division of Engineering, California Institute of Technology, Pasadena, Report No. KH–R–3, April, 1961.

9. COLBY, B. R., Discontinuous rating curves for Pigeon Roost and Cuffawa creeks in Northern Mississippi, U.S. Dept. of Agriculture, Agricultural Publication, A.R.S. 4–136, April, 1960.

10. EINSTEIN, H. A. and BARBAROSSA, N. L., River channel roughness, *Proc. A.S.C.E.* **77**, Sep. No. 78 (July 1951).

11. VANONI, V. A., Some effects of suspended sediment on flow characteristics, *Proc. 5th Hydraulics Conference*, State University of Iowa, Studies in Engineering, Bul. 34, 1953.

12. VANONI, V. A., Transportation of suspended sediment by water, *Trans. A.S.C.E.* **111**, 67–133 (1946).

13. SIMONS, D. B., RICHARDSON, E. V. and ALBERTSON, M. L., *Flume studies using medium sand* (0·45 mm), U.S. Geological Survey Water-Supply Paper 1498–A (1961).

14. SIMONS, D. B. and ALBERTSON, M. L., Uniform water conveyance channels in alluvial material, *Proc. A.S.C.E.* **86**, No. HY5, 33–71 (May 1960).

15. SHEN, H. W., Development of bed roughness in alluvial channels, *Proc. A.S.C.E.* **88**, No. HY3, 45–58 (May 1962).

16. CUBERTSON, J. K. and DAWDY, D. R., *A study of fluvial characteristics and hydraulic variables Middle Rio Grande, New Mexico*, U.S. Geological Survey Water-Supply Paper 1498–F, 1964.

17. ALLEN, J. and SHAHWAN, A., The resistance to flow of water along a tortuous stretch of River Irwell (Lancashire)—an investigation with the aid of scale-model experiments, *Proc. Inst. C.E. (London)*, **3**, Part 3, Paper No. 5914, 144–65 (1954).

18. LEOPOLD, L. B., BAGNOLD, R. A., WOLMAN, M. G. and BRUSH, L. M. Jr., *Flow resistance in sinuous or irregular channels*, U.S. Geological Survey, Professional Paper 282–D, U.S. Government Printing Office, 1960.

19. IPPEN, A. T., DRINKER, P. A., JOBIN, W. R. and SHEMDIN, O. H., *Stream dynamics and boundary shear distribution for curved trapezoidal channel*, Massachusetts Institute of Technology, Hydrodynamics Laboratory, Dept. of Civil Engineering, Report No. 47, Jan. 1962.

20. IPPEN, A. T. and DRINKER, P. A., Boundary shear stresses in curved trapezoidal channels, *Proc. A.S.C.E.* **88**, No. HY5, Part I, 143–79 (Sept. 1962).

21. ROZOVSKII, I. L., *Flow of Water in Bends of Open Channels*. Translated and Published for the National Science Foundation, Washington, D.C. and the Dept. of Interior, U.S.A., by the Israel Program for Scientific Translations, 1961.

CHAPTER 14

Movement of Sand by Water Waves

14.1. Summary of Gravity Wave Theory

The theory of waves of small amplitude, which may be considered the first approximation to the more general problem, yields for the celerity of surface waves of wavelength L on water of depth D

$$c = \sqrt{\left[\left(\frac{gL}{2\pi} + \frac{\sigma 2\pi}{\rho L} \right) \tanh \frac{2\pi}{L} D \right]}. \qquad (14.1)$$

This theory assumes irrotational motion. The effect of surface tension σ is negligible on gravity waves of engineering importance, where L is large. Neglecting surface tension

$$c = \sqrt{\left(\frac{gL}{2\pi} \tanh \frac{2\pi}{L} D \right)} \qquad (14.2)$$

For deep water $(D > L/2)$ this is approximately

$$c = \sqrt{\left(\frac{gL}{2\pi} \right)} = \sqrt{(5 \cdot 12 L)} = 5 \cdot 12 T \qquad (14.3)$$

in ft-lbf-sec units, since $L = cT$, where T is the wave period. Thus $L = gT^2/2\pi$ or $L = 5 \cdot 12 T^2$.

At the other extreme when the water becomes very shallow relative to the wavelength, $\tanh 2\pi D/L$ approaches $2\pi D/L$ and the celerity becomes

$$c = \sqrt{(gD)}. \qquad (14.4)$$

Figures 14.1 and 14.2 show the relationship between the wave period, water depth and wavelength and celerity respectively.

The orbital motion of water particles is shown by theory and experiment to be elliptical. In deep water the ellipses tend to circles with the radius rapidly decreasing with depth below the surface. The horizontal and vertical displacements of a water

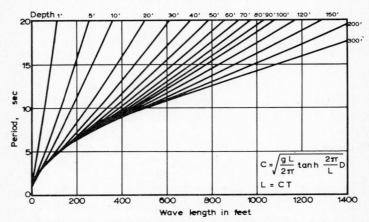

FIG. 14.1. Relationship between wave period, length and depth.

particle from its mean position, a distance y (negative downwards) from the surface of water at rest are

$$\left.\begin{aligned}
X &= \frac{H}{2}\frac{\cosh\left[(2\pi/L)(D+y)\right]}{\sinh\left(2\pi/L\right)D}\cos\left[2\pi\left(\frac{x}{L}-\frac{t}{T}\right)\right], \\
Y &= \frac{Y}{2}\frac{\sinh\left[(2\pi/L)(D+y)\right]}{\sinh\left(2\pi/L\right)D}\sin\left[2\pi\left(\frac{x}{L}-\frac{t}{T}\right)\right].
\end{aligned}\right\} \quad (14.5)$$

Hence the half-axes of the ellipse (amplitude of orbital motions) are

$$\left.\begin{aligned}
a &= \frac{H}{2}\frac{\cosh\left[(2\pi/L)(D+y)\right]}{\sinh\left(2\pi/L\right)D} \\
b &= \frac{H}{2}\frac{\sinh\left[(2\pi/L)(D+y)\right]}{\sinh\left(2\pi/L\right)D},
\end{aligned}\right\} \quad (14.6)$$

with the ratio of $b/a = \tanh\left[(2\pi/L)(D+y)\right]$.

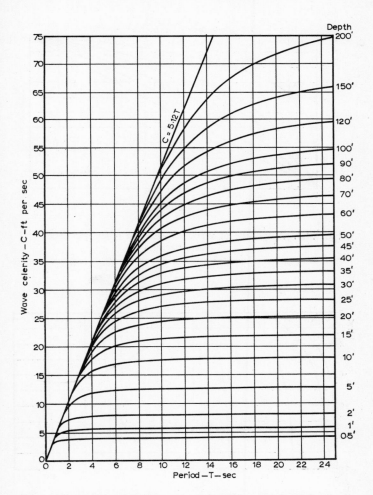

FIG. 14.2. Relationship between wave period, celerity and depth of water.

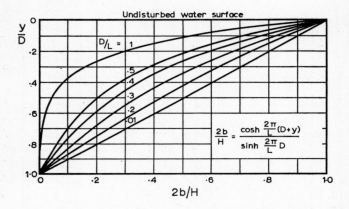

FIG. 14.3. Amplitude of vertical oscillation related to depth and wavelength.

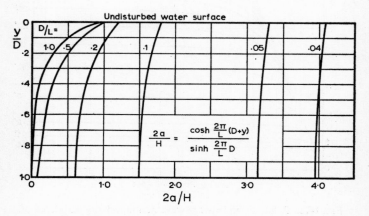

FIG. 14.4. Amplitude of horizontal oscillation related to depth and wavelength.

It is also seen that as the depth approaches infinity the half-axes both approach $(H/2)e^{(2\pi/L)y}$, and that the radius of the orbital circles in deep water decreases exponentially. Near the surface the orbital paths become nearly circular very rapidly as the depth D increases, but in water of finite depth these circles become

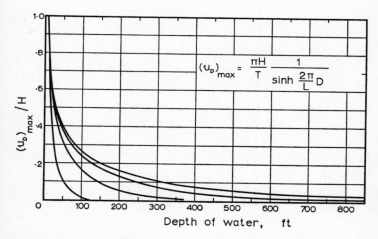

$$(u_p)_{max} = \frac{\pi H}{T} \frac{1}{\sinh \frac{2\pi}{L} D}$$

Fig. 14.5. Relationship between maximum velocity at the bottom per foot of wave height and the depth of water for various wave periods.

increasingly flatter ellipses with increasing distance y below the surface. At the bottom the vertical motion is zero and the water moves only back and forth horizontally. The amplitudes of the horizontal and vertical movements in terms of depth and wavelength are shown on Figs. 14.3 and 14.4.

The velocities of the water particles at an average position a distance y from the centre of the surface orbit are

$$u = \frac{\partial X}{\partial t} = \frac{\pi H \cosh\left[(2\pi/L)(D+y)\right]}{T \sinh (2\pi/L)D} \sin\left[2\pi\left(\frac{x}{L} - \frac{t}{T}\right)\right] \quad (14.7)$$

$$v = \frac{\partial Y}{\partial t} = \frac{-\pi H \sinh\left[(2\pi/L)(D+y)\right]}{T \sinh(2\pi/L)D} \cos\left[2\pi\left(\frac{x}{L}-\frac{t}{T}\right)\right]$$

(14.8)

with

$$u_{max} = \frac{\pi H \cosh\left[(2\pi/L)(D+y)\right]}{T \sinh(2\pi/L)D},$$ (14.9)

$$v_{max} = -\frac{\pi H \sinh\left[(2\pi/L)(D+y)\right]}{T \sinh(2\pi/L)D}.$$ (14.10)

and the average velocities over a half-cycle

$$\bar{u} = \pm \frac{2H \cosh\left[(2\pi/L)(D+y)\right]}{T \sinh(2\pi/L)D},$$ (14.11)

$$\bar{v} = \pm \frac{2H \sinh\left[(2\pi/L)(D+y)\right]}{T \sinh(2\pi/L)D}.$$ (14.12)

At the bottom only the horizontal component of the velocity remains:

$$u_D = \frac{\pi H}{T \sinh(2\pi/L)D} \sin\left[2\pi\left(\frac{x}{L}-\frac{t}{T}\right)\right],$$ (14.13)

$$(u_D)_{max} = \frac{\pi H}{T \sinh(2\pi/L)D},$$ (14.14)

$$\bar{u}_D = \pm \frac{2H}{T \sinh(2\pi/L)D} = \frac{2}{\pi}(u_D)_{max}.$$ (14.15)

The relationship for maximum velocity at the bottom is shown on Fig. 14.5.

These results neglect the viscous effects on the velocity at the immediate vicinity of the boundary.

It has been shown by experiment[1,2,3] that the theory for waves of small amplitude yields results which are sufficiently accurate, for engineering applications, for waves of appreciable height.

The irrotational theory for waves of finite height was developed by Stokes. It was shown that not until the third approximation is introduced does the wave celerity depart from that given by the first approximation for waves of small height. Stokes' results to the third approximation are:

$$c_s^2 = \frac{gL}{2\pi} \tanh \frac{2\pi}{L} D$$

$$\left\{ 1 + \left(\frac{\pi H}{L}\right)^2 \left[\frac{2\left(\cosh \frac{4\pi}{L} D\right)^2 + 2\left(\cosh \frac{4\pi}{L} D\right) + 5}{8\left(\sinh \frac{2\pi}{L} D\right)^4} \right] \right\} \quad (14.16)$$

yielding for deep water

$$c_0 = \sqrt{\left\{ \frac{gL_0}{2\pi} \left[1 + \left(\frac{\pi H_0}{L_0}\right)^2 \right] \right\}}, \quad (14.17)$$

where the subscript 0 signifies the deep water values.

The theory also shows that under the crest the actual particle orbit lies a little above an ellipse, is a little flatter than an ellipse in the trough and that the orbital path is not closed, but the particle moves slightly forward. This theory of Stokes takes into account that the velocity of a particle depends not only upon its mean position, but also upon its displacement from its mean position. Thus it is shown that the particle velocity is greater in its forward movement than in its backward movement with the trough. This results in a movement of water in the direction of the wave propagation. The net forward movement of water is called the mass transport. The expression for the instantaneous fluid particle velocity in the horizontal direction is[4]

$$u = -\frac{\pi H}{L} c \left[\frac{\cosh (2\pi/L)(D+y)}{\sinh (2\pi/L)D} \right] \cos \left[\frac{2\pi}{L}(x-ct) \right]$$

$$+ \left(\frac{\pi H}{L}\right)^2 \frac{c}{[\sinh (2\pi/L)D]^2} \cdot \left[-\frac{1}{2} + \frac{3}{4} \frac{\cosh (4\pi/L)(D+y)}{(\sinh (2/L)D)^2} \right] \cos$$

$$\left[\frac{4\pi}{L}(x-ct) \right] + \left(\frac{\pi H}{L}\right)^2 \frac{c}{2} \left[\frac{\cosh (4\pi/L)(D+y)}{(\sinh (2\pi/L)D)^2} \right], \quad (14.18)$$

where the origin of x is at the trough. Integration of this equation over a complete cycle yields the mass transport velocity.

$$\overline{U} = \frac{1}{T}\int_0^T u\,dt = \frac{1}{2}\left(\frac{\pi H}{L}\right)^2 c\left[\frac{\cosh(4\pi/L)(D+y)}{\sinh^2(2\pi/L)D}\right] \quad (14.19)$$

which for deep water becomes

$$\overline{U}_0 = \left(\frac{\pi H_0}{L_0}\right)^2 c_0 e^{(4\pi/L)y}. \quad (14.20)$$

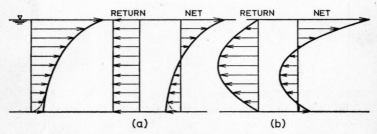

Fig. 14.6. Vertical distribution of mass transport velocity. Dotted lines indicate modification by boundary layer.

The total mass transport is given by

$$q = \int_0^D \overline{U}\,dy = H^2\frac{\sqrt{(\pi g/32L)}}{\sqrt{\tanh(2\pi/L)D}}. \quad (14.21)$$

Continuity requires a return flow of equal magnitude. If uniform return velocity distribution is assumed, then the resultant velocity distribution would be as shown on Fig. 14.6a.

Experimental evidence on the distribution of return flow is very limited, but it indicates a distribution with maximum velocity at mid-depth or possibly somewhat lower (Fig. 14.6b).

The resultant velocity distribution is also sensitive to the wave steepness. With long waves the picture is approximately as shown in Fig. 14.6. However, with steep waves the mass transport is more concentrated into the surface layer and is very small at the bed (Fig. 14.7).

Observations in a laboratory wind-wave tunnel show that with the asymmetrical wind waves the shoreward drift is even more concentrated in the surface layer and over the greater part of the depth from the bed up water is moving off-shore carrying beach material with it.

The foregoing theoretical velocity distribution equations have been developed from the irrotational flow theory. In a real fluid the no-slip boundary condition introduces a periodically varying bottom shear stress, τ_0, and a boundary layer is formed which modifies the velocity distribution in the vicinity of the boundary.

From the irrotational flow theory the local wavelength and wave height can be predicted by assuming that the expression for wave celerity derived for small wave heights on a horizontal bed is also valid on a sloping bed, and that no energy is lost through internal or bottom friction, or reflection from the beach.

Thus it is found that

$$\frac{L}{L_0} = \tanh \frac{2\pi}{L} D \qquad (14.22)$$

and

$$\frac{H}{H_0} = \left[\frac{\sinh (4\pi/L)D}{(4\pi/L)D + \sinh (4\pi/L)D} \frac{1}{\tanh (2\pi/L)D} \right]^{1/2} . \quad (14.23)$$

The ratio of these gives the transformation of wave steepness (Fig. 14.8 and Fig. 14.9) as

$$\frac{H}{L} \cdot \frac{L_0}{H_0} = \left[\frac{\sinh (4\pi/L)D}{(4\pi/L)D + \sinh (4\pi/L)D} \right]^{1/2} \left[\frac{1}{\tanh (2\pi/L)D} \right]^{3/2} .$$

$$(14.24)$$

Viscous damping and wave reflection modify these results. The viscous damping is important in very shallow water and in model studies.[5]

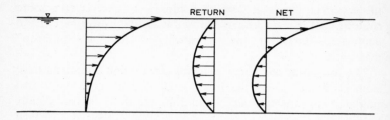

FIG. 14.7. Vertical distribution of mass transport velocity (steep waves).

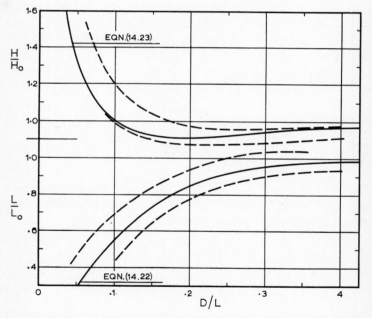

FIG. 14.8. Transformation of wave height and length in shoaling waves. Dotted lines indicate approximate limits of experimental results.

Near the breaker line the continuous wave form characteristics of deep water waves are lost. Individual waves become separated by long, flat troughs and resemble the mathematical concept of solitary wave; see, for example, Munk.[6]

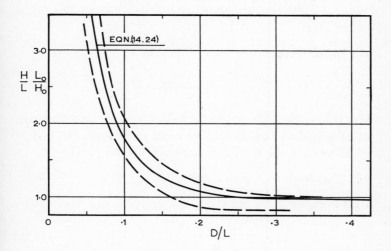

FIG. 14.9. Transformation of wave steepness in shoaling waves. Dotted lines indicate approximate limits of experimental results.

14.2. Theoretical Studies of the Sediment Motion

14.2.1. *Formulation of the analytical model*

As the waves move shorewards, a depth is eventually reached at which the fluid motion caused by waves reaches the bottom. Shoreward from this point the wave steepness, the water particle displacement and its velocity increase with decreasing depth. The oscillating "free stream" velocities can be calculated by the irrotational flow formulae, but the particle movement on the bed will also depend on whether the boundary layer is laminar, in transition or turbulent. At a depth depending on wave height and length, the oscillating fluid forces which act on a sediment particle on the bed will become strong enough to set it in motion.

The analytical models of sediment motion are of the same kind as those discussed when dealing with the particle entrainment in steady flow. The only difference is that the force equilibrium is more complicated in a time variable movement. The forces involved are:

$$\frac{4}{3}\pi r^2 = \frac{4}{3}\pi\left(\frac{d}{2}\right)^3 = \frac{\pi d^3}{6}$$

(1) Gravity force

$$F_G = \frac{\pi d^3}{6}\,\gamma(S_s - S) = (M_s - M)g, \tag{14.25}$$

where γ is the specific weight of fresh water, S_s and S are the specific gravities of solids and sea water respectively, M_s and M are the mass of the solid and displaced water respectively.

(2) Drag force F_D, which consists of:

(a) Form drag

$$F_F = C_1\,\frac{\rho}{2}\,\frac{\pi d^2}{4}\,(u_e - v_s)\,|u_e - v_s|. \tag{14.26}$$

Here u_e is the effective velocity usually assumed at particle crest level and v_s is the velocity of sediment particle, C_1 is the drag coefficient and its value is different for each flow pattern.

(b) Surface drag

$$F_s = C_2 d^2 \rho(u_e - v_s)\,|u_e - v_s|. \tag{14.27}$$

In a laminar boundary layer the drag coefficient over the upper surface of the sphere is

$$C \propto \left[\frac{(u_e - v_s)d}{\nu}\right]^{-1/2} \tag{14.28}$$

and

$$F_s = \,'_2 d^{3/2}\rho(u_e - v_s)^{3/2}\nu^{1/2}. \tag{14.29}$$

This force is likely to be at a small angle to the bed surface, but it may be reasonable to assume it parallel to the bed.

(3) Lift

$$F_L = C_L \rho \frac{\pi d^2}{8} (u_e - v_s)^2. \qquad (14.30)$$

This is augmented by a lift derived from Magnus effect when the particle rolls.

(4) Since the motion of the particle involves acceleration the virtual mass has to be considered, i.e. an added inertial effect arising from acceleration of some fluid mass with that of the particle

$$F_{vm} = C_3 \frac{\pi d^3}{6} \rho \left[\frac{du_e}{dt} - \frac{dv_s}{dt} \right] = C_M M \left[\frac{du_e}{dt} - \frac{dv_s}{dt} \right]. \quad (14.31)$$

The virtual mass coefficient will depend on the particle shape and on the proximity to the boundary.

(5) Pressure force on the particle due to the instantaneous pressure gradients under the wave. This is proportional to the inertia force of the fluid displaced

$$F_p = C_4 \frac{\pi d^3}{6} \rho \frac{du_e}{dt} = M \frac{du_0}{dt}, \qquad (14.32)$$

where u_0 refers to the potential flow velocities of wave motion.

(6) Inertia force

$$F_I = \rho S_s \frac{\pi d^3}{6} \frac{dv_s}{dt} \qquad (14.33)$$

is equal and opposite to the resultant of all external active forces on the particle.

(7) Reaction forces exist at each point of contact with the bed. These act through the point of application of the resultant external active force when the particle is at rest. With a spherical

particle of diameter d resting on a plain bed of spheres of diameter k there are three contact points. The reaction forces make an angle ϕ with the normal to the bed, and from geometry

$$\sin \phi = \frac{2}{\sqrt{3}(d/k+1)},$$

$$\tan \phi = \frac{2}{\sqrt{3}\sqrt{[(d/k)^2 + 2d/k - \frac{1}{3}]}}. \qquad (14.34)$$

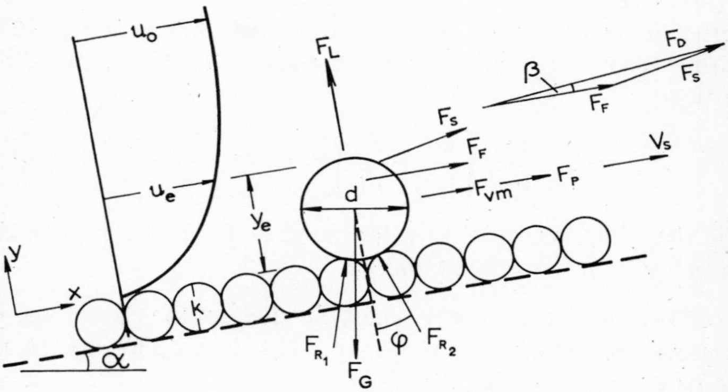

Fig. 14.10. Diagrammatic presentation of forces acting on a spherical particle.

(8) Resistance force due to rolling friction. This is proportional to the normal component of gravity and fluid forces acting on the particle. If ε is the coefficient of rolling friction, then

$$F_{rr} = \varepsilon[F_G \cos \alpha - F_D \sin \beta - F_L] \frac{v_s}{|v_s|}. \qquad (14.35)$$

Here β is the angle between the resultant of viscous resistance forces F_D and beach slope in radians.

Fig. 14.10 shows the instantaneous forces acting on a spherical particle.

The condition of *incipient motion* is given to the first approximation by assuming that the viscous resistance and apparent mass forces act through the upper edge of the particle and all other forces through the particle centre and taking moments about the point of bed particle contact. Thus

$$\Sigma M = 0 = \rho \frac{\pi d^3}{16} u_e^2 [C_D(1+\cos\phi)+C_L\sin\phi] +$$
$$\text{viscous resistance and lift}$$

$$+ \rho \frac{\pi d^4}{12} \left[C_M \frac{du_e}{dt}(1+\cos\phi)+\frac{du_0}{dt}\cos\phi \right] -$$
$$\text{virtual mass and pressure}$$

$$- \rho \frac{\pi d^4}{12} g \left(\frac{S_s}{S}-1 \right) \sin(\alpha+\phi). \qquad (14.36)$$
$$\text{gravity}$$

Here the viscous normal force $F_D \sin \beta$ and the non-viscous normal force F_L are combined in terms of a lift coefficient C_L.

The equation of motion for *established sediment movement* is obtained by writing the equilibrium equation for all forces involved in the direction of motion. Assuming waves of normal incidence to the beach and that the sediment particle is in motion throughout the entire wave cycle and assuming all forces to be parallel to the bed, then the equilibrium requirement yields

$$\Sigma F_x = 0 = M\frac{du_0}{dt}+ {}_M M\left[\frac{du_e}{dt}-\frac{dv_s}{dt} \right]+$$
$$\text{pressure} \qquad \text{virtual mass}$$

$$+ C_D \frac{\pi d^2}{4}\frac{\rho}{2}(u_e-v_s)\,|u_e-v_s| -$$
$$\text{drag (form + surface)}$$

$$- g(M_s-M)\sin\alpha - \varepsilon[F_G\cos\alpha - F_D\sin\beta - F_L]\frac{v_s}{|v_s|}$$
$$\text{gravity} \qquad\qquad\qquad \text{rolling resistance}$$

$$- M_s\frac{dv_s}{dt}. \qquad (14.37)$$
$$\text{inertia}$$

14.2.2. *Established sediment motion*

Eagleson and Dean[7, 8] investigated established sediment motion formulated by eqn. (14.37). The following assumptions were made:

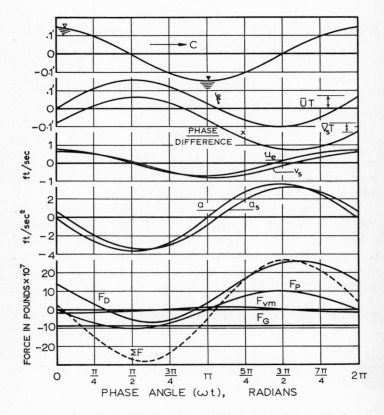

FIG. 14.11. Theoretical kinematics and force history for a particular condition. Here ξ is the displacement of water particle from its mean orbital position parallel to beach near bottom, otherwise horizontal, and x is particle motion parallel to the beach slope. (By permission from ref. 8.)

(1) The drag force and the bottom frictional force are both linear functions of the relative instantaneous velocity $(u_e - v_s)$.

(2) Convective accelerations of the sediment particles are negligible.

(3) The elevation at which the instantaneous velocity and acceleration are applied is independent of time.

(4) The instantaneous fluid particle velocities at the edge of the boundary layer and within the boundary layer at an effective elevation are given by

$$u_0 = \omega A_0 \sin \omega t + 2\omega B_0 \sin 2\omega t + E_0 \qquad (14.38a)$$

and

$$u_e = A \sin \omega t + B \sin 2\omega t + P \cos \omega t + Q \cos 2\omega t + E \qquad (14.38b)$$

respectively. Here $\omega = 2\pi/T$; A, B, P, Q, and E are coefficients associated with wave kinematic properties and are independent of time, and $\omega t = \pi/2$ under the wave crest.

(5) The coefficient of apparent mass C_M is independent of time.

The approximate values of the various terms in the linearized form of eqn. (14.37) were plotted[8] against the phase angle and are shown in Fig. 14.11. This shows the predominance of drag and pressure components over most of the cycle. However, the results depend largely on the phase lag between the fluid and sediment. The phase lag increases with increasing mass of the sediment and this leads to predominance of drag and virtual mass. As the immersed weight of the particles approaches zero all terms except pressure and inertia go to zero also. For the chosen conditions (Fig. 14.11) the net sediment motion is negative, i.e. in offshore direction. Integration of the linearized form of eqn. (14.37) over one wave cycle yields the net sediment velocity

$$\bar{V}_s = \frac{1}{T} \int_t^{t+T} v_s dt = N_9 + \frac{C_2}{N_1 T} e^{-N_1 t} [e^{-N_1 t} - 1], \qquad (14.39)$$

where the numerical constants[8] relate the effects of drag co-efficient, rolling friction coefficient, coefficient of virtual mass, wave kinematic properties, and phase angle. The lift force is taken to be zero. This solution consists of a transient part, the contribution of which decreases exponentially with time, and a steady state part which is essentially independent of the initial boundary conditions. The steady state part becomes

$$\bar{V}_s = E - \left(\frac{M_s - M}{G + G^1}\right) g \sin \alpha. \qquad (14.40)$$

Here

$$F_D = \text{const.} \left[\frac{(u_e - v_s)d}{v}\right]^{-1} \rho \frac{\pi d^2}{8} (u_e - v_s)^2 = G(u_e - v_s) \qquad (14.41)$$

and the rolling resistance force

$$F_{rr} = G^1(u_e - v_s) = C_R \rho \frac{\pi d^2}{8} (u_e - v_s)^2. \qquad (14.42)$$

The term E represents the residual of the instantaneous effective velocities integrated over a complete cycle. But this is the corresponding mass transport velocity, so that

$$E = \bar{U}_e = \frac{1}{T} \int_t^{t+T} u_e dt. \qquad (14.43)$$

Thus is obtained

$$\underbrace{C_D \rho \frac{\pi d^2}{8} (\bar{U}_e - \bar{V}_s)^2}_{\text{drag}} + \underbrace{C_R \rho \frac{\pi d^2}{8} (\bar{U}_e - \bar{V}_s)^2}_{\text{bottom resistance}} = \underbrace{g(M_s - M) \sin \alpha.}_{\text{gravity}} \qquad (14.44)$$

Here both $\bar{U}_e$ and $\bar{V}_s$ are the residues of integration over a complete cycle of much higher instantaneous velocities and are not in themselves dynamically important. Both are what was previously termed mass transport velocities. For application the values of $\bar{U}_e$, $\bar{V}_s$, C_0 and C_R have to be determined experimentally for a given beach, sediment and wave.

At M.I.T. extensive experimental studies were carried out to check the theory discussed above and to determine values of the constants involved. In this work the conditions of incipient motion and of established sediment movement were considered.

It is not difficult to see from eqns. (14.37) and (14.40) that the net sediment velocity may be positive, negative or zero so that three regions of established motion may be expected. Ippen and Eagleson[9] developed criteria for the "null point" of the net sediment velocity; that is, where there is no net movement either shorewards or offshore. In this region of zero net sediment velocity the hydrodynamic forces, taken on average over a complete cycle of motion, balance the component of weight of the particle down the beach slope. Shoreward of this equilibrium region the particle motion is onshore and seaward it is offshore. In the zone of offshore motion the average effect on particle motion of the hydrodynamic forces is smaller than that of the component of the submerged particle weight and vice versa in the shoreward region. Their analysis leads to the following relationship for the null point

$$\left(\frac{H}{D}\right)^2 \frac{c}{w} = \text{const.} \left[\frac{C_{Dss}}{C_D + eC_L}\right]^{1/2} [\sqrt{(e\cos\alpha + \sin\alpha)} -$$

$$- \sqrt{(e\cos\alpha - \sin\alpha)}]. \qquad (14.45)$$

Here w is the terminal velocity of fall of sediment particles in fresh water,

C_D is a drag coefficient and

C_{Dss} is a drag coefficient for steady state conditions,

C_L is a lift coefficient,

$$e = \tan\phi = \frac{2}{\sqrt{3}}\left\{\frac{1}{(d/2k) + \sqrt{[(d/k)^2 + 2(d/k) - \frac{1}{3}]}}\right\}$$

and is analogous to eqn. (14.34); here the resultant of hydrodynamic forces is assumed to pass through the uppermost point of the particle.

By experiment this relationship for the null point was found to be satisfied by a single line

$$\left(\frac{H}{D}\right)^2 \frac{c}{w} = 11\cdot6\,\frac{H}{L} \tag{14.46}$$

or

$$\frac{H}{D} = 3\cdot4\left[\frac{H}{L}\frac{w}{c}\right]^{1/2}, \tag{14.47}$$

irrespective of the values of d/k and δ/y_e (Fig. 14.12).

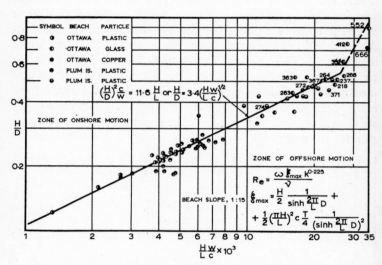

Fig. 14.12. Correlation of sediment motion data; "null" point or point of zero net sediment velocity. Numbers adjacent to experimental points are $Re \times 10^{-2}$. The break in the line is at approximately $Re = 3 \times 10^4$. (From ref. 9, by permission of the U.S. Army Corps of Engineers, Coastal Engineering Research Center.)

An example of the results of laboratory measurement[8] of the net sediment velocity and the net mass transport velocity is shown on Fig. 14.13. This figure shows the three regions of sediment movement. It also shows the variation of the average

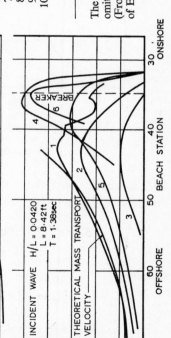

Fig. 14.13. Typical variations in net sediment and water particle velocity with position on the beach. Beach stations at 0·5 ft spacing measured parallel to the bed. Still-water level intersects with beach at station 21.5. Beach slope 1 : 14·8. The numbers at curves denote the following combinations of k and d.

No.	k (mm)	d (mm)	Material	Specific gravity
1	0·79	2·0	Plastic	1·29
2	0·79	3·17	Plastic	1·28
3	0·79	3·0	Plastic	2·44
4	1·83	2·0	Plastic	1·29
5	1·83	3·17	Plastic	1·29
6	1·83	4·0	Glass	2·17
7	Smooth	5·0	Plastic	1·24
8	Smooth	3·0	Glass	2·44
9	Smooth	6·0	Glass	2·12
10	Smooth	3·0		Neutral buoyancy

The curves show mean lines; the observed points are omitted. Velocities are positive in the onshore direction. (From ref. 9, by permission of the U.S. Army Corps of Engineers, Coastal Engineering Research Center.)

net sediment velocity $\bar{V}_s$ and the average mass transport velocity $\bar{U}_e$ along the beach profile. These are important terms in eqn (14.44).

The Stokian irrotational theory of wave motion does not give correct mass transport velocities in the bottom boundary layer.

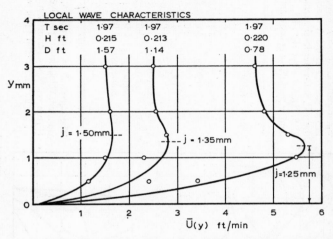

FIG. 14.14. Sample distribution of net fluid velocity within the boundary layer on a smooth bottom. (From ref. 7, p. 64, by permission of the American Society of Civil Engineers.)

Within the boundary layer the theoretical mass transport velocity is given by Longuet-Higgins[10] as

$$2\frac{\overline{U}_{(y)}}{\overline{U}_0} = 5 - 8e^{-(\pi/\nu T)^{1/2}y} \cos\left[(\pi/\nu T)^{1/2}y\right] + 3e^{-(2\pi/\nu T)^{1/2}y} = \Phi$$

(14.48)

where

$$\overline{U}_0 = \frac{1}{2}\left(\pi\frac{H}{L}\right)^2 \frac{c}{\sinh^2(2\pi D/L)}.$$

(14.49)

Net mass transport velocity distributions, as measured by Eagleson and Dean,[7] are shown on Fig. 14.14.

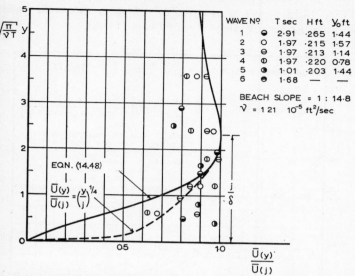

FIG. 14.15. Distribution of net fluid velocity within the boundary layer on a smooth bottom. (From ref. 7, p. 65, by permission of the American Society of Civil Engineers.)

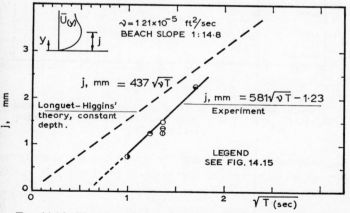

FIG. 14.16. Elevation of maximum mass transport velocity within the boundary layer on a smooth bottom. (From ref. 7, p. 67, by permission of the American Society of Civil Engineers.)

Fig. 14.15 shows a comparison of these measured value
with the theoretical values given by eqn. (14.48).

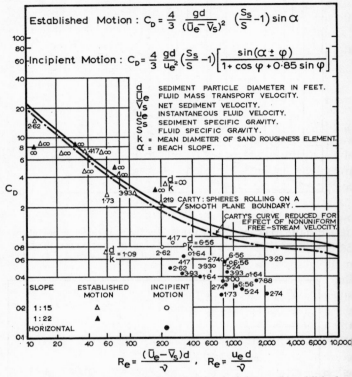

FIG. 14.17. Resistance coefficients defining incipient and established
motion. (From ref. 7, p. 69, by permission of the American Society
of Civil Engineers.)

The ordinate $y = j$ at which the maximum net velocity wa
observed is compared with that given by theory, that is

$$j = 1\cdot30\sqrt{(\nu T)} \qquad (14.5$$

and the comparison is shown on Fig. 14.16.

The two lines appear to approach each other with increasing wave period. At lower values of the wave period, however, the discrepancy between theory and observation is quite pronounced. Neither is it at present clear how these values are affected by varying bottom roughness.

Combining the effect of drag and bottom resistance reduces eqn. (14.44) to

$$C_D \rho \, \frac{\pi d^2}{8} (\overline{U}_e - \overline{V}_s)^2 = F_G \sin \alpha. \qquad (14.51)$$

Values of this combined drag coefficient C_D were calculated[8] by using experimental data in eqn. (14.51). Only the data seaward of the point of inflection on Fig. 14.13 were used because of the action of forces not included in eqn. (14.51). The results are shown on Fig. 14.17 and compared with Carty's resistance coefficients for spheres (Fig. 14.18).

Carty (unpublished B.S. Thesis, M.I.T., 1957) studied the drag on spheres by letting these roll on an inclined plane submerged in still fluid. The relative tangential velocity of the centre of the particle was used as the particle velocity. This form of rolling motion causes a negative dynamic lift (downwards) opposing that caused by circulation arising from viscous flow past the sphere. When applied to problems of viscous flow past boundaries composed of spherical particles errors are introduced by this downward force caused by rotation and by the non-uniform distribution of actual velocity near the bed. Figure 14.18 shows a correction for the non-uniform velocity distribution, but the effect of rotation is neglected and assumed to be very small.

On Fig. 14.17 the calculated points are identified in terms of d/k. It is seen that for high values of d/k, that is for conditions approaching a smooth boundary, the agreement with the theoretical curve is good. It is also seen that for a given value of Reynolds number C_D decreases as d/k decreases, that is as the roughness of the surface increases. This result is to be expected because with increasing roughness the size of the intergranular hollows increases; the uppermost particles settle into these hollows and become increasingly more sheltered. The decreasing C_D values seem to suggest that net sediment velocities over rough surfaces are lower than predicted.

It is predicted that for the range of interest

$$C_D = \frac{19 \cdot 2}{\text{Re}} \qquad (14.52)$$

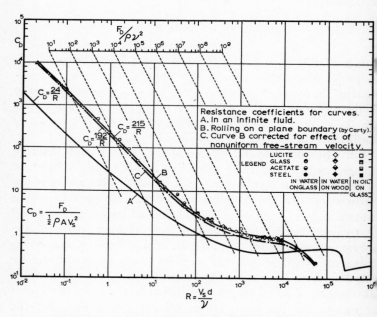

FIG. 14.18. Resistance coefficients for spheres. (From ref. 8, by permission of the U.S. Army Corps of Engineers, Coastal Engineering Research Center.)

and $d/k = 1$ is an acceptable approximation for natural beaches. Introduction of this value of C_D into eqn. (14.51) yields for the equilibrium at the null point where $\bar{V}_s = 0$

$$\frac{gd^2}{v\,\overline{U}_e}\left(\frac{S_s}{S}-1\right)\sin\alpha = 14 \cdot 4 \qquad (14.53)$$

or with $S_s = 2 \cdot 65$, $S = 1 \cdot 03$ and $v = 1 \cdot 45 \times 10^{-5}$ ft^2/sec

$$d^2 \sin \alpha = 4 \cdot 13 \times 10^{-6} \bar{U}_e. \tag{14.54}$$

Eagleson and Dean[7] replaced the Longuet-Higgins expression [eqn. (14.48)] near the bed of natural beaches by the approximation

$$(\pi/vT)^{1/2} y = 0 \cdot 32 \Phi^{7/8}. \tag{14.55}$$

Thus

$$\Phi = 2 \frac{\bar{U}_{(y)}}{\bar{U}_0} = 3 \cdot 68 [\sqrt{(\pi/vT)} y]^{8/7}. \tag{14.56}$$

On a very rough bottom with $d/k = 1$ the lower part of the particle is partially embedded and the fluid velocities around this lower part should be small. Therefore, it is assumed that $\bar{U}_{(y)} = \bar{U}_e$ when $y = d$; that is, the effective fluid velocity acts at the upper edge of the particle. This yields for the equilibrium conditions

$$d^2 \sin \alpha = 7 \cdot 60 \times 10^{-6} [\sqrt{(\pi/vT)} d]^{8/7} \bar{U}_0$$

or

$$d^{6/7} \sin \alpha = 7 \cdot 60 \times 10^{-6} [\sqrt{(\pi/vT)}]^{8/7} \bar{U}_0. \tag{14.57}$$

Here d is measured in feet and $\bar{U}_0$ in feet per second. U_0 is defined by eqn. (14.49).

This relationship for $\bar{V}_s = 0$ between particle size, beach slope and local wave characteristics rests on the assumption that the equilibrium condition of established sediment motion is the controlling mechanism.

14.2.3. Incipient sediment motion

Eagleson and Dean[7,8] also studied the condition where the remaining particle size at all locations cannot be moved by the maximum local instantaneous fluid velocity. It is assumed that the incipient motion occurs for a given d/k, F_G and $\sin \alpha$ at the wave phase angle at which the hydrodynamic portion of the moment given by eqn. (14.36) has its maximum value.

The fluid velocity distribution near the bottom is taken to be

$$u_e = \frac{H}{2} \frac{2\pi/T}{\sinh{(2\pi/L)D}} \{\sin\theta - e^{-(\pi/\nu T)^{1/2}y}\sin[\theta - (\pi/\nu T)^{1/2}]\}$$

(14.58)

as given by Lamb[11] for long waves. Here θ is the phase angle in radians with the origin 90° behind the wave crest.

Equation (14.58) and its first time derivatives are substituted into eqn. (14.36) and it is assumed that

$$\left.\begin{array}{l} u = u_e \quad \text{when } y = d, \\[2mm] \dfrac{du}{dt} = \dfrac{du_e}{dt} \quad \text{when } y = d. \end{array}\right\}$$

(14.59)

Differentiation with respect to θ yields for the location of the maximum hydrodynamic moment

$$\frac{d\Sigma M}{d\theta} = 0 = \frac{d}{d\theta}\left\{\frac{3}{4}\frac{u_e^2}{(2\pi/T)d}[C_D(1+\cos\phi)+C_L\sin\phi] + \right.$$

$$\left. + C_M\frac{du_e}{d\theta}(1+\cos\phi) + \frac{du_0}{d\theta}\cos\phi\right\}.$$

(14.60)

The authors assume that C_M is equal to 0·6 for a sphere on a smooth plane boundary in potential flow[12] and C_L is equal to 0·85C_D.[13] Then it is found that:

(1) If C_D is assumed constant at the appropriate value, determined for established motion at a high Reynolds number, then the drag and lift forces predominate for all $(\pi/\nu T)^{1/2}d$ and the phase angle for incipient motion is close to 90°.

(2) If C_D is assumed inversely proportional to Reynolds number, at a value determined for established motion at low Reynolds number, then for large values of $(\pi/\nu T)^{1/2}d$ inertia forces predominate and the phase angle of maximum force is close to 0°. For small $(\pi/\nu T)^{1/2}d$ drag and lift forces predominate as above.

By assuming that all accelerative effects may be ignored and C_L is equal to $0.85C_D$ the authors obtain from eqn. (14.36)

$$C_D = \frac{4}{3} \frac{gd}{u_e^2} \left(\frac{S_s}{S} - 1\right) \left[\frac{\sin(\alpha \pm \phi)}{1 + \cos\phi + 0.85\sin\phi}\right], \quad (14.61)$$

where u_e is determined from eqns. (14.58) and (14.59) for $\theta = 270°$ or $90°$ depending on whether initial motion is in the offshore or onshore direction.

For small values of $(\pi/vT)^{1/2}d$ an approximate value of u_e is given by

$$u_e = 0.86 \frac{H}{2} \frac{2\pi/T}{\sinh(2\pi/L)D}(\pi/vT)^{1/2}d \ \Bigg\} \quad (14.62)$$

for
$$0.01 < (\pi/vT)^{1/2}d < 1.0.$$

Substituting eqns. (14.52) and (14.62) into eqn. (14.61) yields

$$\frac{gd\pi H}{vT(\pi/vT)^{1/2}\sinh(2\pi/L)D}\left(\frac{S_s}{S} - 1\right)\left[\frac{\sin(\alpha \pm \phi)}{1 + \cos\phi + 0.85\sin\phi}\right] =$$
$$= 12.4. \quad (14.63)$$

For sand in sea water

$$\frac{d}{(\pi/vT)^{1/2}}\sin(\alpha \pm 0.92) = 8.1 \times 10^{-6}\frac{\pi H}{T\sinh(2\pi/L)D}, \quad (14.64)$$

where an experimental value is substituted for $\tan\phi$ for the condition that $d/k = 1$.

This is a relationship between particle size, beach slope and local wave characteristics resting on the assumption that the condition of incipient motion is the controlling mechanism. The above analytical approach to the problem of incipient motion does not include the effect of beach permeability. Flow into the sand under the wave crest will make the bed more stable. Flow out of the bed under the wave trough will reduce the particle stability and may turn the bed temporarily into quicksand.

K*

14.2.4. *The beach profile*

Eagleson, Glenne and Dracup[14] extended the preceding theoretical work. They included the effect of local wave characteristics, in terms of deep water values, and also the effect of wave reflection. The extended analysis yields expressions for particle size and for the beach profile, two for each, based on the assumption that either the incipient conditions of motion or the oscillating established motion conditions control the phenomenon. Although in many respects oversimplified, the work is a significant contribution to the analytical formulation of the beach equilibrium problem. The development follows on the elementary analytical treatment discussed above. For brevity, only the final results are quoted here. These are as follows:

(1) Incipient particle size

$$d_i = 258 \cdot 7 \, \frac{v^{1/2} H_0}{T^{3/2} g} \left(\frac{S}{S_s - S} \right) \frac{f_2(D/L_0)}{\sin \alpha + \tan \phi} \, (1 - R). \quad (14.65)$$

(ii) Equilibrium particle size

$$d_e = \left[6 \cdot 81 \, \frac{H_0^2 N v (1 - R)^2}{g T L_0} \left(\frac{S}{S_s - S} \right) \frac{f_1(D/L_0)}{\sin \alpha} \right]^{7/6} \left[\frac{\pi}{v T} \right]^{2/3}$$

valid for $d_e < d_i$. $\qquad\qquad\qquad\qquad\qquad\qquad\qquad$ (14.66)

Here

$$f_2(D/L_0) = \left[\frac{2\pi D}{L} \tanh^2 \frac{2\pi D}{L} + \sinh^2 \frac{2\pi D}{L} \tanh \frac{2\pi D}{L} \right]^{-1/2},$$

R is the reflection coefficient and equals the ratio of reflected wave height to incident wave height, N is a constant in

$$C_D = \frac{N}{\text{Re}} \doteqdot \frac{19 \cdot 2}{u_e d/v}$$

when

$$d/k = 1$$

$$\tan \phi \doteqdot 1 \cdot 3.$$

(iii) Slope, controlled by incipient conditions

$$\sin \alpha = -\frac{d(D)}{dx} = d_i f_2(D/L_0) - \tan \phi. \qquad (14.67)$$

(iv) Slope, controlled by established motion conditions

$$\sin \alpha = -\frac{d(D)}{dx} = \frac{K}{J} f_1(D/L_0). \qquad (14.68)$$

Here

$$\frac{K}{J} = 6 \cdot 81 \frac{H_0^2 N v (1-R^2)}{g L_0 T d^2} \left[\frac{\pi d^2}{v T} \right]^{4/7} \left(\frac{S}{S_s - S} \right)$$

and

$$f_1(D/L_0) = \frac{\coth^2 (2\pi D/L)}{\sinh^2 (2\pi D/L) + (2\pi D/L_0)}.$$

The last one can be replaced by an approximate expression

$$f_1(D/L_0) \doteqdot g_1(D/L_0) = \frac{0 \cdot 01335}{(d/L_0)^2} - \frac{0 \cdot 0161}{D/L_0}.$$

Substitution of this into eqn. (14.68) facilitates integration, yielding

$$\frac{x}{L_0} = 42 \cdot 73 \frac{J}{K} \left[\ln (0 \cdot 01335 - 0 \cdot 0161 D/L_0) + 0 \cdot 7271 \left(\frac{D}{L_0} \right)^2 + \right.$$
$$\left. + 1 \cdot 206 \frac{D}{L_0} - 1 \cdot 50 \right]_{(D/L_0)max}^{(D/L_0)x}. \qquad (14.69)$$

Assuming an initial beach profile and an incident wave form which are not in equilibrium, then the boundary conditions at the seaward extreme of the profile modification are interpreted as:

(a) The point of incipient motion. If sand size and beach slope are constant an "incipient depth" value could be calculated. If the incipient point is shoreward of the equilibrium point then the slope will be discontinuous at this point. This is because seaward of the incipient point D/L_0 is determined from eqn.

(14.67) with $\alpha = \alpha_0$, whereas shorewards of this point the slope has to satisfy eqn. (14.68) for the established motion. Here α_0 is the constant undisturbed beach slope.

(b) The point of established motion, with the incipient point seaward of it. By neglecting the offshore sediment movement as small this point is approximately given by putting $\alpha = \alpha_0$ in eqn. (14.68).

Laboratory studies showed that eqn. (14.67) yielded very steep slopes which were not in keeping with observation.

Equations (14.65) and (14.66), however, have been found useful for predicting the depth at which profile modification begins. Knowing sand size and original slope α_0 an "incipient depth D_i" and an "equilibrium depth D_e" may be calculated for a given wave. It was found that if $D_i > D_e$ the beach formed a steep profile, and if $D_i < D_e$ the beach developed a flat profile by digging into the initial slope. This classification of the form of beach profile was found to correspond with the empirical criterion of $H_0/L_0 > 0.025$ and $H_0/L_0 < 0.025$ respectively.

The theoretical beach profiles [eqns. (14.68) or (14.69)] were found to be in qualitative agreement with the observed ones in the offshore region, sufficiently far from the breakers. The calculated profile was still steeper than the observed profile. Maximum observed error was 40 per cent for a given depth near the offshore bar. The authors suggested that this overestimate of the slope may have been caused by the actual mass transport velocities being smaller than predicted by the theory. Here it is also necessary to realize that usually the sand bed in this offshore region is covered by ripples, which give rise to an additional resistance to motion (see Chapter 13). How the mass transport velocity is affected by the ripples is, at present, not known.

14.2.5. Sediment sorting

As the given wave moves shorewards into shallowing water the maximum local instantaneous fluid velocity increases. The shoaling wave can move an increasingly larger proportion of the finer particles. Once the initial sorting process is completed the remaining median particle size—offshore of the breakers—will increase along the beach profile as the depth decreases. The maximum particle size is found in the breaker region, that is the region of maximum turbulence. This means that on an equilibrium profile the beach material will be well sorted and the sand size for which the net transport is zero will predominate at any given location. Inman,[15] for example, observed that on a natural beach in equilibrium the median size decreases in the offshore direction and that the skewness of the local size distribution changes from negative to positive in the same direction.

It has to be kept in mind that a natural beach adjusts its slope and sand size by sand transport so that for a given wave the local slope and sand size satisfy equilibrium conditions. Outside the offshore bars the equilibrium profile is concave upwards. Also, towards the breaker line the sorting of beach material is more and more counteracted by deposition of suspended sand. This sand is entrained in the breaker zone and is carried seawards by the return flow.

From the preceding theory the criterion of incipient motion implies increasing slope for a constant sand size or for a constant slope an increasing sand size in the onshore direction.

The direction and quantity of the net movement of sand in terms of the established sediment motion criterion depends on the relative magnitude of the opposing force components parallel to the local beach slope; the gravitational force and the net average of the resultant fluid force over a wave cycle. If a stable state with $\bar{V}_s = 0$ exists simultaneously at all points on the beach, then both the slope and grain size increase in the onshore direction.

Eagleson, Glenne and Dracup[14] also considered the problem of sediment sorting and discussed it in terms of the parameters d_i and d_e as follows.

Assume that the original beach sand had a unimodal sand size distribution and that the beach has reached an equilibrium profile for the given waves. In the process the original size frequency distribution has changed at all points along the profile. The authors reason that the final shape of the local size frequency distribution curve is a function of the local ratio of d_e to d_i (the equilibrium particle size to incipient particle size).

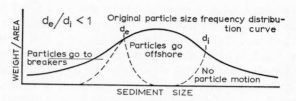

FIG. 14.19. Theoretical sorting of beach material for $d_i > d_e$. (From ref. 8, by permission of the U.S. Army Corps of Engineers, Coastal Engineering Research Center.)

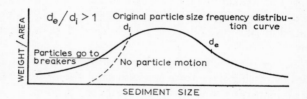

FIG. 14.20. Theoretical sorting of beach material for $d_i < d_e$. (From ref. 8, by permission of the U.S. Army Corps of Engineers, Coastal Engineering Research Center.)

If $d_e/d_i < 1$ the final size frequency distribution on the off-shore profile should be bimodal (Fig. 14.19).

The first peak in distribution corresponds to the oscillating equilibrium particle size, and occurs because particles smaller than d_e move towards the breakers while the larger ones move seawards.

The second peak occurs because the fluid forces cannot move particles larger than the incipient size.

If $d_e/d_i > 1$, the distribution should remain unimodal (Fig. 14.20).

Particles smaller than d_i move towards the breakers, but particles larger than d_i cannot be moved by the fluid forces and remain. This case with d_e larger than d_i could be visualized as a situation where the particles larger than d_i, once in motion, are maintained in an oscillating equilibrium.

Furthermore, since both these characteristic sizes increase with decreasing depth, the size frequency distribution curve should move bodily in the direction of larger particle sizes.

Experimental evidence for the above theory is limited and provides only weak qualitative support.

14.2.6. Some additional methods of approach to the sediment movement problem

This introduction to the theory of sediment movement by water waves will not be complete without reference to methods different from the preceding one. But neither would an attempt to discuss all the theoretical and empirical studies be in keeping with the aim of concentrating the reader's attention on the elementary basic principles of the subject. Therefore, only a few additional methods are reviewed below.

Manohar[16] emphasizes that the movement of sediment takes place in a boundary layer that is developed at the bottom by the action of viscous forces. He started from eqn. (14.13) which is an equation of simple harmonic motion of the form

$$u = a\omega \sin \left(\frac{2\pi}{L} x - \omega t\right), \qquad (14.70)$$

where

$$a = \frac{H}{2} \frac{1}{\sinh (2\pi/L)D} \quad \text{and} \quad \omega = \frac{2\pi}{T}.$$

With surface waves of large wavelength this can be written as

$$u = u_0 \sin \omega t, \qquad (14.71)$$

where

$$u_0 = \omega a.$$

A plane lower boundary is assumed to be oscillating with this velocity in an otherwise still fluid. This is in order to by-pass the difficulty of model scales for experimental work when modelling for both gravity and viscous effects.

For the assumed two-dimensional incompressible flow problem the Navier–Stokes equations (equations of motion) reduce to

$$\frac{\partial u}{\partial t} = v \frac{\partial^2 u}{\partial y^2} \qquad (14.72)$$

when the non-linear terms are neglected and u is assumed to be a function of y and t only. At $y = 0$, $u = u_0 \sin \omega t$ and the solution is

$$u = u_0 e^{-(\omega/2v)^{1/2}y} \sin \left[\omega t - (\omega/2v)^{1/2}y\right]. \qquad (14.73)$$

Equation (14.73) represents a velocity distribution in a laminar boundary layer above an oscillating surface. The transverse vibrations are propagated into the fluid from the boundary with a velocity of $\omega/(\omega/2v)^{1/2} = (2v\omega)^{1/2}$ and with rapidly diminishing amplitude. At $(\omega/2v)^{1/2}y = 4\cdot6$ the amplitude of the oscillatory velocity is about 1 per cent of that of the boundary. This is taken by Li[17] as the boundary layer thickness and is also used here

$$\delta_1 = \frac{4\cdot6}{(\omega/2v)^{1/2}} = 6\cdot5(v/\omega)^{1/2}. \qquad (14.74)$$

Three cases are considered as follows:

(1) $\delta_1 >>> k$
(2) $\delta_1 >> k$
(3) $\delta_1 > k$

In the first case the laminar sublayer thickness is so much larger than the height of the roughness elements that the oscillating bottom acts as a hydraulically smooth one. For this case a Reynolds number is defined as

$$\mathrm{Re}_{\delta_1} = \frac{u_0 \delta_1}{v} = \mathrm{const.} \; \frac{(\sqrt{\omega})a}{\sqrt{v}}. \qquad (14.75)$$

With increasing height relative to the boundary layer thickness the effect of roughness on the flow also increases and the bed can be no longer considered to be smooth. The Reynolds number is now defined as

$$\text{Re}_k = \frac{\omega ak}{v}. \tag{14.76}$$

With still larger roughness formation of wakes and separation takes place at individual roughness elements. For this case the Reynolds number could be expressed as

$$\text{Re}_{f(k)} = \frac{\omega af(k)}{v}. \tag{14.77}$$

Inside the laminar boundary layer only the tangential drag force and the weight force are assumed to act. Using a packing coefficient p_1, defined as d^2 times the number of grains per unit area in the top layer of bed, the applied fluid force on each particle is $\tau d^2/p_1$. The critical condition for incipient motion is

$$\tau_c = \alpha_1 p_1 A_2(\rho_s - \rho)gd \tan \phi = \alpha_1 p_2(\rho_s - \rho)gd \tan \phi, \tag{14.78}$$

where α_1 is a constant depending upon the point of action of the drag force, A_2 is a coefficient defining grain volume, $p_2 = p_1 A_2$. The incipient motion is assumed to occur when

$$\tau_0 = \mu \frac{\partial u}{\partial y} \bigg|_{y=0}$$

is maximum. Thus from eqn. (14.73)

$$\tau_{0(\max)} = \mu v^{-1/2} \omega^{3/2} a. \tag{14.79}$$

Equating to the value of τ_c and solving for ω yields the critical value of angular velocity for condition of incipient motion in the laminar boundary layer

$$\omega_c = \left[\frac{\alpha_1 p_2(\rho_s - \rho)gd \tan \phi}{a\rho v^{1/2}} \right]^{2/3}. \tag{14.80}$$

General movement is defined as the movement of the entire top layer of grains and should also be given by the above equation if the value of $\alpha_1 p_2$ is increased.

Taking moments about the point of particle support and equating the moment due to lift and drag to that due to gravity and combining the coefficients of lift and drag into one function of (ud/v) yields a dimensionless ratio

$$\psi_1 = \frac{b_1 \rho u^2 f(ud/v)}{(\rho_s - \rho)gd}. \tag{14.81}$$

This is the ratio of the weight of a submerged particle to lift force acting on the particle (incorporating drag as less significant), and is the same as the term ψ in the Einstein bed-load function.

Equation (14.73) is extended to yield a solution of the same kind for turbulent flow by replacing the kinematic viscosity by the kinematic eddy viscosity ε. This ignores that ε is not a property of the fluid but varies from point to point as a function of turbulence characteristics. The resulting analytical argument therefore is not physically significant and cannot be taken to explain the mechanism of the phenomenon. However, the data presented in terms of the dimensionless numbers are interesting and provide valuable guidance for future work.

The transition from laminar to turbulent boundary layer was determined experimentally. The results are shown on Fig. 14.21. The dimensionless number [eqn. (14.81)] becomes

$$\psi_1 = b_1 \left[\frac{\omega^2 a^2 \rho f(\omega a d/v)}{(\rho_s - \rho)gd} \right] \tag{14.82}$$

by replacing u by ωa.

Plotting data as d_{50}/a against

$$\omega \bigg/ \left[\frac{(\rho_s - \rho)g \tan \phi}{\rho v^{1/2}} \right]^{2/3}$$

on log–log paper yielded well-defined relationships for both initial and general motion condition (Fig. 14.22).

Assuming that $f(\omega ad/v) \doteq (\omega ad/v)^{1/2}$ allows eqn. (14.82) to be written as

$$\psi_1' = b_1' \left[\frac{\omega a \rho^{0.4}}{(\rho_s - \rho)^{0.4} g^{0.4} v^{0.2} d^{0.2}} \right].$$

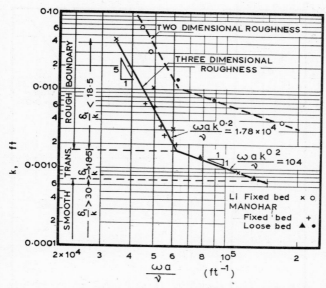

FIG. 14.21. Criterion for transition from laminar to turbulent flow with oscillatory motion. (From ref. 16, by permission of the U.S. Army Corps of Engineers, Coastal Engineering Research Center.)

Figure 14.23 shows experimental results plotted in terms of d_{50} against $\omega a \rho^{0.4} / [(\rho_s - \rho)^{0.4} g^{0.4} v^{0.2}]$.

These experimental results also seem to describe ripple features (Fig. 14.24 and Fig. 14.25). An interesting deduction from the results is that ripples form only when the boundary layer is turbulent. This is in keeping with development of bed features in steady flow, discussed in Chapter 12.

The velocity at the bed under a solitary wave is introduced for sediment calculation, but the treatment is too superficial to be of

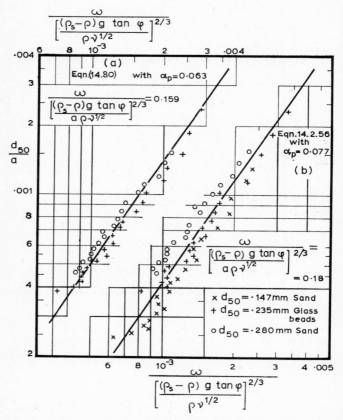

FIG. 14.22. Initial (a) and general (b) motion of sediment in laminar boundary layer. (From ref. 16, by permission of the U.S. Army Corps of Engineers, Coastal Engineering Research Center.)

basic interest. However, plots of experimental data with ψ^1 as the abscissa and the sediment transport rate or the velocity of movement of ripples show consistent trends in fairly deep water, that is in depth greater than 25 ft.

An earlier study of the formation of ripples by Bagnold[18] shows two distinct types: the "rolling-ripple" and the "vortex-ripple". The rolling-ripple occurs when the relative velocity is

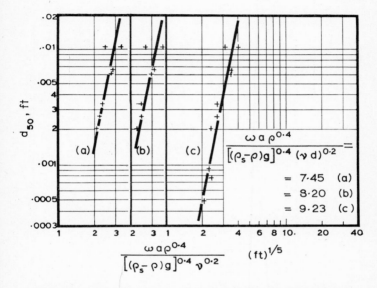

Fig. 14.23. Initial (a) and general (b) motion of sediment in turbulent boundary layer. (c) Initiation of ripples. (From ref. 16, by permission of the U.S. Army Corps of Engineers, Coastal Engineering Research Center.)

just great enough to roll the grains on the bed surface. This peak of the relative velocity lasts only for a short time so that the grain path remains short. Gradually, the grains in this area of motion form a ridge. This ridge shelters a strip of the sand surface. The repetition distance is the width of this sheltered area. With fine sands the area between the ridges remains flat, but with larger grains the profile tends to a flat arc. When the ripples reach a certain height a vortex appears in the lee of the crest. This vortex scoops out sand and deposits it downstream of the vortex,

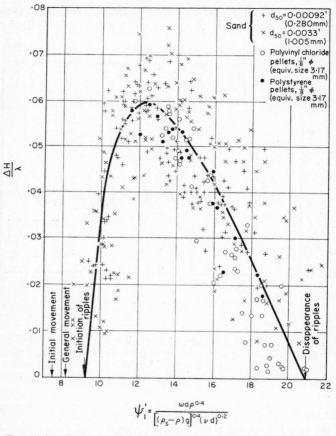

$$\psi_1' = \frac{\omega a \rho^{0.4}}{\left[(\rho_s - \rho)g\right]^{0.4}(\nu d)^{0.2}}$$

FIG. 14.24. Steepness of ripples, $\Delta H/\lambda$, versus ψ'. (From ref. 16, by permission of the U.S. Army Corps of Engineers, Coastal Engineering Research Center.)

thus creating a new crest and so on. Bagnold's experiments were carried out by using an oscillating lower boundary in still water.

Development of an analytical model for the formation of ripples, along the lines of the theory by Exner and others for steady flow, appears to be feasible for this case of oscillating flow. Oscillating flow gives rise to a bed shear stress varying

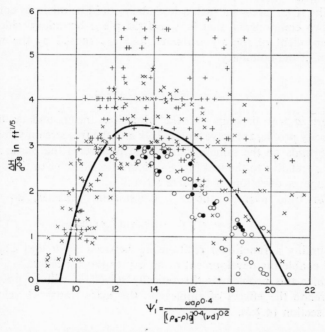

FIG. 14.25. Scale of ripples $\Delta H/d^{0.8}$ versus ψ'. Symbols as defined on Fig. 14.24. (From ref. 16, by permission of the U.S. Army Corps of Engineers, Coastal Engineering Research Center.)

periodically with time in magnitude and direction. Once the critical shear has been exceeded the particle transport depends on the magnitude and direction of the bed shear stress. Thus $d\tau_0/dx > 0$ means erosion and $d\tau_0/dx < 0$ deposition. Assume, for example, that the bed already has a sinusoidal wave form, created by the oscillating motion discussed by Bagnold, and expressed as

$$\eta = \eta_0 \cos kx,$$

where η is the departure of bed surface from the plane bed level and $\eta_{max} = \eta_0$.

The shear stress on such a boundary could be taken to consist of two components, that is τ_{01} of the plane boundary which is independent of the x-coordinate, and τ_{02} caused by the wave form of the boundary.[19,20]

Let

$$\tau_{02} = \pm a\eta_0 \cos (kx \pm \alpha),$$

where $a > 0$ depends on the viscosity, the boundary layer velocity profile, the wave length $2\pi/k$ and the free stream velocity, α depends on the same variables and represents the phase shift of τ_{02} relative to the bed form, $+$ and $-$ signs refer to the cyclic change of direction of the free stream.

On time average the τ_{01} component vanishes, so that

$$\bar{\tau}_0 = \bar{\tau}_{02} \doteqdot -a\eta_0 \sin kx \sin \alpha.$$

Assuming a functional relationship between $d\eta/dt$ and $d\bar{\tau}_{02}/dt$ will enable the development of an expression for $d\eta/dt$.

Once this problem is theoretically solved, it will be possible to relate the effects of ripples on the mass transport velocity (cf. section 14.2.3).

14.2.7. Concluding remarks

The oversimplified analytical models of the various facets of the problem of sediment movement by water waves, discussed above, fall far short of explaining the sediment movement in a rigorous manner. Yet, they do show that this very complex phenomenon can be reduced to simpler models and treated by starting from basic principles of mechanics. Such treatments, carefully compared with experimental and field observations, will lead to a better understanding of coastal problems. Even if it will never be possible to solve the practical problems in a rigorous analytical manner, understanding of the component mechanisms, which combined constitute the problem, will lead to the ability to predict the correct form of such a solution.

These problems become more involved still when the beach is under the action of asymmetrical wind waves. In a laboratory wind-wave tunnel the water at the beach end becomes much more heavily charged with sand for the wind driven waves than it is for paddle-formed shoaling waves of the same height. The wind drag causes a banking-up of the water level, that is an increased mass transport, and the return current is more powerful. This suspended sand can thus be carried beyond the bed-load equilibrium point into deep water and this equilibrium point may also be shifted because of modification of the mass transport velocity distribution and its effective net magnitude.

It hardly needs to be emphasized that the various wave and tide induced currents in the field can modify the results based on theoretical models or even overshadow these completely.

14.3. General Observations on Coastal Movements

The theory of Ippen and Eagleson[9] suggested a null point [eqn. (14.46)] at which the onshore transport of sediment on the bottom by the wave action becomes zero. Careful measurements in the field[21,22] support the existence of such a null point. Shoreward of this null point the net sediment movement is on-shore and seaward it is offshore. Miller and Zeigler[23] compared observations on beaches with the above theory[9] and concluded that gravity force in eqn. (14.44) was not an important factor in moving sand offshore. On exposed beaches the sand movement appears to fade out, in long term average, at about 30 ft depth. Inman[21] observed over a four-year period changes in sand level ranging from 0·15 ft at 70 ft depth to 0·29 ft at 30 ft depth. The data were strongly correlated and showed that erosion at the 30 ft level was frequently accompanied by deposition at the 70 ft level. In 18 ft depth the mean range was 0·62 ft with individual observations exceeding 2 ft.

Trask[22] divides the seabed into three zones as follows:

(1) Beyond 60 ft depth with little or no movement. The grain size diminishes with increasing depth.

(2) Intermittent zone between 30 and 60 ft depth, where the particles are moved at times and the particle size is nearly constant.

(3) Active zone in depth less than 30 ft. Here grain size increases with decreasing depth.

Generally, the null point may be assumed to move up and down the beach slope with varying wave size and wave steepness. Steep waves erode the near shore profile and deposit the material further out. An onshore wind augments this process by increasing wave steepness and asymmetry and the strength of the return current. Conversely, waves of long wave length move this material back onshore. An offshore wind assists this process by reducing the wave height of the swell and thus flattening the wave. Inside the breaker line (Fig. 14.26) steep waves move material seawards whereas flat waves move material landwards. The critical values of wave steepness quoted by various investigations range from $H/L = 0·01$ to $0·03$. This has led to classification of beach profiles as (Fig. 14.27), cf. section 14.2.3:

(a) winter, storm or bar type;
(b) summer, ordinary or berm type.

When the waves move into shoaling water they become increasingly more asymmetrical. Qualitatively seen, the trough in front of a crest is in shallower water than the trough behind it and moves more slowly so that the crest behind it catches up on the trough in front. This leads to a steeper leading face of the crest. The asymmetry increases with the slope of the beach. Eventually, the wave height becomes so great in relation to water depth that the wave becomes unstable and breaks. This occurs when the ratio of water depth to wave height is approximately 4 : 3 (Fig. 14.26), where the wave height is the vertical distance between the trough and crest of the wave. At this point the velocity of water particles in the wave crest exceeds the wave form celerity and the wave breaks.

Depending on the form of the breakers they are called:

(1) plunging breaker: originates from a fairly low wave moving on to a steep beach;

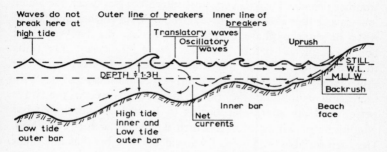

FIG. 14.26. Diagrammatic presentation of the surf or breaker zone.

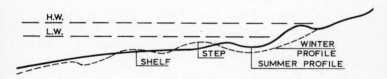

FIG. 14.27. Diagrammatic comparison of winter and summer profiles.

(2) spilling breaker: originates from a steeper wave moving on to a gently sloping beach.

These are the two limiting forms and a large variety of intermediate breaker forms is possible.

Kemp[24] suggests that the type of beach profile depends on the ratio of the time the wave takes to travel from the breaker point to the limit of uprush to the wave period. This ratio is termed phase difference. With increasing wave height the breaker distance increases, but the phase difference in laboratory experiments was observed to remain constant at 0·3. The motion of water up and down the beach profile is likened to a simple pendulum, the velocity of movement increasing with the increasing amplitude of incident wave. The beach steepens and retreats seaward. This is called the surge condition and corresponds to the summer profile. There is very little intermixing between the water masses at either side of the breaker line. With further increase of wave height the phase difference increases, the backrush not being completed before the next wave plunges. This leads to an exchange of water with that outside the breaker line. The flow is somewhat unstable and lateral circulation is present. With increasing amplitude the phase difference exceeds the wave period and this marks (according to Kemp) the developed bar conditions or winter profile, which is called the surf condition. Here appreciable exchange of water across the breaker line takes place. The phase difference from 0·3 to 1·0 identifies the transition region between surge conditions and surf zone.

The winter profile is characterized by an eroding shoreline and pronounced offshore bars. These bars are the direct result of the steep winter waves breaking in shallow water. The sand scoured on the breaker line is dropped out again just seaward of the breaker leading to a bar.

A bar can also develop with the very flat waves which produce the summer profile. This bar has been called the swash bar and it develops shorewards from the break-point by the action of the uprush or swash. Flat waves cause a net sand transport landwards on both sides of the breaker line and lead to accumulation of sand. The wave backwash down the upper beach has its maximum velocity in the surface. On approaching the breaker line this return flow is rapidly retarded by the rising water level of the next wave. The velocity difference in the vertical leads to the formation of a vortex, scooping up sand. The uprush picks it up and carries it shorewards. Not all of it is brought back by the backwash which has lost some of its energy in dissipation and some water by percolation. Thus sand can pass through the breaker line, although experiments show that there is very little exchange in the water masses on either side of the breaker line. The sand accumulates and the swash bar is formed. This can grow above the water line up to the height of the uprush and leads to the building up of the beach. Observations show that the height of the uprush, the berm height, is about 1·5 to 1·8 times the wave height.

The bottom profile is generally covered by ripples. The ripples are symmetrical in profile in the vicinity of the null point and asymmetrical to either side of this. Shorewards of the null zone the ripples have a steep shoreward and a flat seaward slope. These ripples are of the kind called vortex ripples and move fairly quickly. As the crest of a wave passes, the surface layer of sand moves over the flat slope of the ripple and slides down the steep shoreward slope. At the same time a vortex develops at the lee of the ripple crest and scoops up sand. With the passage of the trough the water velocity reverses and the sand picked up by the vortex is carried back on to the seaward slope of the ripple. Some sand, however, remains in suspension and is carried along with the movement of water and currents. Seawards of the null zone the ripples are again asymmetrical, but the steep face is on the seaward side and the ripple form moves seaward. Here the combined effect of gravity and the seaward velocity exceeds that of the shoreward velocity. From measurements on the seabed, for example, by Inman,[25] it has been found that the size of the ripples depends on the water depth, wave height and length and on the sand size, the larger ripples forming in the coarser sand. Amplitudes vary up to about 6 in. and ripple length from about 2 in. to over 4 ft. The ripple pattern can change, disappear and reappear in a few hours with changes in waves on the water surface. Ripples have been observed in water 170 ft deep. It appears that the actual transport of sand by these ripples seaward of the null point is very small.

On sandy beaches suspension plays a very important role. Material put in suspension in the breaker zone can be carried by the various currents and these do not need to be strong currents as the material is put in suspension by wave action.

The concentration of sand is high at the breaker line and drops steadily in the uprush. In the backwash the sand movement is close to the bottom. Seaward of the breaker line the concentration drops rapidly and the sand is confined to layers close to the bed. The thickness of this layer of suspended sediment above the bed is closely linked with the wave height and increases with it. It is also sensitive to the onshore wind which increases the return

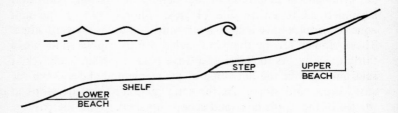

FIG. 14.28. Diagrammatic profile of shingle beach.

current to the sea so that more material in suspension is carried seawards. The oscillatory motion and vorticity over the ripples help to maintain suspension just over the bed. Suspension is the major mode of transport by which sand, particularly the finer fractions, is steadily lost into the deeps of the sea. In particular, with steep waves and a fairly thick suspended sediment layer over the bed there may be transport in the onshore direction on the bed. But integrated over the depth the net sediment transport may be offshore.

These suspensions also give rise to an offshore density current, contributing to a seaward movement of solids.

The profile of a shingle beach is similar to the summer profile of a sand beach (Fig. 14.28).

Bagnold[26] found in the laboratory that the depth of the shelf below still water is approximately equal to the incident wave height. This agrees with observations in the field when currents are absent. There is very little movement of shingle on the shelf after it has been established by the given waves. Material which

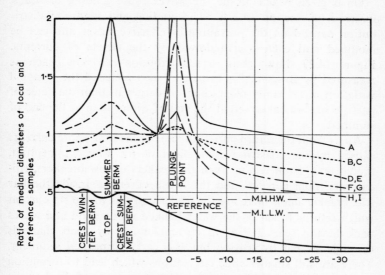

FIG. 14.29. Particle size distribution across a beach.

Location	A	B	C	D and E	F	G	H	I
Median diameter (in mm) of reference sample	0·42	0·22	0·19	0·35	0·44	0·40	0·36	0·30

Reference sample at mid-tide beach face used as 100 per cent. (From ref. 27, by permission of the American Geophysical Union.)

has been scoured by the waves in forming the shelf is thrown up on the upper beach. But, as the shingle is porous, much of the water in the uprush percolates into the beach and the backwash is feeble. Therefore the slope of the shingle beach is very steep compared with that of a sandy beach.

On a given beach profile the waves cause grading of beach material, cf. section 14.2.4. The grading and sand size distribution depend on the prevailing or effective waves and can be modified and even overshadowed by the effects of currents. Figure 14.29 shows grain size distribution across a beach as measured by Bascom.[27] Inman[15] also included the seasonal variation in his study of grading. A larger median diameter of particle size was observed at the end of winter than at the end of summer.

Apart from the return current, there are the long-shore currents caused by the coastwise component of the wave momentum, the currents from regions of high breakers to low breakers, rip-currents, tidal currents and the ocean currents. Inside the bar (the breaker line), there are the feeder currents to the rip current which returns much of the water banked up by wind and waves back to the sea. These rip currents not only keep channels through the bar by erosion but also carry suspended sediment. There are still smaller scale circulations which lead to formation of the beach cusps. The coastwise wave components lead to the littoral drift of material which takes place mainly in shallow water.

The focusing of waves by refraction caused by the underwater contours leads to coastwise currents which can carry suspended material from regions of high breakers to low breakers.

Ocean and tidal currents can carry material into great depth or even cause scour in deep water. The tidal flood current will flow faster than the ebb when the tide runs into shallowing channels and will cause a net sediment transport. Tidal currents deflected by headlands can lead to large-scale coastal eddies which again can carry suspended material.

These coastal currents, even if they are not capable of eroding material, are an important factor in sand transport by suspension. Wave motion and disturbance caused by the ripples help to maintain the suspension. The currents give rise to the formation and movement of sandbanks in open sea.

In many locations the currents are very powerful. Between the Isle of Wight and the south coast of England spring tide currents are said to be $4\frac{1}{2}$ knots and scour shingle at a depth of about 30 fathoms. Off Deal in the North Sea end of the Straits of Dover there are moving shingle banks in depths down to 40 ft.

The purpose of the brief discussion of these currents, sand and shingle banks, etc., is to draw attention to the complexity of the problem of coastal movements of sediment. While it is not possible to solve these problems in a rigorous manner, an understanding of the oversimplified models of movement discussed above, combined with careful observation, should go a long way towards understanding a particular problem.

References

1. —— —— —— ——, *A Study of Progressive Oscillatory Waves in Water*, Beach Erosion Board TM No. 1 (1941).
2. MORISON, J. R., The effect of wave steepness on wave velocity, *Trans. Amer. Geophys. Union*, **32**, 201–6 (1951).
3. WIEGEL, R. K., Experimental study of surface waves in shoaling water, *Trans. Amer. Geophys. Union*, **31**, 377–85 (1950).
4. WIEGEL, R. L. and JOHNSON, J. W., Elements of wave theory, *Proc. First Conference on Coastal Engineering*, Oct. 1950.
5. EAGLESON, P. S., Laminar damping of oscillatory waves, *Proc. A.S.C.E.* **88**, No. HY3, Part I, 155–81 (May 1962).
6. MUNK, W. H., The solitary wave theory and its application to surf problems, *Ann. New York Acad. Sci*, **51**, Art. 3, 376–424 (1949).
7. EAGLESON, P. S. and DEAN, R. G., Wave-induced motion of bottom sediment particles, *Proc. A.S.C.E.* **85**, No. NY10, 53–79 (Oct. 1959).
8. EAGLESON, P. S. and DEAN, R. G., The mechanics of the motion of discrete spherical bottom sediment particles due to shoaling waves, Beach Erosion Board TM No. 104, 1958.
9. IPPEN, A. T. and EAGLESON, P. S., A study of sediment sorting by waves shoaling on a plane beach, Beach Erosion Board TM No. 63, 1955.
10. LONGUET-HIGGINS, M. S., Mass transport in water waves, *Phil. Trans. Roy. Soc., London* (A) **245**, No. 903, 585–91 (1953).
11. LAMB, H., *Hydrodynamics*, The University Press, Cambridge, also Dover Publication, New York.
12. MILNE-THOMSON, L. M., *Theoretical Hydrodynamics*, MacMillan, 1949, p. 481.
13. CHEPIL, W. S., The use of evenly spaced hemispheres to evaluate aerodynamic forces on a soil surface, *Trans. A.G.U.* **39**, No. 3, 397–404 (June 1958).

L

14. EAGLESON, P. S., GLENNE, B. and DRACUP, J. A., Equilibrium characteristics of sand beaches in the off-shore zone, U.S. Army Beach Erosion Board TM 126, July 1961.

15. INMAN, D. L., Areal and seasonal variations in beach and nearshore sediments at La Jolla, California, U.S. Army Beach Erosion Board TM 39, 1953.

16. MANOHAR, MADHAO, Mechanics of bottom sediment movement due to wave action, U.S. Army Beach Erosion Board TM No. 75, 1955.

17. LI, HUON, Stability of oscillatory laminar flow along a wall, U.S. Army Beach Erosion Board TM No. 47, 1954.

18. BAGNOLD, R. A., Motion of waves in shallow water. Interaction between waves and sand bottoms, *Proc. Roy. Soc., London* (A) **187**, 1–18 (Oct. 1946).

19. BENJAMIN, T. B., Shearing flow over a wavy boundary, *J. Fluid Mech.* **6** (1959).

20. BECKER, E., Die laminare, incompressible Grenzschicht an einer durch laufende Wellen deformierten ebenen Wand, *Zeitschrift fuer Flugwissenschaften*, **8**: 10–11; 308–16 (1960).

21. INMAN, D. L. and RUSNAK, G. S., Changes in sand level on the beach and shelf at La Jolla, California, U.S. Army Beach Erosion Board, TM No. 82, 1956.

22. TRASK, P. D., Movement of sand around southern California promontories, U.S. Army Beach Erosion Board TM No. 76, 1955.

23. MILLER, R. L. and ZEIGLER, J. M., A model relating dynamics and sediment pattern in equilibrium in the region of shoaling waves, breaker zone, and foreshore, *Journal of Geology*, **66**, No. 4, 417–41 (July 1958).

24. KEMP, P. H., The relationship between wave action and beach profile characteristics, *Proc. of Seventh Conference on Coastal Engineering*, The Hague, Aug. 1960, vol. 1, ch. 14, pp. 262–77.

25. INMAN, D. L., Wave generated ripples in nearshore sands, U.S. Army Beach Erosion Board TM 100, 1957.

26. BAGNOLD, R. A., Beach formation by waves; some model experiments in a wave tank, *J. Inst. C.E.* **15–16** (1940–41), Paper No. 5237, 27–52 (Nov. 1940).

27. BASCOM, W. N., Relationships between sand sizes and beach face slope, *Trans. Amer. Geophys. Union*, **32**, No. 6, 866–74 (Dec. 1951).

CHAPTER 15

Remarks on Related Topics

THIS chapter is intended as an introduction—a reminder—to topics which are important and closely related to loose boundary hydraulics, but are outside the scope of this book. Only a very brief outline of these topics is offered and the student is referred to the literature from which a few lead-in references are given at the end of the chapter.

15.1. Watercourse Geometry

A river is not only a drainage channel but also a conveyor of detritus eroded along its upper reaches. This detritus or sediment is gradually transported downstream and broken into finer and finer fractions by wear and weathering. Finally, the sediment is discharged into the oceans or deposited in deltas. Deltas of the past may now be alluvial plains.

This process of erosion is slow in terms of human time, but it will continue until the catchment is transformed into flat land, called a peneplain by geomorphologists. However, in many rivers the rate of change is so slow that for engineering purposes one can speak of equilibrium or regime, as was done in preceding chapters.

The regime equations discussed were derived from data obtained from essentially straight canals. However, the natural watercourse has an inherent tendency to run along a winding or meandering course. In the upper reaches topographical features control the shape and path of the river and the course could be straight or tortuous. Where the river flows over shingle deltas it tends to braid. On these steep shingle deltas, usually at the foot of mountains, the discharge still ·fluctuates violently and the oscillating or meandering pattern of the river is broken up by spill-overs. Spill-over refers to the river running over the inside bank of the bend, that is, it is taking the short course when the level rises sufficiently. This spill-over erodes a "cut-off" channel and gradually with time and fluctuating discharges the braided pattern is evolved.

On alluvial plains rivers seldom run straight but tend to meander, that is to flow in a sinuous pattern. Attempts to explain the mechanism of meandering have been numerous, but as yet there is no generally accepted theory. It is not surprising when one considers the complexity of the problem. Any small disturbance of an initially straight flow would lead to changes in velocity and shear stress distribution. This in turn causes changes in cross-sectional as well as in plan geometry of the channel and a complicated pattern of secondary and spiral currents is created. The dynamic equilibrium between erosion and deposition and the associated distributions of boundary shear stresses and velocity appear to lead to a sinuous course. The wavelength and amplitude of the meander pattern vary with discharge; both have been found to be proportional to the square root of discharge.

This sinuous course, once established, displays the well-known pattern of deeps and shallows. The reasons for these features can be illustrated by using a very simple analytical model for the flow through a bend.[1] For a bend with concentric inner and outer banks of radii R_1 and R_2 respectively, and an approximately constant velocity V_s in the surface layers the condition of equilibrium between centrifugal and pressure forces in a horizontal plane is given by

$$g\,dz = \frac{V_s^2}{R}\,dR$$

or with $z = 0$ when $R = R_1$

$$z = \frac{V_s^2}{g}\ln\frac{R}{R_1}.$$

The result from this simple analytical model is in surprisingly good agreement with observation. However, the velocity on the vertical is not constant, but decreases with increasing depth below the surface. This means that the centrifugal force also decreases and as a result there is a hydrostatic pressure excess and a radially inward pressure gradient in the bottom region of the bend. This

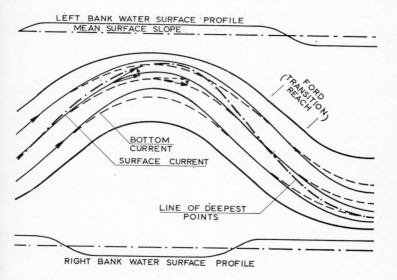

FIG. 15.1. Diagrammatic picture of flow through a bend.

gives rise to an inward current along the bottom and an outward current on the surface to satisfy continuity. This simple explanation shows the reason for the direction of the secondary current. The dynamics of the established flow, of course, is much more complicated. Superimposed on the flow through the bend it leads to the pattern of flow shown diagrammatically in Fig. 15.1.

It is seen that the flow into the bend converges towards the outer bank and in flowing out of the bend it diverges and so on. Where the flow converges it excavates a deep into the bed of the river. Some of this material is carried downstream and the bottom currents move it towards the inner bank. The diverging flow downstream of the bend cannot carry all of this sediment and deposits some, leading to the shallow banks or fords at inflection points. A deposited beach also forms along the inner bank just downstream from the point of maximum curvature. The sediment transport to some extent tends to be along the shortest path, or steepest gradient, that is cutting across the bend. This is augmented by the spiral current, but the deposition along the inner bank is mainly caused by the retarded flow where the water surface slope is reduced or even adverse; see also Fig. 13.17.

This simple model helps to understand the pattern of flow and cross-sectional geometry in a meandering stream. It does not explain why equilibrium leads to a sinuous pattern, with the "wave form" translating downstream at celerities to be measured in geological time. Space here does not permit a study of the various theories attempting to explain the reasons for meandering and the student is referred to the literature.

The literature also contains much empirical information which permits the estimation, for engineering purposes, of meander width and length and depth of the deeps as a function of the radius of the bend, etc.

15.2. Scour at Bridge Piers and Below Hydraulic Structures

In principle scour is caused by a lack of balance between the transport capacity of the flow and the sediment in motion. For example, a river flowing into a man-made reservoir will drop its sediment load into the reservoir and a delta is formed. The same discharge of clear water out of the reservoir control structure will re-enter the river without sediment content and the river will scour until equilibrium is established. The principles of particle equilibrium and transport involved are the same as discussed in preceding chapters. The major problem in connection with scour below a hydraulic structure, such as a weir, spillway, etc., is the

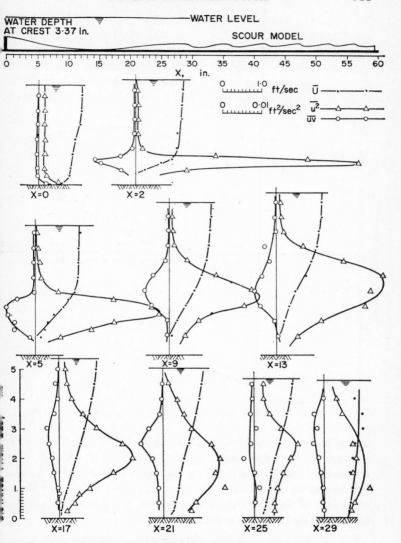

FIG. 15.2. Scour model: profiles of the mean and fluctuating longitudinal velocities and the turbulent shear.

insufficient knowledge of the velocity distribution and flow pattern involving separation and wakes. This hydraulics problem is difficult enough without the added complication of sediment.

In a wake, not only the velocity distribution, but also the increased turbulent agitation influences the size and shape of the scour hole. Figure 15.2 shows some results of velocity measure-

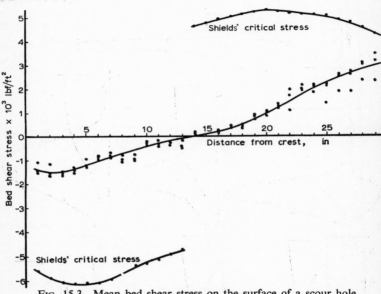

Fig. 15.3. Mean bed shear stress on the surface of a scour hole.

ments made at the University of Auckland.[10] The features are similar to those of the wake problem discussed in Chapter 12 in connection with ripples. Figure 15.3 shows results of bed shear measurements on the same scour model. This figure also shows the value of Shields' critical shear stress $\bar{\tau}_c$ adjusted for various bed slopes by using the expression

$$\bar{\tau}_{cs} = \bar{\tau}_{ch} \frac{\sin (\phi - \alpha)}{\sin \phi},$$

where $\bar{\tau}_{cs}$ and $\bar{\tau}_{ch}$ are the critical entrainment shear stresses on sloped and horizontal beds respectively, ϕ is the angle of repose of the sand, and α is the angle of the bed to the horizontal, positive when the bed slopes downwards with respect to the direction of the local velocity of flow.

It is seen that on the downward sloping part of the established scour the shear acts towards the structure (upstream) and is never greater than 25 per cent of the theoretical critical value. This lower magnitude of the threshold shear must be caused by the increased turbulent agitation, by the strong intermittent eddies present in the wake. Thus, if one could predict the velocity field and the turbulent eddy pattern it should also be possible to predict the scour. However, at present this is not possible for engineering works and the engineer has to rely on empirical data and model tests. For both of these the student is referred to the engineering literature from which a few references are given at the end of this chapter. From scour studies around model bridge piers and abutments, Laursen and Toch[11] concluded:

> ... At least as a first approximation the equilibrium scour depth, with certain qualifications as to the flow conditions, appears to be a function only of the geometry, i.e. the relative depth of flow, the shape of the pier and the angle of attack.
> Two important corrollary conclusions based on this finding are immediately apparent. In so far as the equilibrium depth of scour in a model is concerned, the velocity of flow, the sediment size, and the rate of sediment transport do not need to be scaled. Exactly the same depth of scour should result in the model, no matter what velocity or sediment is used, as long as there is general bed-load movement and the Froude number is everywhere less than unity ...

This statement underlines the previous discussion, that is that the geometry of the problem determines the wake and flow pattern, so that the sediment size and viscous effects are of minor importance.

In practice the river channel downstream of stilling basins and the like is protected by a cover of large-size stones—called riprap—designed to prevent or reduce the risk of undermining and damage of the structure. Many factors affect the stone size required. Among them are:

the size of individual stones,
the weight of individual stones,
the shape, particularly of the larger stones,
the gradation of the riprap,
the thickness of the riprap layer.

The pattern of flow leaving the stilling basin, weir or past a bridge pier is equally important. Here one must consider:

the magnitude and direction of the mean velocity near the bed,
wake pattern,
eddy intensity,
waves and surges.

From model experiments and comparison with prototype successes and failures various relationships between the stone size and bottom velocity have been proposed, such as[12,13]

$$V_b = 2{\cdot}57 \sqrt{d},$$

where V_b is velocity near the bed (in ft/sec), d is stone diameter in inches for stones with specific gravity of 2·65.

The riprap should be composed of a well graded mixture where about 60 per cent of the stones should be equal to or larger than that given by the formula and the stones must not be flat. It is a very sound practice to place riprap on a graded gravel layer— an inverted filter. This filter prevents the washing out of fines and the collapse of the riprap. The thickness of the riprap should be not less than 1·5d.

15.3. Density Currents

Density currents, or stratified flow, occur where motion in the gravitational field is caused or influenced by variations of density. The single fluid open channel flow is strictly also a layered flow, but here the difference between the densities of air and water is so large that the density and inertia effects of air may be neglected. However, in very many problems there are small density differences which may arise from temperature difference, suspension of solids, or chemical solutions. In hydraulic engineering such density differences occur when sediment laden flow enters reservoirs or lakes, when salt and fresh water—with or without sediment load—meet in tidal estuaries, as internal currents of sediment laden flow, in ocean currents, etc. The simplest problems are two layered flows with discontinuous density gradient, but multi-layered systems are possible and the density gradients are usually continuous. Also diffusion between layers may take place, or interfacial waves, like the surface waves in the water–air interface, may be present.

These density currents are important when dealing with silting of reservoirs. The sediment laden flow entering a lake disappears beneath the surface at the "plunge-point". The larger particles form the delta and the fine particles—usually less than 20 μ in diameter—create underflows in the reservoir. These underflows are important when designing clear water outlets or outlets designed to pass the fine sediment through the reservoir. Again, in estuaries there may be a seaward flow of fresh water and a landward flow of salt water underneath. These currents affect sediment movement and have to be studied carefully.

15.4. Transport of Solids in Closed Conduits

The transport of solids in pipelines has wide application ranging from dredging and placing of hydraulic fills to many industrial processes and handling of bulk goods, for example, coal. The material transported can also range from heterogeneous mixtures such as gravel and mud or sewage to muds of well-drilling rigs, finely graded products of industrial processes or paper pulp. Industrial, metallurgical and chemical plants use pipelines to transport raw materials, materials in process and even finished products. The transporting medium can be either liquid or gas.

Transport in pipelines is fundamentally similar to that in open channels and can be transport in suspension, or as bed load, or both. However, in many applications the flow may have a distinctly non-Newtonian stress–strain relationship and this can

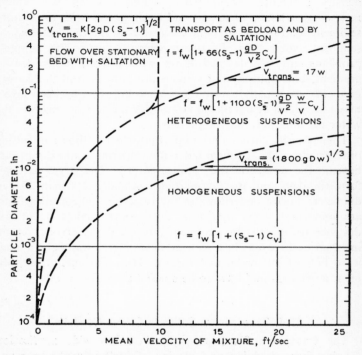

FIG. 15.4. Flow regimes in a 6 in. diameter pipeline carrying water and solids with specific gravity of 2·65, according to Newitt, et al.[23].

add to the complexity of the problem. To date, no single comprehensive theory of transport of solids in pipelines exists and published work—theoretical as well as experimental—is confined to particular fields of application. It is outside the scope of this book to treat the existing theories or to attempt to unify these. This brief discussion is intended for introduction only.

Assume a pipeline of given size and carrying a suspended solid–fluid mixture of a given concentration. As the velocity decreases a critical condition will be reached at which some of the particles will settle out and form a deposit over which some particles will move as a bed load. If the rate of feed remains constant and the

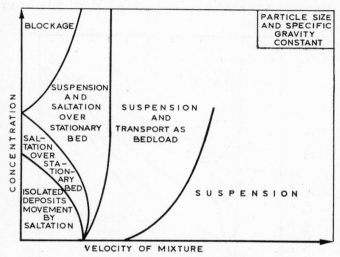

FIG. 15.5. Flow regimes as a function of concentration.

velocity drops below such critical value, the thickness of the deposit will grow until the cross-sectional area is reduced sufficiently for a new state of equilibrium to be established. If the velocity is later increased a gradual degrading will take place until the deposit is carried away and all the solids are once more carried in suspension.

For homogeneous and heterogeneous suspensions of solids Newitt et al.[23] classified the flow regions as shown on Fig. 15.4.

For constant particle size and specific gravity the dependence of flow regimes on concentration is shown diagrammatically on Fig. 15.5.

The questions posed by the designer are:

(1) What is the minimum carrying velocity for given conditions?

(2) What is the head loss for these conditions?

The minimum carrying velocity and friction loss depend on the concentration and density of the solid–fluid mixture, relative

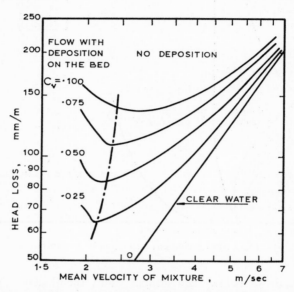

FIG. 15.6. Head loss as a function of concentration and velocity according to Durand and Condolios.[24] Velocity is defined as the volumetric discharge divided by cross-sectional area.

densities of fluid and solids, the size of pipeline, the slope of pipeline, and the grading of the solids as well as their shape. For example, Durand and Condolios[24] showed the effect of concentration on head loss to be as shown in Fig. 15.6.

The minimum values of head loss correspond to the lowest velocity at which no deposit is formed—all particles moving in suspension and saltation.

Durand and Condolios classified the flow according to the particle size as follows:

1. Homogeneous slurries, equivalent to a fluid.

   (a) Colloids of particle size less than 1 micron; maintained by Brownian motion even at zero velocity.

   (b) Plastic pastes of $1\ \mu < d < 40\ \mu$. At higher concentrations these pastes have a yield stress τ_y. Behave like solids when at rest. Viscosity is a function of velocity.

2. Heterogeneous slurries.

   (a) $40\ \mu < d < 150\ \mu$. Fluid turbulence maintains the suspension. These particles settle according to Stokes' law.

   (b) $0\cdot15\ \text{mm} < d < 1\cdot5\ \text{mm}$, carried by suspension and saltation.

   (c) $d > 1\cdot5\ \text{mm}$, carried by saltation.

For 1 (b) they concluded that in laminar flow the head loss was greater than that for clear fluid. But for turbulent flow the head loss can be calculated as for clear fluid, the answer being in terms of feet of the mixture. The transition Reynolds number was found to be approximately 2000. The transition velocity (in ft/sec) is

$$V = \frac{1000 + 1000\ \sqrt{(\eta^2 + \rho D^2 \tau_y / 3000)}}{\rho^D},$$

where η is the viscosity of the mixture (M/LT).

For the heterogeneous regime they give the critical velocity—when there is no deposit on the bottom of the pipe—as

$$V_{\text{crit}} = K[2gD(S_s - 1)]^{1/2}, \qquad \text{(ft/sec)}$$

where K is a numerical factor depending on volumetric concentration and particle size, Fig. 15.7.

This critical velocity is very little affected by concentration and particle size for particles greater than 2 mm in diameter.

The resistance to flow, according to their experimental results, is given as

$$f = f_w \left\{ 1 + 81 \left[\frac{gD}{V^2} (S_s - 1) \right]^{3/2} \frac{C_v}{C_D^{3/4}} \right\},$$

where f_w is the Darcy–Weisbach friction factor for water, C_v is the volumetric concentration, and C_D is the drag coefficient of the particle falling through still water. For mixtures the C_D of an

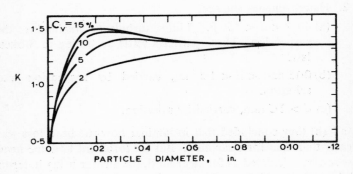

Fig. 15.7. Factor K in the Durand and Condolios expression for critical non-deposit velocity as a function of particle size and concentration.

equivalent sphere is used, the diameter of which is equal to the weighted average diameter.

The corresponding expressions given by Newitt and others are shown on Fig. 15.4.

With materials, such as paper pulp, the flow can have a core of suspended material and a clear water layer between the core and pipe wall.[25] In most applications there is an optimum concentration for conveyance. With increasing concentration the flow may "freeze" solid. An intriguing feature is the flow of oil bubbles in water and transport of solid capsules at velocities greater than that of the supporting fluid.[26]

The slope of the pipeline is a further factor on head loss. Head loss has been found to increase with increasing slope, that is that the loss in a vertical pipeline is greater than in a horizontal one.

References

1. THOMPSON, J., On the origin of windings of rivers in alluvial plains with remarks on the flow of water round bends in pipes, *Proc. Roy. Soc.* (*London*) **25**, 8–15 (May 1876).

2. INGLIS, Sir Claude, *The Behaviour and Control of Rivers and Canals*, Res. Publication Central Board of Irrigation, India, No. 13, Simla 1949.

3. INGLIS, SIR CLAUDE, *Meanders and Their Bearing on River Training*, Inst. of Civil Engineers, London, Maritime and Waterways Engineering Division, January, 1947.

4. LEOPOLD, L. B. and MADDOCKS, T., *The Hydraulic Geometry of Stream Channels and some Physiographic Implications*, U.S. Geological Survey, Prof. Paper 252, 1953.

5. LEOPOLD, L. B. and WOLMAN, M. G., *River Channel Patterns: Braided, Meandering and Straight*, U.S. Geological Survey Prof. Paper 282–B, 1957.

6. MATTHES, GERARD, Basic aspects of stream meanders, *Trans. Amer. Geophys. Union*, Part III, 632–6 (1941).

7. STRAUB, Lorenz G., in *Hydrology* edited by Meinzer, Dover Publications, "Mechanics of rivers".

8. TANNER, W. F., Helicoidal flow, a possible cause of meandering, *Journal of Geophysical Research*, **65**, 993–5 (March 1960).

9. HJULSTROM, F., *A Study of the Meander Problem*, Bulletin No. 51 of the Institution of Hydraulics at the Royal Institute of Technology, Stockholm, 1957.

10. SHEEN, S. J., Turbulence over a sand ripple. Thesis submitted as part requirement for the degree of Master of Engineering at the University of Auckland, 1964.

11. LAURSEN, E. M. and TOCH, A., *Scour Around Bridge Piers and Abuttments*, Bulletin No. 4, Iowa Highway Research Board, the Iowa State Highway Commission and the Bureau of Public Roads, May 1956.

12. MAVIS, F. T. and LAUSHEY, L. M., *A Re-appraisal of the Beginnings of Bed Movement*—Competent Velocity, Report on the Second Meeting of the International Association for Hydraulic Structures Research, Stockholm, 1948, p. 217.

13. PETERKA, A. J., *Hydraulic Design of Stilling Basins and Energy Dissipators*, Water Resources Technical Publication, Engineering Monograph No. 25, U.S. Department of Interior, Bureau of Reclamation, 1964.

14. LAURSEN, E. M., *Scour at Bridge Crossings*, Bulletin No. 8, Iowa Highway Research Board, The Iowa State Highway Commission and the Bureau of Public Roads, August 1958.

15. BRADLEY, J. N., *Hydraulics of Bridge Waterways*, Hydraulic Design Series No. 1 by the Division of Hydraulic Research, Bureau of Public Roads, U.S. Dept. of Commerce, August, 1960.
16. LELIAVSKY, S., *Irrigation and Hydraulic Design*, Chapman & Hall, 1955, vol. 1.
17. SCHOKLITSCH, A., *Handbuch des Wasserbaues*, Springer Verlag, 1950, vol. II.
18. HARLEMAN, D. R. F., Section 26 in *Handbook of Fluid Dynamics*, edited by V. L. Streeter, McGraw-Hill, 1961.
19. ―――― ―――― ――――., *Proceedings of the Eighth Congress of the International Association for Hydraulic Research*, vol. 2, Subject C, Canada, 1959.
20. SCHULTZ, E. A. and SIMMONS, H. B., *Fresh Water–Salt Water Density Currents, a Major Cause of Siltation in Estuaries*, Techn. Bulletin No. 2, April, 1957, U.S. Army Corps of Engineers Committee on Tidal Hydraulics.
21. ―――― ―――― ――――., Sediment transportation mechanics: density currents, *Proc. A.S.C.E.* **89**, No. HY5, 77–87 (Sept. 1963).
22. KNAPP, R. T., Density currents: their mixing characteristics and their effect on the turbulence structure of the associated flow, *Proc. Second Hydraulics Conf.*, State Univ. of Iowa, 1942.
23. NEWITT, D. M., RICHARDSON, J. F., ABBOTT, M. and TURTLE, R. B., Hydraulic conveying of solids in horizontal pipes, *Trans. Inst. Chem. Eng.* **33**, 93 (1955).
24. DURAND, R. and CONDOLIOS, E., The hydraulic transport of coal and solid materials in pipes, *Proc. Colloq. on Hydraulic Transportation*, London, Nov. 1952.
25. BAINES, W. D., *Laminar Flow of Dilute Fibre Suspensions*, National Research Council of Canada Report No. MH–73, 1958.
26. ELLIS, H. S., REDBERGER, P. J. and BOLT, L. H., Transporting solids by pipeline, *Industrial and Eng. Chemistry*, **55**, Nos. 8 and 9 (August and September 1963).
27. WORSTER, R. C., The hydraulic transport of solids, *Proc. Colloq. on Hydraulic Transportation*, London, Nov. 1952.
28. CRAVEN, J. P., The transportation of sand in pipes: full-pipe flow, *Proc. Fifth Hydraulics Conference*, State University of Iowa, June 1952, pp. 67–76.
29. AMBROSE, H. H., The transportation of sand in pipes: free surface flow, *Proc. Fifth Hydraulics Conference*, State University of Iowa, June 1952, pp. 77–86.
30. ―――― ―――― ―――― ――――., *Correlation of Data Derived from Two Surveys on Velocity and Friction Losses Involved in Pumping of Fluid–solid Mixtures*, Hydraulic Institute, New York, Nov. 1959.
31. BREBNER, A., *An Introduction to Aqueous Hydraulic Conveyance of Solids in Pipelines*, C. E. Research Report No. 21, July, 1962, Queen's University at Kingston, Ontario.
32. WILSON, W. E., Mechanics of flow with non-colloidal inert solids, *Proc. A.S.C.E.* **67**, 1434 (1941).

33. —— —— —— ——., *The Transportation of Solids in Steel Pipelines*, Colorado School of Mines Research Foundation, Inc., Golden, Colorado, 1963.

34. DURST, R. E. and JENNESS, L. C., The flow properties of paper pulp stocks, *TAPPI*, **37** (Oct. 1954).

35. DURST, R. E., A correlation of pulp stock flow data with properties of the pulp stock, *Pulp and Paper Magazine of Canada*, **57**, No. 3 (1956).

Index